McGRAW-HILL PUBLICATIONS IN THE
BOTANICAL SCIENCES

EDMUND W. SINNOTT, Consulting Editor

CRYPTOGAMIC BOTANY

Volume II

BRYOPHYTES AND PTERIDOPHYTES

CRYPTOGAMIC BOTANY

VOLUME II
BRYOPHYTES AND PTERIDOPHYTES

BY

GILBERT M. SMITH

Stanford University

FIRST EDITION
SEVENTH IMPRESSION

McGRAW-HILL BOOK COMPANY, Inc.

NEW YORK AND LONDON

1938

COPYRIGHT, 1938, BY THE
McGRAW-HILL BOOK COMPANY, INC.

PRINTED IN THE UNITED STATES OF AMERICA

PREFACE

In preparing the illustrations for this volume, most of the habit sketches of Bryophyta were drawn by Mrs. Carl F. Janish, and those of the Pteridophyta were drawn by Maximo V. Rodrigo.

I am deeply indebted to Professor D. H. Campbell for placing at my disposal his extensive collections of preparations and preserved material of bryophytes and pteridophytes. These unique collections, many of them made in inaccessible tropical countries, have made possible a much fuller series of original illustrations of bryophytes and pteridophytes. Professor G. S. Bryan has furnished preparations of *Andraea*.

Many of the illustrations are based upon preparations made especially by Dr. D. A. Johansen. My thanks are again due him for helpful aid in securing illustrative material at the proper stage of development and for his technical skill in preparing it for microscopical study.

Gilbert M. Smith.

Stanford University,
March, 1938.

CONTENTS

CRYPTOGAMIC BOTANY

VOL. II

BRYOPHYTES AND PTERIDOPHYTES

CHAPTER I

BRYOPHYTA—INTRODUCTION

The Bryophyta have a sharply defined alternation of generations in which the diploid asexual generation, although morphologically distinct from the haploid sexual generation, is always attached to it and wholly or partially dependent upon it for nutrition. This condition is in contrast with that in Pteridophyta and more advanced plants, where the asexual generation, the sporophyte, is always an independent plant at maturity. The sporophytes of plants higher than Bryophyta are internally differentiated into xylem and phloem; whereas Bryophyta lack these tissues.

The sexual generation of Bryophyta, the gametophyte, is always an independent plant at maturity and one that is nutritionally self-sustaining because of the presence of chloroplasts within its body. In many cases the plant body is a thallus, that is, without differentiation into root, stem, and leaf. In those cases where it is externally differentiated into stem and leaf, there are never any roots; only one-celled absorptive organs (rhizoids).

All Bryophyta are oögamous, and the gametes are produced within multicellular sex organs in which there is an outer sterile layer of jacket cells. In this respect they are immediately distinguishable from algae since sex organs of the latter, when multicellular, always have all cells gamete-producing.

Life Cycle of Bryophyta. The life cycle of a bryophyte consists of a regular alternation of an asexually reproducing generation with a sexually reproducing one. This was first clearly demonstrated by Hofmeister in 1851,[1] but the periodic doubling and halving in the number of chromosomes associated with the alternation was not clearly recognized until 1894.[2] This alternation of generations is obligatory in the sense that a zygote resulting from gametic union always grows into a sporophyte and

---

[1] Hofmeister, 1851.   [2] Strasburger, 1894.

that spores produced by a sporophyte always germinate to form a gameto-phyte. It is not obligatory in the sense that gametophyte and sporophyte must always alternate with each other, because vegetative propagation of the gametophyte may result in a life cycle in which there is a succession of gametophytic individuals before there is the formation of a sporophyte. It should also be noted that vegetative budding does not always result in a generation similar to the parent one. Thus, vegetative budding of gametophytic tissue may result in the formation of a sporophyte. This production of a sporophyte from a gametophyte and without any union of gametes is *apogamy*. Conversely, a sporophyte may bud off a mass of cells which develops into a gametophyte. Production of a gametophyte from a sporophyte without the formation of spores is *apospory*. Apogamy and apospory are of rare occurrence in Bryophyta as compared with Pteridophyta.[1] Most of the recorded cases among bryophytes are among the Musci where a wounding of sporophytes[2] induces an aposporous production of gametophytes. The Anthocerotae are also known to be aposporous.[3]

Origin of the Bryophyta. The Bryophyta are undoubtedly a series of great antiquity, but the paleontological evidence in support of this contention is very meager. This is not surprising when one takes into consideration the delicate tissues of the bryophytes and the consequently poor chance of their becoming fossilized. However, anacrogynous Jungermanniales are known to have been present in the middle Car-boniferous.[4] The presence of Musci in the upper Carboniferous is not established with as great certainty,[5] but there seem to be good reasons for believing that moss-like plants existed at that time. Fragments of typical *Sphagnum* leaves have been found in the Cretaceous.[6]

Although it is generally agreed that the Bryophyta have arisen from the green algae, the manner in which they have arisen is a matter of speculation since there is a wide gap between the Chlorophyceae and the simplest known bryophyte. It is generally agreed that the progenitors of the Bryophyta belonged to the ulotrichaceous series of the Chloro-phyceae. Typical Ulotrichales are filamentous and have a plant body primarily fitted for an aquatic existence. The Bryophyta are largely terrestrial, and those of them that are aquatic in habit, as *Riella*, are land plants in which the aquatic habit is secondarily acquired. The transfer of algae from an aquatic to a terrestrial environment is thought to have lead to a development of a more massive plant body in which the reduced surface, in proportion to the volume, tended to prevent undue drying of the thallus. The primitive Bryophyta, similar to many present-

[1] See p. 132 for a fuller account of these phenomena.
[2] Marchal and Marchal, 1911.   [3] Bornhagen, 1926; Rink, 1935.
[4] Walton, 1925.   [5] Walton, 1928.   [6] Arnold, 1932.

day species, probably grew where there was an abundance of moisture in the soil. Thus there was but little evolution of water-absorbing tissues, except for the elongation of certain of the cells on the under surface into rhizoids. The abundance of moisture also resulted in a retention of the method of gametic union typical of algae, that is, by one or both of a pair of uniting gametes moving freely in all directions by swimming through water. The persistence of this primitive method of gametic union among all pteridophytes and in certain of the lower gymnosperms is one of the striking features in the evolution of plants.

Origin of the Sex Organs. Although it is relatively easy to visualize the manner in which the plant body of an alga may be evolved into a plant body such as is found in bryophytes, it is much more difficult to

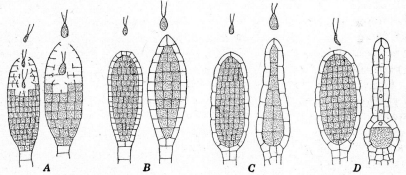

Fig. 1.—Diagrams showing the hypothetical origin of sex organs of Bryophyta. (*Based upon Davis*, 1903.)

envisage how the sex organs typical of Bryophyta have evolved from those of algae. The advantage of the sterile jacket layer present in sex organs of Bryophyta is obvious—it protects the delicate gametes from undue drying as they develop. The need of this protection is shown by the widespread occurrence among Bryophyta of additional features protecting the sex organs against loss of water. These include: embedding of the organs within the thallus; the development of accessory envelopes; and the surrounding of the organs by leaves.

The most attactive hypothesis explaining the origin of the sex organs characteristic of bryophytes holds that archegonia and antheridia are fundamentally alike and that they arose by sterilization of the outermost cells of a multicellular gametangium, similar in general appearance to the gametangium of *Ectocarpus*. One of the weaknesses of the hypothesis is that such gametangia, although widespread among brown algae, are not known for any green algae. However, certain green algae, as *Schizomeris*, produce reproductive cells in a structure essentially like a multicellular gametangium, and others, as *Chaetonema*, have multicellular antheridia resembling the gametangia of *Ectocarpus*. The gametangial hypothesis[1] holds that the hypothetical ancestral green algae were probably heterogamous and had both sorts of gametes motile (Fig. 1). In both the male and the female gametangia the outermost cells lost their gamete-producing capacity and matured into a sterile layer that enclosed the fertile cells. Retention of the gamete-producing capacity of all the fertile cells within the male gametangium resulted in the antheridium typical of Bryophyta. Archegonial evolution was accompanied by a sterilization of all but the lowermost of the interior cells. The single fertile cell lost the power of motility and became an egg. According to this interpretation the neck canal cells and ventral canal cell of an archegonium are homologous with the first-formed fertile cells within an antheridium. The evidence supporting this hypothetical origin of

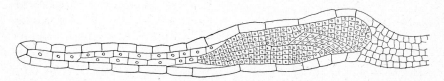

Fig. 2.—Abnormal archegonium of *Mnium*, showing an antheridium-like internal tissue. (× 215.)

bryophytan sex organs comes largely from the abnormal sex organs occasionally developed by various Hepaticae and Musci.[2] These reversionary sex organs are almost always archegonia. In some of them interior cells other than the lowermost become fertile. Sometimes these cells mature into eggs, but more often they divide and redivide to form masses of cubical cells identical in appearance with those within antheridia (Fig. 2). Reversion of the superficial cells to a fertile condition is most unusual, only one or two such cases having been recorded.[3]

Origin of the Sporophyte. Two theories have been advanced to account for the dissimilar alternating generations of Bryophyta and plants higher in the evolutionary scale. According to the *homologous theory*,[4] the sporophyte is a direct modification of the gametophyte and not an entirely new structure. Advocates of this theory hold that the sporophyte is to be interpreted as a neutral generation, modified from the sexual generation, and as one especially adapted for spore formation. The direct proliferation of one generation from the other in apogamous and aposporous individuals is the chief argument in favor of this theory.

[1] Davis, 1903.

[2] Bryan, 1927; Florin, 1923; Haupt, 1926; Holferty, 1904; Meyer, 1912.

[3] Meyer, 1912.

[4] This theory, first proposed by Pringsheim (1878) has Scott (1896) and Eames (1936) as its most ardent advocates. Lang (1909) and Coulter (1899), although taking a noncommittal stand, incline toward it.

The *antithetic theory*[1] holds that the sporophyte is an entirely new structure intercalated in the life cycle. According to this theory the zygote, instead of immediately undergoing a reduction division and forming spores, divided to form a number of diploid cells, each of which divided reductionally and formed spores. The result was a rudimentary type of sporophyte in which all the cells were sporogenous. From this was evolved a sporophyte in which the superficial cells matured into sterile cells instead of into reproductive cells. The Ricciaceae are the only present-day Bryophyta with this simple type of sporophyte. Further evolution of the sporophyte came about as a result of additional sterilization of the sporogenous tissue. In the higher Bryophyta this has resulted in a sporophyte differentiated into foot, seta, and capsule. The theory that there has been this progressive sterilization of sporogenous tissue rests largely upon the comparison of supposedly primitive and advanced sporophytes. Evidence supporting this assumption is also to be seen in abnormal individuals where, as in *Porella*,[2] the internal tissues of seta and foot revert to a fertile condition and form spores. Green algae showing beginning of an evolution toward the simple *Riccia* type of sporophyte are unknown. At one time *Coleochaete*, with its formation of several zoospores by the zygote, was thought to show this, but it is now known that the first division of the zygote nucleus of *Coleochaete* is reductional and that there is nothing corresponding to a rudimentary diploid generation.

The origin of a diploid asexually reproducing generation seems to be best explained by the antithetic theory, that is, by an intercalation of vegetative cell divisions between gametic union and meiosis. However, such an origin of the sporophyte does not explain the dissimilarity of the two generations among Bryophyta. The dissimilarity of the two is probably associated with the retention of the zygote within the archegonium and the resultant parasitism of the intercalated generation upon the sexual generation. On the other hand, parasitism may not be the sole cause of the dissimilarity since many brown algae have free-living alternating haploid and diploid generations that are dissimilar in appearance.

Three major evolutionary series (Hepaticae, Anthocerotae, Musci) are recognizable among the Bryophyta, but their relationships one to another are obscure. All three series appear to have diverged early from the hypothetical primitive Bryophyta evolved from the Chlorophyceae (Fig. 3).

From the standpoint of structure of the sporophyte, the Hepaticae are nearest to the hypothetical ancestors since they include the genera

---

[1] This theory outlined by Celakovsky in 1874 was first fully elaborated by Bower (1890). Its strongest champions are Campbell (1918) and Bower (1908, 1935).

[2] Anderson, 1923.

with the simplest known sporophytes.   Evolution among the Hepaticae has been chiefly in the gametophytic generation and has been either an elaboration of external complexity with a retention of internal simplicity, or has been an elaboration of an internal complexity with a retention of external simplicity.   Most sporophytes of Hepaticae show considerable sterilization of sporogenous tissue, but none of them shows any tendency toward unlimited (indeterminate) growth.   For this reason alone, the Hepaticae may be considered an evolutionary sideline that ends blindly.

The Musci also seem to be a blindly ending evolutionary sideline. Their gametophytes are externally complex and with some internal differ-

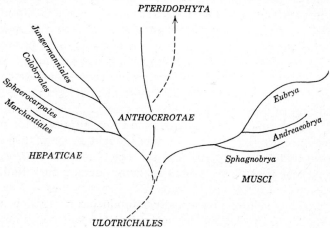

Fig. 3.—Diagram showing the suggested interrelationships among the Bryophyta.

entiation of tissues.   Most of them have sporophytes with a greater internal differentiation of tissues than do those of any Hepaticae, but growth of all sporophytes of Musci is also definitely limited.   The Musci are sometimes thought to have been evolved from the leafy Hepaticae (Jungermanniales, Calobryales), but this appears improbable when ontogeny of sex organs of the two and the early embryology are taken into consideration.

Gametophytes of the Anthocerotae, except for their embedded sex organs, are less advanced than those of Hepaticae and Musci.   On the other hand, the sporophytes are of a much more advanced type in that their growth is indeterminate.   Their indeterminate growth is thought to be a feature of fundamental importance which has made possible an evolution of a pteridophytic type of plant (page 114).

Classification of Bryophyta.   The conventional treatment of the Bryophyta is to range them in two classes, Hepaticae and Musci.   Within the past quarter century there has been a growing tendency to accept the proposal[1] that the Anthocerotales be placed in a class coordinate with the Musci and Hepaticae. When the Anthocerotales are placed in a separate class, the Bryophyta are divided into the three following classes:

The *Hepaticae* which have gametophytes that are dorsiventrally differentiated and either externally simple or externally differentiated into leaf and stem. The interior of the gametophyte may be homogeneous or composed of various tissues. Sex organs, except when terminal in position, are always formed from superficial cells on the dorsal side of the thallus. The sporophyte may be simple or with a foot, seta, and capsule. In either case it is determinate in growth and entirely parasitic upon the gametophyte.

The *Anthocerotae* which have gametophytes that are dorsiventrally differentiated, of simple external form, and internally homogeneous. The male sex organs are formed from hypodermal cells on the dorsal side of the thallus. The sporophyte is differentiated into a capsule and foot. The lower portion of a capsule is meristematic and continually adding to the upper portion. Sporogenous tissue in a sporophyte arises from the outer layer (amphithecium) of an embryo.

The *Musci* which have gametophytes with a transitory prostrate stage bearing sexual branches which continue growth as independent plants after disappearance of the prostrate portion. The sexual branches are differentiated into stem and leaves, radially symmetrical, and the sex organs are formed from superficial cells. The sporophyte consists of a foot, seta, and capsule. Frequently it has an internal differentiation of the sterile tissues and is only semiparasitic upon the gametophyte. Growth of the sporophyte is always determinate.

Bibliography

ANDERSON, FLORA. **1923.** *Proc. Ind. Acad. Sci.* **1922:** 261–262. 1 fig. [Abnormal sporophytes.]
ARNOLD, C. A. **1932.** *Papers Mich. Acad. Sci.* **15:** 51–61. 4 pl. [Fossil Bryophyta.]
BORNHAGEN, HEDWIG. **1926.** *Biol. Zentralbl.* **46:** 578–586. 7 figs. [Apospory.]
BOWER, F. O. **1890.** *Ann. Bot.* **4:** 347–370. [Origin of sporophyte.]
  1908. The origin of a land flora. London. 727 pp. 359 figs.
  1935. Primitive land plants. London. 658 pp. 449 figs.
BRYAN, G. S. **1927.** *Bot. Gaz.* **84:** 89–101. 20 figs. [Abnormal sex organs.]
CAMPBELL, D. H. **1918.** The structure and development of mosses and ferns. 3d ed. New York. 708 pp. 322 figs.
COULTER, J. M. **1899.** *Bot. Gaz.* **28:** 46–59. [Origin of sporophyte.]
DAVIS, B. M. **1903.** *Ann. Bot.* **17:** 477–492. 2 figs. [Origin of sex organs.]
EAMES, A. J. **1936.** Morphology of vascular plants. Lower groups (Psilophytales to Filicales). New York. 433 pp. 215 figs.
FLORIN, R. **1923.** *Ark. Bot.* **18,** Nr. 5: 1–58. 1 pl. 25 figs. [Abnormal sex organs.]
HAUPT, A. W. **1926.** *Bot. Gaz.* **82:** 30–54. 2 pl. 16 figs. [Abnormal sex organs.]

[1] Howe, 1899.

HOFMEISTER, W. **1851.** Vergleichende Untersuchungen der Keimung, Entfaltung und Fruchtbildung höherer Kryptogamen (Moose, Farrn, Equisetaceen, Rhizocarpeen und Lycopodiaceen) und der Saamenbildung der Coniferen. Leipzig. 179 pp. 33 pl.

HOLFERTY, G. M. **1904.** *Bot. Gaz.* **37**: 106–126. 2 pl. [Abnormal sex organs.]

HOWE, M. A. **1899.** *Mem. Torrey Bot. Club* **7**: 1–208. 35 pl. [Hepaticae and Anthocerotae of California.]

LANG, W. H. **1909.** *New Phytol.* **8**: 1–12. [Origin of sporophyte.]

MARCHAL, E., and E. MARCHAL. **1911.** *Bull. Cl. Sci. Acad. Roy. Belgique* **1911**: 750–778. 1 pl. [Apospory.]

MEYER, K. **1912.** *Biol. Zeitschr. Moskau* **1912**: 177–187. 12 figs. [Abnormal sex organs.]

PRINGSHEIM, N. **1878.** *Jahrb. Wiss. Bot.* **11**: 1–46. 2 pl. [Origin of sporophyte.]

RINK, W. **1935.** *Flora* **130**: 87–130. 28 figs. [Apospory.]

SCOTT, D. H. **1896.** *Rept.* of 66th. Meeting British Assoc. Adv. Sci. **1896**: 992–1010. [Origin of sporophyte.]

STRASBURGER, E. **1894.** *Ann. Bot.* **8**: 281–316. [Alternation of chromosome numbers.]

WALTON, J. **1925.** *Ann. Bot.* **39**: 563–572. 1 pl. 1 fig. [Fossil Bryophyta.]
    1928. *Ibid.* **42**: 707–716. 1 pl. 1 fig. [Fossil Bryophyta.]

CHAPTER II

HEPATICAE

There is great diversity in external form among gametophytes of the various genera of the Hepaticae, but all of them are fundamentally alike in that they are dorsiventrally differentiated and develop sex organs terminally or from superficial cells on the dorsal side of the thallus. The sporophytes are all alike in that they are strictly limited in growth and wholly parasitic upon the gametophyte. The class includes some 8,500 species grouped in about 175 genera.

The Hepaticae are less advanced than are other Bryophyta, but the decision as to which is the most primitive order of the class depends upon the criteria established. From the standpoint of gametophytic structure, *Sphaerocarpos* is the simplest of living liverworts. From the standpoint of sporophytic structure, the Ricciaceae are the simplest. Since the great phylogenetic sweep from Bryophyta upward is in the evolution of the sporophyte, the liverworts with the simplest sporophytes, the Ricciaceae, are best placed first among the Hepaticae, even though they belong to an order which shows the greatest internal differentiation of any gametophyte.

Until the beginning of the present century, the families here placed in the Hepaticae were segregated into two orders (Marchantiales and Jungermanniales). Recent investigations show that *Sphaerocarpos* and its immediate relatives should be placed in a separate order. The Calobryaceae merit the same consideration. Acceptance of these proposals results in a segregation of the Hepaticae into four orders.

ORDER 1. MARCHANTIALES

The gametophytes of Marchantiales differ from those of other Hepaticae in that they are internally differentiated into various tissues. The structure and development of the sex organs differ from that of all other Hepaticae but the Sphaerocarpales. The sporophytes are also distinct from other Hepaticae except the Sphaerocarpales in that the jacket layer surrounding the sporogenous tissue is but one cell in thickness. The order includes about 25 genera and 400 species.[1]

[1] All estimates of the number of genera and species for the various orders and families of the Hepaticae and Anthocerotae are based upon Stephani (1900–1924).

The gametophytes of Marchantiales are ribbon-shaped, dichotomously branched, and dorsiventrally differentiated. From the standpoint of complexity of internal structure, they are the most advanced of the Hepaticae. The dorsal part of the thallus is internally differentiated into air chambers, opening externally by a pore, and the ventral part is internally differentiated into a storage tissue comprised of two or three types of cells. In some cases there is a rudimentary conducting tissue of elongate cells in the sagittal axis of the storage tissue. Gametophytes of most Marchantiales differ from those of other Hepaticae in the presence of two kinds of rhizoids and in the presence of scales on the ventral surface.

In addition to these vegetative features all members of the order have antheridia developing in the same manner as will be described for *Riccia*. The archegonia also differ from those found in most other genera of Hepaticae in that the neck typically consists of six tiers of cells.

Sporophytes of Marchantiales differ from those of other Hepaticae (except Sphaerocarpales) in that the jacket layer never becomes more than one cell in thickness. From the standpoint of complexity of sporophytes, the order includes the family (Ricciaceae) with the simplest known sporophytes. The simplicity of this sporophyte is generally ascribed to its primitiveness, but there are those[1] who consider it a reduced rather than a primitive type.

If one accepts the primitiveness of the Ricciaceae, two general tendencies are evident in the Marchantiales. One of these is in the sporophyte. From the simple condition where the entire sporophyte is a capsule, there has been a partial sterilization of the sporogenous tissue to form a foot and a seta. In addition, advanced members of the order have a further differentiation of the sporogenous tissue into cells which produce spores and sterile cells (*elaters*) which assist in spore dispersal. The other general evolutionary tendency is in the manner in which the archegonia are borne. In the most primitive family, the Ricciaceae, the archegonia are borne in a longitudinal dorsal strip of indefinite extent. The family above this, the Corsiniaceae, produces archegonia in definitely circumscribed areas (*receptacles*), but a succession of receptacles may be formed by a branch. Intermediate families (Targioniaceae and Monocleaceae) have but one receptacle on a branch, and this lies just posterior to the growing apex. The most advanced family, the Marchantiaceae, also has a restriction of the female receptacle to a branch apex, but it only produces female receptacles on special erect branches. The nature of the receptacle, the manner in which it is borne, and the structure of the sporophyte are the bases for a segregation of the order into five families.

[1] Goebel, 1910.

FAMILY 1. RICCIACEAE

The Ricciaceae differ from other Marchantiales in that the sex organs are borne in a longitudinal strip extending the entire length of thallus. They are also the only family in which the sporophyte is not differentiated into foot, seta, and capsule. The family includes five genera and 141 species.

FIG. 4.—*Riccia trichocarpa* Howe. (× 3.)

Riccia is the most widely distributed member of the family. There are more than 135 species in the genus, and all but two of them are terrestrial in habit.

The gametophyte of *Riccia* is wholly prostrate and is typically rosette-like because of several dichotomous branchings (Fig. 4). Each branch of the thallus is linear to wedge-shaped, is thickened in the sagittal axis, and has a conspicuous median longitudinal furrow on the dorsal side. The ventral surface of the growing apex of a branch bears transverse rows of scales, one cell in thickness, which project forward and overlap the growing point. Near the growing point, the scales are very close to one another; back from it, they are some distance apart. Increase

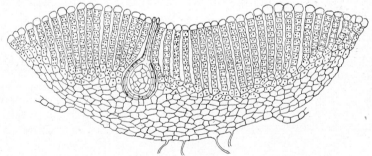

FIG. 5.—Semidiagrammatic transverse vertical section of gametophyte of *Riccia glauca* L. (× 80.)

in breadth of the median portion of a branch posterior to the growing point tears each scale in half. As a result, older portions of a branch appear to have two rows of scales, one near each lateral margin. Certain of the cells between the scales in older portions of the thallus give rise to unicellular rhizoids. As is the case with most other Marchantiales, these are of two sorts; those with smooth walls, and those with rod-like or plate-like ingrowths of the wall which project into the lumen of the rhizoid.

The lower portion of a thallus is a colorless parenchymatous tissue in which the cells may contain starch (Fig. 5). Above this is a single layer of air chambers which are vertical canals with their long axes approximately vertical. In most cases the canals are bounded by only four cells, but in some cases[1] the walls of the canals are plates of variable size. The cells constituting the walls of the air chambers contain numerous chloroplasts. Unlike most Marchantiales, but similar to other Ricciaceae, the air chambers of *Riccia* have no plate-like or filamentous ingrowths which increase the photosynthetic surface of the thallus. Above the air chambers is an "epidermal" layer, one cell in thickness. The air pores, through which there is an interchange of gases between the interior and exterior of the plant, are simple intercellular spaces bounded by four to six "epidermal" cells.

The growing distal end of each branch is occupied by a transverse row of three to five or more apical cells laterally joined to one another.[2] Each apical cell is triangular in vertical longitudinal section, and rectangular in surface view or in horizontal longitudinal section. Segments are cut off largely from the dorsal and ventral faces of each apical cell, but from time to time a segment may be cut off from a lateral face. The growing apex lies in a deep notch because maturation of embryonic tissue lateral to the group of apical initials is more rapid than of embryonic tissue posterior to the initials. Now and then certain of the median members in a row of apical cells divide vertically, and the original set of initials becomes segregated into two sets. This is the beginning of a dichotomy of the thallus and one which becomes more and more pronounced as more tissue develops between the two sets.

Although the apical initials cut off segments alternately to the dorsal and the ventral faces, the greater bulk of the thallus is derived from those produced at the dorsal face. The ventral segments have been described[3] as contributing only to the lowermost cell layer of the thallus and to its appendages (rhizoids and scales), but this seems to be too radical a statement. The first division in a segment from the dorsal face of an apical initial is parallel to the surface of the thallus (Fig. 6). The inner daughter cell, by division and redivision, contributes to the colorless parenchymatous tissue in the lower portion of a thallus. Derivatives from the outer daughter cell give rise to the air chambers and to the "epidermal" layer. Differentiation of the epidermal layer takes place quite early and there are sometimes but three or four cells intervening between the apical cell and the first embryonic epidermal cell. Differentiation of the air

[1] Black, 1913; Juel, 1910.   [2] Campbell, 1918.   [3] Pietsch, 1911.

chambers takes place farther back from the apical cell. There are those[1] who hold that the air chambers are formed by a cessation of upward growth in certain portions of the thallus and a vigorous upward growth in adjoining portions of the thallus. The more widely accepted view[2] holds that the air chambers arise schizogenously, that is, by a splitting of vertical cell walls in a compact embryonic tissue below the surface of the thallus. The splitting eventually extends upward to the epidermal layer and there forms an air pore.

Riccia, similar to other Hepaticae with dichotomously branching prostrate thalli, reproduces vegetatively by the progressive death of older

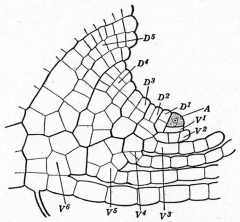

FIG. 6.—Longitudinal vertical section through growing apex of *Riccia glauca* L. The outlines of the portions derived from the last five dorsal segments (D^1–D^5) and from the last six ventral segments (V^1–V^6) cut off from the apical cell (A) are drawn with a heavy line. ($\times$ 325.)

parts, reaching a dichotomy and the two surviving branches continuing growth as two separate plants. In regions with a prolonged dry season, as in California, all the plant but the growing apices is killed by the summer drought. Resumption of growth by the persistent apices during the succeeding rainy season may result in a rosette of new plants. Several species of *Riccia* produce adventitious branches from the ventral surface of the thallus. Detachment of these adventitious branches, as in *R. fluitans* L., may result in numerous vegetatively formed individuals.[3] Cell divisions at the apices of young rhizoids may also result in a gemma-like mass capable of developing into a new plant.[4]

Most species of *Riccia* are homothallic, but in at least two cases, *R. Bischoffii* Hubner and *R. Curtisii* James [*Thallocarpus Curtisii* (James) Lindb.], the gametophytes are heterothallic. In *R. Curtisii* there is a

[1] Black, 1913; Hirsch, 1910; Leitgeb, 1879; Orth, 1930.
[2] Barnes and Land, 1907, Evans, 1918.   [3] Cavers, 1903.   [4] Campbell, 1918.

genotypic determination of sex at the time the spores are formed, two of the spores in a tetrad developing into female plants and two into male plants.[1]   In *Riccia*, as in other Marchantiales, the sex organs are formed in acropetalous succession and begin to develop in segments but one or two removed from the dorsal face of an apical cell.   The production of sex organs is long continued, and all stages of their development are to be found on the same thallus.   They lie in a more or less linear file within the longitudinal furrow on the dorsal side of the thallus.   Homothallic species successively form a few antheridia and then a few archegonia. Coincident with the development of sex organs, there is an upward growth of adjacent vegetative tissue.   A developing antheridium becomes completely enclosed by the upwardly growing adjacent tissue, and the *antheridial chamber* thus formed is connected with the exterior by a narrow

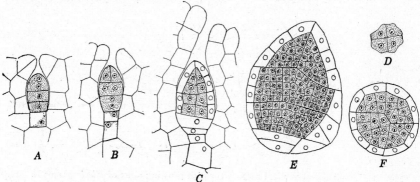

Fig. 7.—Stages in development of antheridia of *Riccia glauca* L.   A–C, E, in vertical section; D, F, in transverse section.   (× 485.)

cylindrical canal.   There is never a complete enclosure of the developing archegonium, and even at the time of fertilization the distal portion of its neck projects above the adjacent tissues.

Antheridial development[2] begins with the capitate enlargement of a superficial dorsal cell which is only two or three cells removed from an apical initial.   This *antheridial initial* soon divides transversely into a *basal cell* which is embedded in the thallus and an *outer cell* which projects somewhat above the thallus.   The basal cell develops into the embedded foot portion of the antheridial stalk and the outer cell into the remainder of the antheridium.   Successive transverse divisions of the outer cell result in a filament of four cells, which are easily distinguished from the basal cell and its derivatives by their denser protoplasts (Fig. 7A).   The two upper cells of the row are *primary antheridial cells* which eventually produce the antheridium proper, and the two lower cells are *primary*

[1] McAllister, 1916, 1928.   [2] Black, 1913; Campbell, 1918.

stalk cells from which is developed the stalk portion of an antheridium. Each of the two primary antheridial cells, by two successive vertical divisions at right angles to one another, gives rise to four cells (Fig. 7*B*, *D*). In both of the two tiers of four cells derived from primary antheridial cells, there is a periclinal division into four sterile *jacket initials* that encircle four fertile *primary androgonial cells*. Each primary androgonial cell, by division and redivision, gives rise to many cubical *androgonial cells* which become progressively smaller in each succeeding cell generation. The blocks of androgonial cells derived from the various primary androgonial cells may be distinguished from one another by their arrangement and by the fact that all descendents from a particular primary cell divide simultaneously (Fig. 7*C*, *E–F*). Increase in size of the androgonial tissue is accompanied by compensating anticlinal division in the sterile jacket layer. Each cell (*androcyte mother cell*) of the last cell gener-

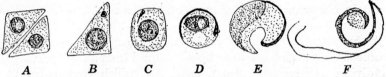

| A | B | C | D | E | F |

Fig. 8.—*Riccia Frostii* L. Stages in metamorphosis of androcytes into antherozoids. (*After Black*, 1913.)

ation of androgonial cells divides diagonally, instead of vertically or transversely, to form two *androcytes*.

The androcytes are the cells which are metamorphosed into *antherozoids*. Shortly after the androcytes are formed, there is the appearance of a single minute extranuclear granule, the *blepharoplast*, in each of them.[1] This is not identical with the centrosome-like granules evident in certain dividing androcyte mother cells. The metamorphosis of an androcyte into an antherozoid begins with an elongation of the blepharoplast (Fig. 8) into a cord-like structure that lies at the periphery of the cytoplasm and encircles about three-fourths of its circumference. One end of the elongating blepharoplast is enlarged to form a distinct head. The nucleus now becomes crescent-shaped and homogeneous in structure. It next migrates to the periphery of the protoplast where it comes to lie in contact with the posterior portion of the blepharoplast. There is then a development of two long flagella from the anterior portion of the blepharoplast. Recent studies of the finer structure of antherozoids of Marchantiales, though not of *Riccia*, show that one flagellum is inserted slightly behind the other.[2] The mature antherozoid, except for the blepharoplast portion comprising its apex, is almost wholly nuclear in

[1] Black, 1913.   [2] Mühldorf, 1931.

origin.   The androcyte cytoplasm not utilized in formation of the flagella persists as a small vesicle at the posterior of the antherozoid.

During the maturation of antherozoids there is a complete disappearance of all cell walls within an antheridium so that the antherozoids eventually lie within a common cavity.   Antheridia that have discharged their antherozoids are described as having inwardly distended jacket cells.[1]   However, there is considerable evidence at hand to show that there may be a complete gelatinization of the jacket layer before the antherozoids are liberated.   Discharge of antherozoids is due to an imbibitional absorption of water by the jacket layer, and ripe antheridia may retain their antherozoids for a considerable time if moisture conditions are unfavorable.   Evidence for this is to be seen in thalli bearing fairly well-advanced sporophytes adjacent to antheridia with ripe antherozoids.   The exact manner in which the antherozoids are discharged is as yet unknown.   It is not known whether this takes place explosively, as in certain Marchantiaceae,[2] or by exudation in a gelatinous mass, as in other Marchantiaceae.[3]

Archegonial development[4] begins with the upward projection of a superficial dorsal cell but two or three removed from an apical cell.   This cell divides transversely into a *basal cell*, which contributes to the embedded portion of the archegonium, and an *outer cell*, which develops into the remainder of the archegonium (Fig. 9*A*).   The first division of the outer cell is in an excentric vertical plane and cuts off a *peripheral initial*.   Two further excentric vertical divisions of the sister cell cut off two more peripheral initials.   These three peripheral initials so intersect one another that they lie lateral to a fourth cell, the *primary axial cell* (Fig. 9*B–C*).   Vertical division of each of the three peripheral initials results in the primary axial cell being surrounded by six *jacket initials*.   This is soon followed by a transverse division of each jacket initial to produce a tier of six *neck initials* which lie above a tier of six *venter initials* (Fig. 9*E*).   Transverse division of the neck initials and of their daughter cells ultimately produces an archegonial neck some six to nine cells in height.   The number of vertical rows of neck cells in a mature archegonium, a character more or less constant throughout an order, is correlated with the number of jacket initials formed.   Marchantiales typically have six rows of neck cells, Jungermannials have five rows, and Calobryales four rows.

Coincident with the formation of the jacket initials there is an unequal transverse division of the primary axial cell into a small upper *primary cover cell* and a large lower *central cell* (Fig. 9*D*).   During the development of the neck the primary cover cell, by two successive vertical divisions,

[1] Black, 1913.   [2] Cavers, 1903*A*; Peirce, 1902.
[3] Andersen, 1931.   [4] Black, 1913; Campbell, 1918.

forms four *cover cells*.   Mature cover cells are of greater diameter than the neck cells and separate from one another along the line of mutual contact when the archegonium is mature (Fig. 9*F–I*).   It is very probable that separation of cover cells from one another is due to a breaking down of the middle lamellae.   Development of the venter differs from that of the neck in that divisions of the six venter initials and of their daughter cells are not all in the same plane.   The mature venter is therefore 12 to 20 cells in perimeter instead of six cells as in the neck.   However,

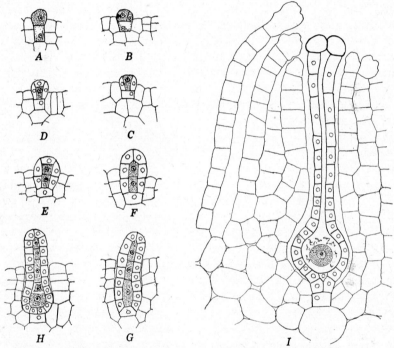

Fig. 9.—Stages in development of archegonia of *Riccia glauca* L.   (× 325.)

absence of periclinal divisions prior to fertilization results in a venter only one cell in thickness.

During the early development of neck and venter, there is a transverse division of the central cell into a *primary canal cell* and a *primary ventral cell* (Fig. 9*E–F*).   At first the two are of the same size; later the primary ventral cell becomes greater in diameter.   During the course of development of the neck, the primary canal cell divides to form four *neck canal cells*.   Soon after the four neck cells are formed, there is an unequal transverse division of the primary ventral cell into a small *ventral canal cell* and a large *egg* (Fig. 9*H*).   Shortly before fertilization the canal cells and the ventral canal cell disintegrate into a mucilaginous mass, and the cover cells separate from one another.

Free-swimming antherozoids discharged from an antheridium require a film of water to enable them to reach an archegonium. However, the gametophytes need not be inundated, since the dorsal furrow functions as a capillary tube which takes in sufficient water to permit movement

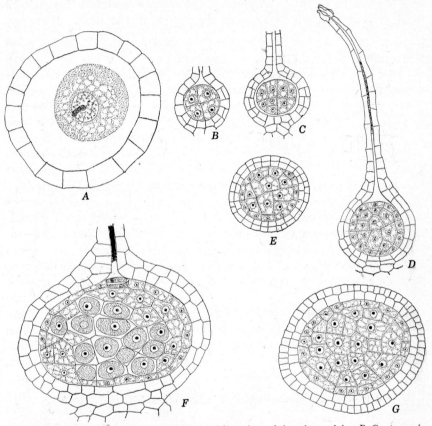

Fig. 10.—*Riccia glauca* L.   *A*, zygote with male and female nuclei.   *B–G*, stages in development of sporophytes.   *A, E, G*, in transverse section; *B–D, F*, in vertical section. (*A*, × 650; *B–G*, × 215.)

of the antherozoids. Antherozoids swimming near an archegonium swim into the neck and down it to the egg. Entrance into the neck is undoubtedly a response to a chemical stimulus, and it has been definitely shown for *Marchantia*[1] that the antherozoids are positively chemotactic to certain proteins and to certain inorganic salts, especially those of potassium. Several antherozoids may enter the venter of an arche-

[1] Åkerman, 1910; Lidforss, 1904.

gonium, but usually only one of them penetrates the egg. It is very probable that gametic union in homothallic species is generally between antherozoids and eggs produced on the same thallus. The details of gametic union have not been as fully described as they have for *Sphaerocarpos* and for certain Jungermanniales, but it has been shown[1] that after the antherozoid enters the egg the male gamete nucleus may be found lying close to the female nucleus (Fig. 10*A*).

Shortly after gametic union, the zygote secretes a wall and increases in volume until it nearly fills the cavity within the venter. Fertilization also stimulates division of venter cells, and, even before the first division of the zygote, there is a periclinal division of all cells in the venter. The venter remains two cells in thickness throughout the entire development of the sporophyte, and all further cell divisions are anticlinal. The first division of the zygote is transverse or approximately so.[2] The two daughter cells then divide in a plane at right angles to that of the first division. The fact that other Ricciaceae may have the first two divisions parallel, thus producing a filament of four cells,[3] is of no particular significance since both filamentous and quadrate four-celled embryos are to be found in other families of Marchantiales,[4] and sometimes even in the same genus.[5] Another series of divisions, at right angles to the preceding series, results in a globose embryo of eight cells (Fig. 10*B*). Succeeding divisions are in irregular sequence. At the stage where the embryo consists of 20 to 30 cells, there are periclinal divisions which differentiate it into an outer layer (the *amphithecium*) and an inner mass (the *endothecium*). In *Riccia*, where the entire sporophyte is a capsule, the ampithecium becomes the *jacket layer* of the capsule (Fig. 10*D–E*). The endothecium is the first cell generation (*archesporium*) of the sporogenous tissue. Division and redivision in cells of this tissue result in a considerable increase in the number of sporogenous cells (Fig. 10*F*). All members of the last cell generation of the sporogenous tissue are potential *spore mother cells* or *sporocytes*, but certain of them may degenerate. These sterile sporogenous cells of *Riccia* and of certain other Ricciaceae[6] have been considered[7] the forerunners of the elaters found in more advanced members of the order.

The spore mother cells destined to form spores are to be distinguished by the rounding up of their protoplasts and the beginning of a disintegration in the walls separating them one from another (Fig. 10*G*). Disintegration of walls of spore mother cells, together with disintegration of the nonfunctional sporogenous cells, jacket cells of the sporophyte, and the inner-cell layer of the surrounding venter, results in a viscous fluid

---

[1] Black, 1913.   [2] Campbell, 1918; Pagan, 1932; Pande, 1933.
[3] Garber, 1904; Lewis, 1906.   [4] Haupt, 1926.   [5] Lang, 1905.
[6] Sealey, 1930.   [7] Pagan, 1932.

in which the dividing spore mother cells are suspended.   The chief function of the immersing fluid is that of a food supply for the developing spores.   The reductional divisions of spore mother cells are similar to those found in other plants,[1] and they halve the number of chromosomes. The cytokinesis following the first division is incomplete, and the cell plates delimiting the four spores are formed simultaneously after the second division.   The four spores of a tetrad usually remain apposed to one another and embedded within a common spherical sheath until the spore walls are nearly mature (Fig. 11B–C).   In one species, $R.$ $Curtisii$ James, the spores of a tetrad remain united to one another even after

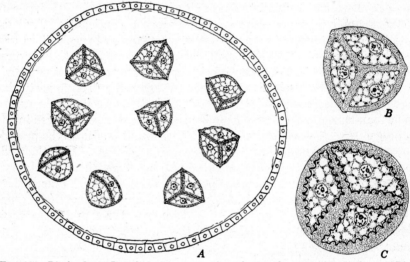

Fig. 11.—*Riccia glauca* L.   *A*, transverse section of a nearly mature sporophyte.   *B–C*, maturing tetrads of spores.   (*A*, × 215; *B–C*, × 485.)

they are fully mature and have been shed from a plant.[2]   The mature spore wall is composed of three layers which are laid down in centripetal succession.   The outermost layer, the *exosporium*, is thin and strongly cutinized.   The median layer (*mesosporium*) is thick and composed of three concentric zones.   The last-formed and innermost layer (the *endosporium*) is a homogeneous layer composed of pectose and callose.[3] The entire spore wall is irregularly thickened and folded.

The jacket layer of a sporophyte and the inner layer of the surrounding venter disappear long before these spores are mature (Fig. 11A).   The resultant spore mass, surrounded by a venter layer one cell in thickness, is usually called the mature sporophyte.   In the strict morphological sense, this is incorrect since the structure to which the term is applied consists

[1] Beer, 1906; Lewis, 1906.   [2] McAllister, 1916.   [3] Beer, 1906.

of a mass of spores, the first cells of the new gametophyte, surrounded by an envelope belonging to the preceding gametophyte.

The Ricciaceae, unlike other Hepaticae, do not have a liberation of the spores immediately after they are mature, and spores remain within a thallus until after the death and decay of the surrounding gametophytic tissues. Under ordinary conditions this does not take place until a year or so after the spores are formed. Germination of a spore begins with a rupture of the two outer wall layers and the protrusion of a tubular outgrowth in which the surrounding wall is continuous with the endosporium.[1] This *germinal tube* attains a length several times the diameter of the spore before a transverse wall is laid down near its distal end. Previous to formation of the cross wall most of the protoplasm has migrated to the distal end of the tube. Coincident with cross-wall formation, there is a development of a rhizoid near the region of emergence of the germinal tube from a spore. A second division, parallel to the first, results in two cells at the distal end of the tube. Each of these cells, by successive vertical divisions, gives rise to a tier of four cells. Further divisions in the proximal tier are transverse, and the daughter cells so formed elongate greatly in their longitudinal axes to form the distinctly cylindrical and elongate posterior portion of a young gametophyte. It is very probable that one of the four cells in the distal tier functions as an apical cell with two cutting faces. This cell functions actively and forms several derivatives. The other three cells of the tier divide but once or twice. Fairly early in development of the gametophyte, there is a replacement of the single apical cell by a transverse row of apical cells. From then onward further growth is identical with that at the apex of a mature thallus.

FAMILY 2. CORSINIACEAE

The Corsiniaceae differ from other Marchantiales in that branches of a female gametophyte bear a linear series of circumscribed receptacles. The sporophytes differ from those of other Marchantiales with a differentiation into foot, seta, and capsule in that they lack typical elaters. The family has but two genera. *Corsinia*, with the single species *C. coriandrina* (Spreng.) Lindb., occurs in North America (Texas), South America, Europe, Africa, and Japan. The other genus, *Funicularia* (*Boschia*), has two species: *F. Weddellii* (Mont.) Trev. in Brazil, and *F. japonica* Stephani in Japan.

The gametophyte of *Corsinia* resembles that of *Marchantia*, but its branching is restricted to two or three dichotomies. The ventral scales are more or less ovate and have acute to filamentous apices. Unlike most other Marchantiales, the scales are irregularly distributed over the

[1] Campbell, 1918.

entire ventral surface.   The lower portion of a thallus is a relatively thick, colorless, parenchymatous tissue.   Above this is a single layer of air chambers, each of which opens externally by a simple pore surrounded by one or two rings of thin-walled cells.   The floor of the chamber may have short filaments of chloroplast-containing cells or may lack them.

Most individuals of *Corsinia* are heterothallic, but some are homothallic.   The antheridia are borne in definitely localized areas (*receptacles*) on the median axis of the dorsal surface.   Each receptacular area is surrounded by a low ridge resulting from more active growth of the adjacent thallus tissue.   Antheridial development is according to the method typical of Marchantiales, and each mature antheridium lies within an antheridial chamber.[1]

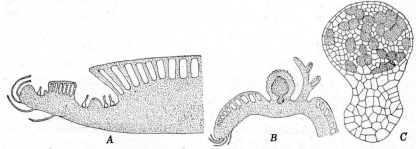

Fig. 12.—*Corsinia coriandrina* (Spreng.) Lindb.   *A–B*, vertical sections of gametophytes. *C*, vertical section of a sporophyte.   (*A–B, after Leitgeb,* 1879; *C, after K. Meyer,* 1912.)

The archegonia are also restricted to definitely localized areas on the dorsal surface of the thallus.   The female receptacle lies in a conspicuous sunken pit resulting from a suppression of upgrowth of tissue between and lateral to the archegonia (Fig. 12*A*).   Each receptacle contains 6 to 10 archegonia surrounded by numerous filamentous proliferations (*paraphyses*) from the surface of the receptacle.   One, two, or more sporophytes are developed on each receptacle.   Periclinal division of cells of the venter is more extensive than in *Riccia*, and the enlarged venter (*calyptra*) surrounding the sporophyte is a massive structure several cells in thickness.   The calyptra with its enclosed embryo is partially ensheathed by an *involucre*. This structure is first evident on the receptacular floor as a small meristematic hump which lies either between or posterior to the archegonia.   Depending on whether the involucre adjoins one sporophyte or a group of sporophytes, it either develops into a curved and irregularly branched shield at one side of a sporophyte (Fig. 12*B*), or it develops into a radially symmetrical, peltately lobed structure in which each lobe shields a sporophyte.   The upper portion of the mature involucre is internally differentiated into air

[1] Leitgeb, 1879.

chambers. The involucre of the Corsiniaceae has been interpreted[1] as the evolutionary forerunner of the archegoniophore of the Marchantiaceae, but one that differs from it in being developed subsequent to fertilization. This interpretation does not appear logical since the involucre is merely an upgrowth of tissue posterior to the growing point, whereas the archegoniophore is formed by an upward growth of the growing point itself.

The sporophyte is more advanced than that of *Riccia* since it is differentiated into *foot, seta,* and *capsule.*[2] It is to be considered more primitive than the sporophyte of Marchantiaceae because the foot and seta are composed of relatively few cells. The sporogenous tissue becomes differentiated into two types of cells, spore mother cells, and sterile cells that persist until the spores are mature (Fig. 12C). The sterile cells are homologous with the elaters of Targioniaceae and Marchantiaceae, but they are a very primitive type of elater in which there is no fibrous thickening of the cell walls.

FAMILY 3.   TARGIONIACEAE

The Targioniaceae differ from other Marchantiales in having female receptacles that are enclosed by a sheath developed from tissues lateral to it. The two genera of the family, *Targionia* and *Cyathodium,* have three and five species, respectively.

Targionia hypophylla L., the species here selected as illustrative of the family, is world wide in distribution and is a common liverwort in the western part of the United States. The gametophyte (Fig. 13) is ribbon-like, is sparingly dichotomous, and has adventitious branches formed in abundance from the ventral side of the midrib. Most of these branches arise laterally, but some of them arise near the thallus apex and grow anterior to it. Death and decay of the slender connection between the branch and the parent plant result in extensive vegetative propagation of the gametophyte.[3]

When viewed from above, the upper surface of a gametophyte is divided into small polygonal areas, each area indicating the position of an air chamber just beneath the epidermal layer. Each chamber opens externally by a small pore that is encircled by four to six concentric rings of cells so arranged that the pore is at the summit of a small hump. The chambers, which have the same schizogenous origin as those of *Riccia*,[4] lie in a single layer at the upper surface of the thallus and are laterally separated from one another by vertical plates one cell in thickness (Fig. 14A). The floor of a chamber has numerous simple or branched, erect, photosynthetic filaments. A filament is generally three cells in height, the spherical distal cell being much larger than the others. The colorless tissue below the air chambers is about 20 cells in thickness in the region

[1] Cavers, 1910.   [2] Meyer, 1914.   [3] Cavers, 1904.   [4] Deutsch, 1912.

of the midrib and is composed of elongate cells whose long axes parallel the long axis of the thallus. Toward the lateral margins of a branch the colorless tissue is composed of fewer and more nearly isodiametric cells, and at the extreme margin it is but one cell in thickness. Many of the cells in the colorless tissue contain starch grains. Intermingled with the starch-containing cells are isolated cells containing either mucilage or a large oil body. Isolated cells containing an oil body are characteristic of most genera in the Marchantiales. Superficial cells of the ventral surface produce obliquely inserted scales, which lie in two rows, one on either side of the midrib. The scales are one cell in thickness except in the basal portion. The ventral surface of a thallus also bears the two types of rhizoids characteristic of Marchantiales. Apical growth

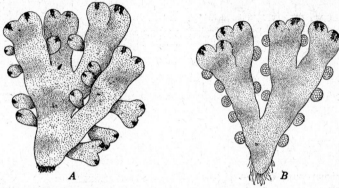

Fig. 13.—*Targionia hypophylla* L.   *A*, female gametophyte with adventitious branches. *B*, male gametophyte.   (× 1½.)

is due to a single wedge-shaped apical cell that alternately cuts off segments ventrally and dorsally.[1]

Antheridia are produced only on short lateral branches which arise adventitiously from the ventral surface of a midrib (Fig. 13B). Antheridia develop according to the same sequence as those of *Riccia*. Development of antheridia is accompanied by an upward growth of adjacent vegetative tissue, and each mature antheridium lies within an antheridial chamber (Fig. 14C). These chambers are externally recognizable as small pores irregularly distributed over the upper surface of an antheridial branch.

Archegonia begin to develop from superficial dorsal cells only two or three removed from the apical cell (Fig. 14A). The history of their development is essentially the same as in *Riccia*. As in the Corsiniaceae, there is a definitely restricted receptacular area, but, unlike the Corsiniaceae, the receptacle never comes to lie a considerable distance posterior to the thallus apex. *Targionia* is essentially *acrogynous* (with a

[1] Deutsch, 1912; O'Keefe, 1915.

cessation of apical growth following the production of archegonia), but there is no proof that the last-formed archegonium is developed from the apical cell itself as in the acrogynous Jungermanniales.

Development of archegonia is accompanied by a maturation and enlargement of tissues posterior to them that push the archegonial receptacle to the ventral side of the thallus (Fig. 14A). However, in

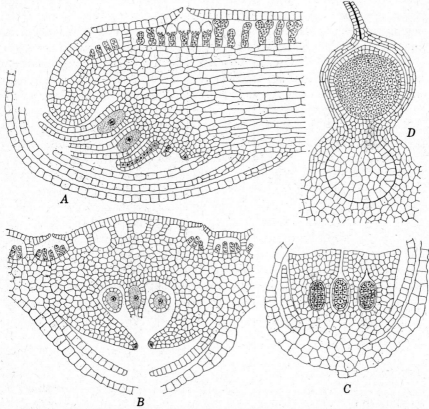

Fig. 14.—*Targionia hypophylla* L.   *A–B*, longitutinal and transverse vertical sections of gametophytes.   *C*, vertical section of an antheridial branch.   *D*, vertical section of a sporophyte.   All figures semidiagrammatic.   (*A–C*, × 160; *D*, × 120.)

spite of its ventral position, the archegonial receptacle is a dorsal structure since it lies posterior to the dorsal face of the apical cell.   Inversion in position of the receptacle is accompanied by the outgrowth of a conspicuous plate-like mass from either lateral flank of the receptacle.   These two outgrowths eventually become apposed to each other to form a sheath, the *involucre*, which surrounds the developing sporophyte.   In most cases development of the involucre takes place subsequent to fertilization, but instances have been noted where it is well along in development before fertilization.[1]   Each lobe of the involucre is to be interpreted as an adventitious branch from the dorsal surface of the thallus, and one which grows in length by the functioning of a single apical cell (Fig. 14*B*).   The posterior portion of each of these adventitious branches develops air chambers on its morphologically dorsal surface, but these lack photosynthetic filaments.   Late in the development of the involucre, there is a heavy cutinization of the cells at the outer face.   In addition to being enclosed by the involucre, the sporophyte is ensheathed by a calyptra, three or four cells in thickness, resulting from anticlinal and periclinal divisions in the venter of the surrounding archegonium (Fig. 14*D*).

Cell divisions in the early development of an embryo are variable, and at the four-celled stage the cells may lie in a quadrant[2] or in a linear file.[3]   The lower half of the embryo becomes differentiated into a broad foot and a narrow seta; the upper half, into a spherical capsule.   The foot attains its full size relatively early in development of the sporophyte, and its superficial cells become short papillate haustoria which obtain food from the adjoining gametophyte tissues.   The seta is composed of many isodiametric embryonic cells until the capsule is mature.   There is then a rapid elongation of these embryonic cells that ruptures the calyptra and pushes the capsule through the two flaps of the involucre and to some distance beyond the apex of the gametophyte.

The capsule has a relatively early differentiation into amphithecium and endothecium.   The jacket layer matured from ampithecial cells is one cell in thickness at maturity and with the cells having band-like fibrous thickenings of their walls.   The apex of the jacket is differentiated into a well-defined circular lid.   Dehiscence of the capsule is by the shedding of this lid in one piece or by its breaking into several fragments.[4]   After shedding of the lid, the remainder of the capsule wall splits into five to eight lobes which bend back upon themselves.   The sporogenous cells within the capsule increase greatly in number after they are differentiated.   About half of the cells of the last cell generation in the sporogenous tissue function as spore mother cells, each dividing to form four spores.   The other half of the sporogenous cells elongate greatly and mature into elongate cells (*elaters*) with two or three spiral thickenings on their walls.   The cells maturing into elaters are indiscriminately mixed with those dividing to form spores.   Elaters are sensitive to hygroscopic changes, curling and abruptly uncurling as they become alternately dry and moist after dehiscence of the capsule.   The abrupt spring-like uncoiling of the elaters aids in discharge of spores from the capsule.

FAMILY 4.   MONOCLEACEAE

The Monocleaceae are placed in a separate family because of the unique hood-like sheath posterior to the female receptacle.   The elongate

---

[1] Deutsch, 1912.   [2] Campbell, 1918.   [3] O'Keefe, 1915.   [4] Cavers, 1904.

capsule of the sporophyte is also distinctive. The single genus *Monoclea* has but two species, *M. Forsteri* Hook., found in New Zealand and Patagonia, and *M. Gottschei* Lindb., found in tropical North and South America.

The thallus of *M. Forsteri* (Fig. 15) is twice or thrice dichotomously branched and is the largest known thallose gametophyte among Bryophyta (length up to 12 cm., breadth to 2.5 cm.). There is no distinct midrib, but the thallus is some 10 cells in thickness in the sagittal axis and tapering to a thickness of one or two cells at the lateral margins. The thallus is a solid parenchymatous tissue in which the chloroplasts are restricted to the dorsal epidermis and the cells immediately beneath. This lack of air chambers might be considered a justification for excluding the genus from the Marchantiales were it not known that two other genera of the order (*Dumortiera*[1] and *Monoselenium*[2]) form only rudimentary chambers. Isolated cells in the thallus of *Monoclea* have the oil bodies characteristic of Marchantiales. Scales are never matured from segments cut off from the ventral face of the initials, but there is a formation of unicellular mucilage hairs which project forward and overarch the delicate growing point.[3] The ventral surface of the thallus has two kinds of rhizoids, thin-walled ones and those in which the walls are irregularly thickened. Terminal growth of a thallus is by means of a transverse row of wedge-shaped apical cells.

Fig. 15.—*Monoclea Forsteri* Hook. (*After Cavers*, 1904.)

Monoclea is heterothallic. The antheridia are borne in sessile male receptacles which project slightly above the dorsal surface of the thallus. Since the apical initials are not destroyed in receptacular formation, there is continued apical growth and a production of a succession of male receptacles. The antheridia of each receptacle are produced in acropetalous succession, and their development is typical of that of Marchantiales.[4] Development of antheridia is accompanied by an upward growth of adjoining tissue, so that a mature antheridium lies within an antheridial chamber opening to the exterior by a long narrow canal (Fig. 16*A*). Certain of the cells lining the antheridial chamber develop unicellular mucilage hairs similar to those on the ventral surface of the growing apex.

The first stages in development of archegonia are to be found only a few segments back from the apical initials. Production of archegonia is not long continued, only a dozen or so being formed. *Monoclea* is

[1] Campbell, 1918*A*.   [2] Goebel, 1910.
[3] Cavers. 1904, 1904*A*.   [4] Johnson, 1904.

anacrocynous, that is, production of archegonia does not check apical
growth.   However, the portion of a thallus developed anterior to the
female receptacle does not subsequently form new receptacles.   Shortly
after the female receptacle is differentiated, there is a thickening of the
portion of the thallus posterior to it, after which the front edge of the
thickening grows forward to form a hood-like outgrowth.   Elongation of
the hood is at the same rate as that of the growing point anterior to the
receptacle.   The tubular *involucre* resulting from elongation of hood and
thallus apex may attain a length of 15 mm. before growth ceases (Fig.
16*B*).   Subsequent apical growth of a branch bearing a female receptacle
is due to the activity of two new sets of initials which appear one on either

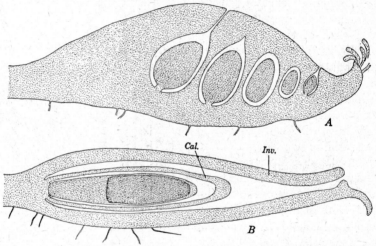

FIG. 16.—*Monoclea Gottschei* Lindb.   *A,* longitudinal vertical section through a male
gametophyte.   *B,* longitudinal vertical section through a female gametophyte showing a
sporophyte surrounded by calyptra (*Cal.*) and involucre (*Inv.*).   (*A,* × 34; *B,* × 16.)

side of the involucre which remains in the angle between the two new
branches.[1]   A mature archegonium has a swollen venter and a long neck.
The neck has the six vertical rows of jacket cells typical of Marchantiales,
but there may be as many as 10 neck canal cells.
    The young sporophyte has an early differentiation into foot, seta, and
capsule.   The great length of the seta and the elongate capsule in the
mature sporophyte are features more typical of Jungermanniales than of
Marchantiales.   However, this resemblance is only superficial since the
jacket layer of the capsule is but one cell in thickness and never has the
dehiscence into four valves characteristic of Jungermanniales.   Late in
development of the sporogenous tissue there is a vertical elongation of all
the cells.   Certain of these cells mature directly into elaters.   Other of

[1] Johnson, 1904; Cavers, 1904, 1904*A.*

them divide transversely to form eight isodiametric spore mother cells.[1] Thus, unlike *Targionia*, elaters and spore mother cells are not members of the same cell generation. Quadripartition of the spore mother cell to form spores is by furrowing, a type of cytokinesis more commonly found in Jungermanniales than in Marchantiales.

Monoclea has been referred both to the Marchantiales[2] and to the Jungermanniales.[3] The features showing its affinities with the Marchantiales include: external appearance of the thallus, oil bodies in isolated cells, two types of rhizoids, structure of male receptacle, ontogeny of antheridia, structure of neck of archegonia, and structure and dehiscence of capsule wall. The chief arguments for placing the genus in the Jungermanniales are the shape of the capsule, lack of air chambers in the thallus, lack of ventral scales, and general resemblance of the female receptacle, involucre, and sporophyte to those of certain anacrogynous Jungermanniales.

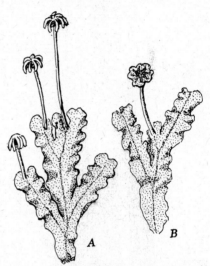

FAMILY 5. MARCHANTIACEAE

The Marchantiaceae include all of the genera in which the archegonia are borne on special, stalked, vertical branches (*archegoniophores*). There are 17 genera and some 235 species. These are separated into three subfamilies, sometimes given the rank of separate families,[4] which are superficially distinguishable from one another by the structure of the air pore.

FIG. 17.—*Marchantia polymorpha* L. *A*, female gametophyte. *B*, male gametophyte. (× ¾.)

The most advanced genus of the family, *Marchantia*, has about 65 species, of which *M. polymorpha* L. (Fig. 17) is the best known and most widely distributed. In many respects this widely studied genus is not typical of the family since most of the genera do not have the stalked antheridiophores and the asexual reproduction by gemmae that are found in *Marchantia*.

Marchantiaceae, except *Dumortiera* and *Monoselenium*, are readily recognized in the field by their prostrate dichotomously branched thalli in which the dorsal surface is divided into rhomboidal to polygonal areas, each with a small but conspicuous pore in the center. The dichotomous

---

[1] Johnson, 1904.   [2] Campbell, 1898; Cavers, 1904; Johnson, 1904.
[3] Schiffner, 1893–1895, 1913.   [4] Evans, 1923.

branching so prominent in *Marchantia* is sometimes obscured in other genera because of a development of adventitious branches from the ventral thallus surface.

The apex of a thallus usually has a transverse row of apical cells, but in some genera[1] there is a single apical cell. Air chambers begin to develop in the embryonic tissue a short distance posterior to the thallus apex. The preponderance of evidence favors the view that they arise schizogenously[2] rather than by upward growth of limited areas of the dorsal surface.[3] Air chambers may be in a single horizontal layer just beneath the epidermis, as in *Marchantia* (Fig. 18A); or in two or more lay-

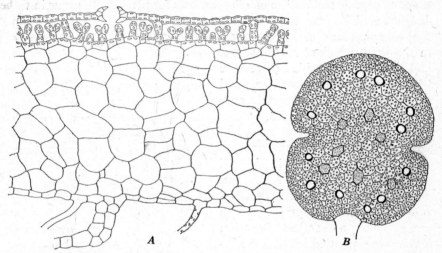

Fig. 18.—*Marchantia polymorpha* L. *A*, vertical section through a gametophyte. *B*, a gemma. ($\times$ 160.)

ers, at least in the median portion of a thallus, as in *Reboulia*. About half of the genera in the family have chambers of the first type. Air chambers of the *Marchantia* type have simple or branched filaments of chloroplast-containing cells arising from the floor of the chamber; those of the *Reboulia* type usually lack filamentous or plate-like outgrowths. Both types of air chamber have well-defined pores in which the bounding cells are either in concentric rings or superimposed in tiers to form a barrel-like structure. The portion of the gametophyte below the air chambers is several cells in thickness, except near the lateral margins, and usually lacks chloroplasts. These closely fitting parenchymatous cells are isodiametric except along the midrib. Most of them contain starch grains. Isolated cells may contain a single large oil body or be filled with mucilage. The cells

[1] Haupt, 1926, 1929.

[2] Barnes and Land, 1907; Dupler, 1921; Evans, 1918; Haupt, 1929.

[3] Leitgeb, 1879; Orth, 1930.

comprising the midrib portion of this colorless tissue are elongate in the saggital axis of the thallus and with locally thickened walls. The lower surface of a gametophyte bears two or more rows of scales, never a single row as in the Ricciaceae. Between the scales are both the smooth-walled and tuberculate rhizoids typical of Marchantiales.

Marchantiaceae regularly reproduce vegetatively as a result of apical growth, branching, and progressive death at the posterior end of the thallus reaching a dichotomy. Vegetative multiplication is also due to the production of adventitious branches from the ventral face of the thallus, followed by the death and decay of the tissue connecting branch with parent plant. In *Marchantia* and *Lunularia* special asexual reproductive bodies, *gemmae*, are produced in cup-like or crescent-shaped *cupules* on the dorsal surface of the thallus. The efficiency of this method of propagation is shown by the wide distribution of *Lunularia cruciata* (L.) Dum. throughout various areas in the United States. In this country, where the plant has been introduced from Europe with nursery stock, a formation of sporophytes is of very rare occurrence and has thus far only been found in California. The cupules of *Marchantia* arise a short distance back from the growing point. They are circular areas which soon become pit-like depressions through the upward growth of the surrounding vegetative tissue.[1] The cells lining the floor of the cupule are all potential initials of gemmae, and many of them soon begin to function as initials by developing into papillate outgrowths. By two transverse divisions the initial becomes divided into a basal cell, a stalk cell, and the primary cell of the gemma proper. The primary cell divides transversely to form a filament of four to five cells, after which divisions are in both the vertical and the horizontal planes. The stalk cell does not divide. A mature gemma is disciform, several cells thick in the median portion, and with a marginal growing point in a shallow indentation on either lateral margin (Fig. 18*B*). Most of the cells contain chloroplasts, but isolated superficial cells on the central area of both flattened faces are colorless. Isolated cells just within the margin may contain oil bodies instead of chloroplasts. Certain of the cells on the floor of the cupule develop into club-shaped mucilage cells. The discharge of mucilage from these cells and the swelling of the mucilage as it imbibes water break the gemmae away from their stalks and force them out of the cupule. Gemmae coming to lie on soil then develop rhizoids from the colorless cells on the face next the soil. The growing points in the two marginal indentations begin to function in the same manner as the growing point of a vegetative branch. Continued apical growth and dichotomous branching of the two growing points are in the opposite direction.

[1] Barnes and Land, 1908.

Death and decay of the tissue originally comprising the gemma results in two separate plants.

The stalked female sexual branches (*archegoniophores* or *carpocephala*) are structures peculiar to the Marchantiaceae. They are modified prostrate branches of the thallus. An archegoniophore begins development with an upward bending of a prostrate vegetative branch. In most cases, including *Marchantia*, there is a precocious dichotomy in the upturned branch.[1] The branch-like nature of the mature archegoniophore is shown by the dorsiventrality of the stalk portion; the side corresponding to the ventral face usually having two longitudinal furrows each containing scales and rhizoids, whereas the side corresponding to the dorsal face has an internal differentiation of air chambers. The presence of two furrows is evidence that the growing point divided early even if the

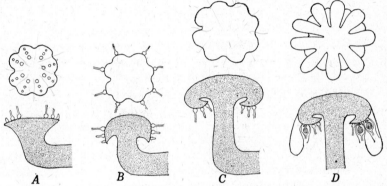

Fig. 19.—*Marchantia polymorpha* L.   Diagrams of top view and vertical section of stages in development of an archegoniophore.

stalk itself remains undivided. After the stalk portion of female branches of *Marchantia* has elongated slightly, there is a dichotomy of the forked swollen apex, followed by a second dichotomy of each of the lobes. The apex of a stalk thus becomes a rosette-like eight-lobed disk, which seems to be radially symmetrical but which actually is bilaterally symmetrical (Fig. 19*A*). Not all members of the family have the apex of the female branch becoming eight-lobed. In certain of them, as in *Asterella* (*Fimbriaria*), which has but a single furrow in the stalk portion, two successive dichotomies result in four apical lobes. In other cases, as in *Conocephalum*, there are but six lobes because of a failure of two of the four lobes to branch again.

Shortly after apical branching ceases, there is an acropetalous formation of archegonia from segments cut off on the dorsal face of the apical initial or initials. In *Marchantia* this results in a group of archegonia

[1] Cavers, 1904*B*.

posterior to each growing point, that is, a formation of eight receptacular areas. The entire apex of the archegoniophore is frequently termed the receptacle, but this is incorrect since it really is a composite structure with eight receptacles.

The archegonia are mature and fertilization is effected at a time when the disk of the archegoniophore is but slightly elevated above the remainder of the thallus. After fertilization and as the stalk portion of the female branch is elongating, there is a conspicuous expansion of the tissue comprising the central area of the disk (Fig. 19*B*). This upwelling, which resembles the raising of a loaf of bread dough in a pan, inverts the marginal portion of an archegoniophore so that the archegonia lie with their necks downward. The oldest archegonia are now nearest the periphery of the disk and the youngest nearest the stalk (Fig. 19*C*). In *Marchantia*, following this inversion, there is the development of a plate of tissue on either side of the eight receptacular surfaces. Thus the eight groups of archegonia each becomes surrounded by a two-lipped curtain-like involucre. Coincident with development of the involucre, *Marchantia* has an intercalary development of stout cylindrical processes from the periphery of the disk (Fig. 19*D*). In *M. polymorpha* L., as in most other species of the genus, these rays are alternate to the receptacular surfaces. Most individuals of *M. polymorpha* have nine rays; seven representing middle lobes between adjoining dichotomies and two representing lateral lobes.

In most genera of the family, including *Marchantia*, growth in length of a thallus branch ceases with development of an archegoniophore. In a few genera, including *Clevea*, the apex of the thallus continues to grow in length after differentiation of an archegoniophore. The origin of the archegoniophore of *Clevea* as a hump of meristematic tissue two or three cells back from the dorsal face of the apical cell[1] would seem to show that it should be interpreted as an adventitious branch arising on the dorsal surface of the thallus.

There is great variation in the manner in which the antheridia of Marchantiaceae are borne. In the simplest case the antheridial receptacles are comparable to those of Ricciaceae and Monocleaceae, since they are localized antheridia-bearing areas on the dorsal surface of a vegetative branch. The production of antheridia may be a continuous process, as in *Asterella californica* (Hampe) Underw.;[2] generally, however, differentiation of fertile areas is intermittent and results in receptacular surfaces separated from one another by sterile tissue. The most advanced condition is found in *Marchantia* and a few other genera. Here, there is a special male branch (the *antheridiophore*) with the same dichotomy as is found in the archegoniophore. An antheridiophore differs from an

[1] Bergdolt, 1926.   [2] Haupt, 1929.

archegoniophore in its lack of an inversion of the receptacular surfaces and in the lack of such accessory structures as rays or involucres.

The ontogeny of the sex organs of Marchantiaceae is the same as in the Ricciaceae and other Marchantiales (Fig. 20).   The neck of an archegonium typically has a jacket layer of six vertical rows of cells, but there is variation both in the number of canal cells and in the time at which the primary ventral cell divides to form the ventral canal cell and egg.

Fertilization takes place in *Marchantia* at a time when the sexual branches are but slightly elevated above the thallus.   The antherozoids are exuded in a gelatinous mass,[1] instead of explosively as in certain

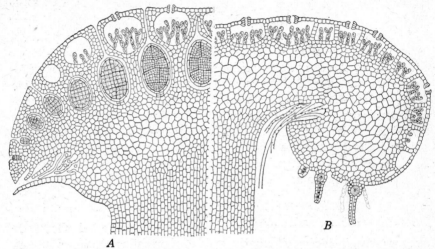

B

A

Fig. 20.—*Marchantia polymorpha* L.   *A*, semidiagrammatic vertical section of an antheriodiophore.   *B*, semidiagrammatic vertical section of an archegoniophore.   (× 50.)

genera of the family.[2]   Free-swimming antherozoids have been shown to be positively chemotactic to certain chemical compounds, especially proteins and inorganic salts of potassium,[3] and it is very probable that the entrance of an antherozoid into the neck of an archegonium is a chemotactic response.   Union of antherozoid and egg takes place as in other Hepaticae, but the male gamete nucleus seems to lie next the female nucleus for some time before the two unite with each other.[4]   As is the case with other liverworts, fertilization stimulates periclinal division of cells in the venter, and this tissue develops into a *calyptra* that surrounds the sporophyte until the latter is nearly mature.   Fertilization also stimulates a division of cells immediately below the archegonium and their division and redivision produces a sheet-like cylindrical outgrowth, one cell in thickness, the *pseudoperianth*.   Thus, there are three con-

[1] Andersen, 1931.   [2] Cavers, 1903*A*; Peirce, 1902.
[3] Åkerman, 1910; Lidforss, 1904.   [4] Andersen, 1929.

centric protective sheaths around the sporophyte; the calyptra, the pseudoperianth, and the involucre.

The first division of the zygote is transverse or approximately so. Most species of *Marchantia*[1] have the second division at right angles to the first and a quadrate disposition of the cells at the four-celled stage. The two uppermost (epibasal) of the four cells develop into the capsule

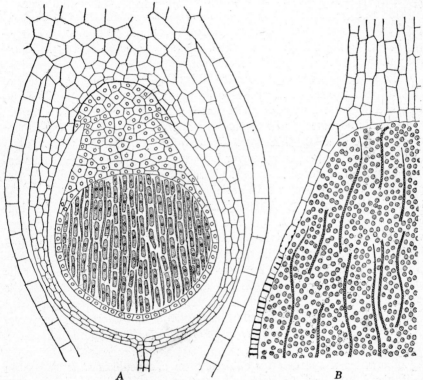

Fig. 21.—*Marchantia polymorpha* L.   *A*, longitudinal section of a young sporophyte surrounded by a calyptra and pseudoperianth.   *B*, longitudinal section of a portion of a nearly mature sporophyte.   (*A*, × 215; *B*, × 120.)

and the upper portion of the seta, and the two lowermost (hypobasal) cells develop into the remainder of the seta and the foot.   One species of *Marchantia* has one cell of a two-celled embryo dividing transversely[2] and the three cells of the filamentous embryo developing respectively into, foot, seta, and capsule of a mature sporophyte.

The lower portion of the foot of *M. polymorpha* develops a mushroom-like expansion which increases the surface for the absorption of food from the adjoining gametophytic tissue (Fig. 21*A*).   Cells of the seta

---

[1] Andersen, 1929; Durand, 1908; Heberlein, 1929.   [2] McNaught, 1929.

are approximately isodiametric and in vertical rows.   Late in the sporophytic development there is a rather sudden increase in the length of the
seta by an elongation of its cells.   This growth in length of a seta ruptures
the calyptra and pushes the capsule beyond the pseudoperianth and
involucre, thus permitting scattering of the spores when the capsule
dehisces.   The embryonic capsule portion of the sporophyte has a rather
early periclinal division into amphithecium and endothecium.   The
jacket layer (amphithecium) remains but one cell in thickness throughout
further development of the capsule.   Maturation of jacket cells is accompanied by a deposition of ring-like thickenings of their walls.   When
fully mature the jacket splits from the apex to about the middle and into
an indefinite number of segments.   There are no definite longitudinal
lines of dehiscence.   The archesporium (the endothecium) divides and
redivides to form a massive sporogenous tissue.   Frequently[1] the apical
tier of cells becomes sterile so that the apex of the jacket appears to be
more than one cell in thickness.   However, the jacket-like cells derived
from the sporogenous tissue never have walls with the ring-like thickenings characteristic of jacket cells.   Except for the sterile group of apical
cells, all the sporogenous cells are elongate and divide diagonally at the
time of cell division.   Eventually there comes a time when about half
the sporogenous cells undergo two or three successive divisions to form
vertical files of isodiametric spore mother cells (Fig. 21A).   The other
half of the sporogenous cells elongate still more and mature into elaters
with two spiral thickenings on their walls (Fig. 21B).   In most cases the
elaters and spore mother cells are evenly distributed throughout the
capsule, but certain individuals of M. polymorpha[2] have been found with
the elaters in a fasciculate group arising from the floor of the capsule,
much the same as in the elaterophore of Pellia.   Each spore mother cell
divides to form four spores.

Liberation of spores after dehiscence of a capsule is assisted by the
coiling and uncoiling of elaters as a result of hygroscopic changes in their
walls.   Spore germinating[3] begins with a considerable increase in the
size.   There is no formation of a germinal tube as in Riccia, but the spore
immediately divides to form an irregular filament of six to eight cells
which may be two cells broad at the distal ends.   A cell at the filament
apex then begins to function as an apical cell with two lateral cutting
faces that alternately produce five to seven segments right and left.
Derivatives from the first-formed segments divide but two or three times;
those of later-formed segments divide and redivide to form a large number
of cells.   After it has cut off five to seven segments, the two-faced apical
cell itself divides and redivides to form a many-celled sheet in which

---

[1] Andersen, 1929; Cribbs, 1918; Heberlein, 1929; McNaught, 1929.
[2] Cribbs, 1918.   [3] Menge, 1930; O'Hanlon, 1926.

there is soon the establishment of the transverse row of apical initials typical of Marchantiales.

ORDER 2. SPHAEROCARPALES

There are three genera in which the vegetative structure of the gametophyte is similar to that of anacrogynous Jungermanniales, but in which development and structure of the sex organs, as well as structure of the sporophyte, is similar to that of Marchantiales. Because of this, these genera are placed in a separate order, the Sphaerocarpales. The chief diagnostic feature by which one may recognize Sphaerocarpales is the presence of an involucre around each of the archegonia. The order is divided into two families.

FAMILY 1. SPHAEROCARPACEAE

The Sphaerocarpaceae have bilaterally symmetrical gametophytes in which each sex organ is surrounded by an involucre. There are two genera in this family, *Sphaerocarpos* and *Geothallus*. *Sphaerocarpos* has seven species, four of which have been reported from this country. These are found chiefly in the Gulf and the Pacific Coast states. *Geothallus* has not been recorded since first described[1] from Southern California.

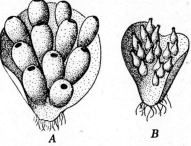

A

B

Fig. 22.—*Sphaerocarpos californicus* Aust. *A*, female gametophyte. *B*, male gametophyte. (× 1½.)

The gametophyte of *Sphaerocarpos* is relatively small, orbicular to cuneate in outline, and simple or dichotomously branched. There is a broad midrib, several cells in thickness; on both lateral margins of it is a wing-like expansion, one cell in thickness. Depending upon environmental conditions, the marginal wings are more or less continuous throughout the length of the thallus or incised to form distinct leaf-like lobes. The entire dorsal surface of the midrib is covered with numerous ovoid or flask-shaped involucres, each of which surrounds a single sex organ (Fig. 22). The ventral surface of the thallus lacks the scales characteristic of Marchantiales, and all rhizoids borne on the ventral surface are of the smooth-walled type. Multicellular glandular hairs, of the type found in many anacrogynous Jungermanniales, are often present on the ventral surface and just back of the growing point. There is no internal differentiation of tissues within the gametophyte (Fig. 23*A*). As in the Marchantiales, apical growth is due to a group of apical initials.[2] Segments cut off from the dorsal and ventral faces of the initials contribute

[1] Campbell, 1896.   [2] Rickett, 1920.

to the midrib; those cut off lateral to the initials contribute to the marginal wings. Certain species, as *S. Donnellii* Aust., are long-lived and multiply vegetatively by progressive growth and death of the thallus. Other species, as *S. cristatus* Howe, are so short-lived that there is no vegetative multiplication in this manner. Vegetative multiplication may also take place by a formation of proliferous outgrowths from the midrib, from the lateral lobes, or from the involucres.[1] In many cases

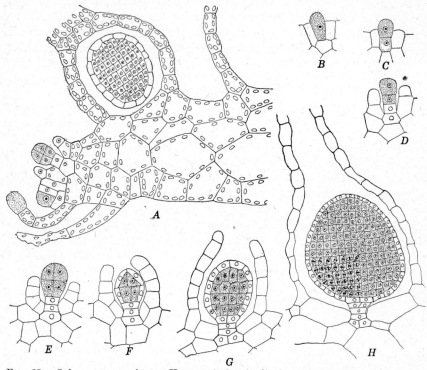

Fig. 23.—*Sphaerocarpos cristatus* Howe. *A*, longitudinal vertical section through the apex of a male gametophyte. *B–H*, stages in development of antheridia. (× 325.)

the plants produced by regeneration come from a single cell of the parent.

All species of the genus are heterothallic, and sexual differentiation has been shown to be due to a sex chromosome.[2] Male plants may be distinguished from female ones by their smaller size, their flask-shaped involucres, and by the fact that they are often tinged with purple. Antheridia are developed from dorsal derivatives one or two removed from the apical initials (Fig. 23*A*). The ontogeny of an antheridium is very much like that of Marchantiales, the chief difference being in the capitate enlargement of the antheridial initial before it divides into basal

[1] Rickett, 1920*A*.   [2] Allen, 1919.

cell and outer cell (Fig. 23*B–H*). The metamorphosis of androcytes into antherozoids also takes place in much the same fashion as in *Riccia*.[1] The two flagella of an antherozoid are unequal in length and the shorter one is inserted anterior to the longer one. Development of the involucre around an antheridium begins as soon as the antheridial initial is differentiated, and upward growth of the involucre is more rapid than that of the antheridium (Fig. 23*D–H*). The involucre surrounding a mature antheridium is flask-shaped and with the relatively broad neck

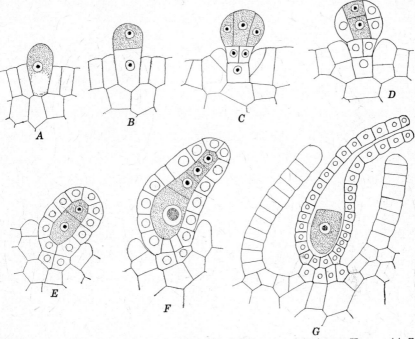

Fig. 24.—Stages in development of archegonia of *Sphaerocarpos cristatus* Howe. (*A–F*, × 485; *G*, × 325.)

portion above the level of the antheridium. Ripe antherozoids exude through the apex of the involucre and there accumulate as a whitish droplet of sticky consistency. The individual antherozoids begin to swim freely when the extruded mass is moistened or flooded with water. Archegonia may either develop from dorsal segments just back of the apical initials or from superficial dorsal cells lateral to the midrib but some distance back from the growing point. The sequence of development in an archegonium is similar to that in Marchantiales, with the formation of six jacket initials (Fig. 24). Development of the involucre begins shortly after the archegonial initial is differentiated, but its devel-

[1] Nevins, 1933.

opment is at a slower rate than that of the archegonium. When the archegonium is mature, the involucre only ensheaths its venter (Fig. 24*G*). After fertilization there is a very rapid upward growth of the involucre, and within two or three days its apex stands higher than the top of the archegonium (Fig. 25*A*).

The male nucleus begins to enlarge and assume a spherical shape immediately after an antherozoid has entered an egg.   Fusing male and female nuclei have definitely organized chromosomes, and fusion of the two begins 60 to 70 hours after entrance of the antherozoid.[1]   The first

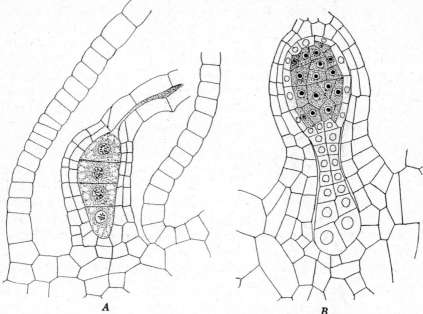

A   B

Fig. 25.—*Sphaerocarpos cristatus* Howe.   *A*, four-celled embryo.   *B*, a young sporophyte after differentiation of the sporogenous tissue.   (× 325.)

divisions in sporophyte development are transverse, and the embryo becomes a filament four to six cells long before vertical divisions appear (Fig. 25*A*).   By this time the venter of the archegonium has become two cells thick in the upper portion and three to four cells thick in the lower portion.   After the embryo is four to six cells long, there is a double vertical division of each of the cells.   Periclinal division in the upper two or three tiers of four cells results in the differentiation of an amphithecium and an endothecium.   The young capsule thus formed soon becomes much broader by division and redivision of the endothecial (sporogenous) cells (Fig. 25*B*).   At the same time the foot portion of the developing

[1] Rickett, 1923.

sporophyte becomes broader, chiefly through lateral expansion of its cells. There is but little division or expansion in the seta portion of the sporophyte, and it frequently remains but two cells in diameter. Most cells of the last cell generation of the sporogenous tissue function as spore mother cells and divide to form four spores each. The remaining sporogenous cells mature into rounded starch-containing cells, morphologically equivalent to elaters but without their characteristically thickened walls. Most species of *Sphaerocarpos* have the four spores from a mother cell adhering to one another after they are mature, but certain species have the spores separating from one another at maturity or as they mature. The jacket layer of the capsule is one cell in thickness at maturity, and its cell walls are without localized thickenings. There is no dehiscence of the capsule when it is mature, and spore liberation is effected by death and decay of the tissues surrounding them.

When the spores germinate, two of the spores of a tetrad develop into female and two develop into male plants.[1] The first step in germination is a sending out of a relatively long germinal tube.[2] The first division in a germinal tube is transverse, into a small terminal cell densely filled with protoplasm and a large scantily filled basal cell. The basal cell does not divide again. The terminal cell divides transversely and vertically to form a short ribbon three to four cells in length and two cells in breadth. The ribbon then becomes two cells in thickness by a horizontal division of each of the cells. Cells in the terminal tier of four then divide and redivide to form a *germinal disk* that lies at right angles to the remainder of the young gametophyte. Growth of the disk becomes asymmetrical after a time because of a differentiation of a group of rapidly dividing initials at one side of the disk. Further growth after the differentiation of the apical initials is similar to that at the apex of an adult thallus.

FAMILY 2. RIELLACEAE

The Riellaceae are segregated from the Sphaerocarpaceae because of their asymmetrical gametophytes. The single genus of the family, *Riella*, has eleven species, each more or less local in distribution. *R. americana* Howe and Underwood, found in Texas and South Dakota,[3] is the only species in this country. The scarcity of records on the occurrence of this and other species is in part due to the fact that the genus is aquatic in habit and grows entirely submerged in pools.

The gametophyte of *Riella* consists of a thickened stem-like portion bearing at one side a conspicuous plate-like wing (Fig. 26). One species has two wings. The wing is usually interpreted as a dorsal outgrowth of the thallus, but a recent careful study[4] of germlings and of juvenile

[1] Allen, 1919.   [2] Campbell, 1896*A*; Rickett, 1920.
[3] Howe and Underwood, 1903; Studhalter, 1931.   [4] Studhalter, 1931.

stages seems to show that there is no dorsiventral differentiation of the thallus. *Riella* may be homothallic or heterothallic. The antheridia are borne serially on the margin of the wing and in small pockets. The archegonia are borne on the edge of the stem-like portion and each is surrounded by an involucre. Development of the sex organs is essentially the same as in *Sphaerocarpos*.[1] The sporophyte is also similar to that of *Sphaerocarpos*.[2]

ORDER 3.   JUNGERMANNIALES

Gametophytes of the Jungermanniales may be either of a simple foliose type or differentiated into stem and leaves. In either case there is but little internal differentiation of tissues. Early stages of antheridial development are of a distinctive type and result in a globose or subglobose antheridium that is generally borne on a long stalk. The archegonia have a neck composed of five vertical rows of cells.

Fig. 26.—*Riella americana* Howe and Underwood, gametophyte bearing young sporophytes. (× 5.)

The capsule of a sporophyte has a jacket layer more than one cell in thickness and one which usually dehisces longitudinally into four parts. The order includes some 145 genera and 7,800 species.

The Jungermanniales are often called the leafy liverworts because the vast majority of them have gametophytes with a sharp differentiation into stem and leaves. However, the order also includes genera in which the gametophyte is strictly thallose and genera which are intermediate between a thallose and a leafy organization. External complexity of form is not accompanied by a corresponding internal complexity of structure, and, except for a few genera in which there are elongate conducting cells, there is no internal differentiation of tissues within gametophytes of Jungermanniales. In fact, from the standpoint of internal differentiation, members of this order have more primitive gametophytes than do those of the Marchantiales.

All rhizoids borne by a gametophyte are of the smooth-walled type. In many genera certain of the rhizoids near the apical region may develop into *mucilage hairs* that enfold and protect the embryonic apex. There may also be a development of scales, one cell in thickness, on the ventral

[1] Kruch, 1890; Leitgeb, 1879.   [2] Leitgeb, 1879.

side of a thallus.   These are homologous with those of the Marchantiales. Certain genera have scale-like outgrowths axillary to sex organs on the dorsal side of a thallus.   Scales of this type have been considered homologous with the involucres surrounding sex organs of the Sphaerocarpales.

Growth of the gametophyte is always initiated by a single apical cell, and the thallose or foliose structure of the gametophyte is due to the method of development of segments cut off by the apical cell.

Vegetative multiplication of the gametophyte may be due to progressive growth and death, but this method of reproduction is not of as frequent occurrence as in the Marchantiales.   Several of the Jungermanniales produce gemma-like adventitious branches, which may become detached from the parent thallus and develop into independent plants.[1] These adventitious branches may be developed from superficial cells in any portion of the thallus, but in most cases they are developed from those near the growing point.

True gemmae are formed by many of the Jungermanniales.   Thalloid genera may have them developing from any superficial cell of the gametophyte.   Some thallose genera produce gemmae on special parts of the plant body and either on gemmiferous branches, as in *Metzgeria;* or in the flask-shaped gemmiferous receptacles, as in *Blasia.*   Foliose genera usually have the gemmae developing from isolated cells of the leaves or have them developing in abundance in the axils of the leaves.

Several genera with a foliose plant body also give rise to one- or two-celled reproductive bodies that are often called gemmae.   These bodies may be formed in abundance, either on the leaf margin, leaf apices, or stem apices, by a rounding up of the cells and their dissociation from one another to form a pulverent mass.   Reproductive structures formed in such a manner have much more in common with the akinetes of the Chlorophyceae than with true gemmae.   The two-celled asexual reproductive bodies formed within cells of *Riccardia* (page 51) are often called endogenously formed gemmae.   A much better interpretation of them is to consider them homologous with the aplanospores found in so many of the Chlorophyceae.

Sex organs are regularly developed by most of the Jungermanniales. Genera with thallose gametophytes may have the antheridia developing on special branches (*Riccardia*) or on the dorsal surface of the midrib region of a main axis (*Pellia*).   Genera with foliose gametophytes have the antheridia developing in the axils of the leaves and have either one, two, four, or more antheridia in each axil.

Antheridia develop from superficial cells close to the apical cell.   The first evidence of antheridial development is a protrusion of a superficial cell above adjoining ones.   This initial soon divides transversely into a

[1] Cavers, 1903; Goebel, 1930.

basal cell, which lies embedded in the thallus, and an *outer cell,* which projects above the thallus (Fig. 27*A*). Transverse division of the outer cell results in a *primary antheridial cell* and a *primary stalk cell* (Fig. 27*B*). In most cases the primary stalk cell develops into a stalk two cells in diameter and several cells in height, but there are genera in which the stalk is a single file of four to eight cells in height.

The primary antheridial cell divides vertically into two daughter cells of equal size. Each of the daughter cells also divides vertically but in a plane diagonal to that of the first division (Fig. 27*D*). In each pair of unequal-sized daughter cells, one is a jacket initial which contributes only

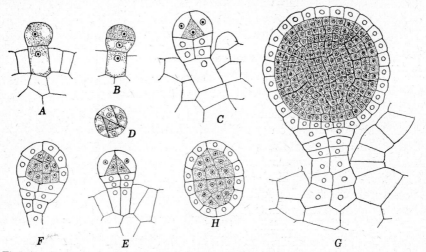

Fig. 27.—Stages in development of antheridia of *Fossombronia angulosa* (Dicks.) Raddi. *A–C, E–G,* in vertical section; *D, H,* in transverse section. (× 325.)

to the jacket layer of the antheridium; the other is a cell which divides periclinally into an outer cell, a *jacket initial,* and an inner cell, a *primary androgonial cell* (Fig. 27*C, E*). At this stage of development, best seen in vertical view, the body of an antheridium consists of two primary androgonial cells enclosed by four jacket initials.

The foregoing sequence in early stages of antheridial development has been found in all investigated species of Jungermanniales, but atypical individuals are sometimes present in which there is a different sequence of development. Instances have been recorded[1] where antheridia have the same sequence of development as in *Calobryum* (page 69) and in which the primary antheridial cell, by successive vertical divisions, gives rise to three jacket initials surrounding a single primary androgonial cell.[1] Cases have also been reported where development is as in the Mar-

[1] Hutchinson, 1915.

chantiales where the primary antheridial cell divides into four daughter cells, each of which divides periclinally into a jacket initial and a primary androgonial cell. Possibly the Jungermanniales do have such a marchantiaceous type of antheridial development, but it has also been held[1] that the reported cases are due to a misinterpretation of typical jungermanniaceous antheridia.

Successive division and redivision of the two primary androgonial cells (Fig. 27F–H) eventually results in the formation of the *androcyte mother cells*, each of which divides diagonally into two *androcytes*. Computations based upon measurements of antheridia of *Fossombronia*[1] show that there are 12 cell generations from the primary androgonial cells to the androcytes. If all of the androgonial cells divide every time, this would result in 8,192 androcytes. Division of the androgonial tissue is accompanied by division and redivision of the jacket initials, and the combined result of the two is the globose antheridium characteristic of the Jungermanniales (Fig. 27G). Metamorphosis of androcytes into antherozoids is much the same as in other bryophytes, and the blepharoplast does not appear until the adrocyte mother cell stage. Mature antherozoids are biflagellate, and several genera have been shown to have the flagella unequal in length and attached to different parts in the body of the antherozoid.[2]

Cells in the jacket of a mature antheridium are strongly hygroscopic and have a marked tendency to separate from one another when moistened. Separation of jacket cells begins at the apex of an antheridium and is due to an outward curvature immediately after they are wetted. The exposed mass of antherozoids emerges from the antheridium as a cloud-like mass in the surrounding water, and within a short time the antherozoids begin to move freely in all directions. Several of the Marchantiales are known to have an explosive discharge of the antherozoids into the air, but this has not been observed in any of the leafy liverworts.[3]

Archegonia may be borne on lateral branches or on the main axis. The initials giving rise to archegonia almost always lie close to an apical cell: in one suborder of the Jungermanniales (the *Acrogynae*) the apical cell itself also develops into an archegonium. Genera with the apical cell developing into an archegonium always have the archegonia terminal in position, those which do not have the apical cell developing into an archegonium may have the archegonia coming to lie some distance back from the growing point by the time they are fully mature. Some of the thallose genera and practically all the foliose genera have the group of archegonia surrounded by one or another type of protective structure.

[1] Chalaud, 1929–1931.   [2] Showalter, 1926; Steil, 1923.
[3] Campbell, 1918; Chalaud, 1929–1931; Horne, 1909; Humphrey, 1906; Showalter, 1926.

Development of the archegonium up to the stage where three *peripheral cells* surround a *primary axial cell* is identical with that of the Marchantiales and of other orders (Fig. 28*A–C*).   During subsequent development, vertical divisions are restricted to two of the three peripheral cells, probably the first two formed.   As a result the jacket layer surrounding the primary axial cell in Jungermanniales is composed of five *jacket initials*, instead of six as in the Marchantiales.   Transverse division of each of the jacket initials results in the differentiation of five *neck initials* and five *venter initials* (Fig. 28*D*).   In most cases division of the

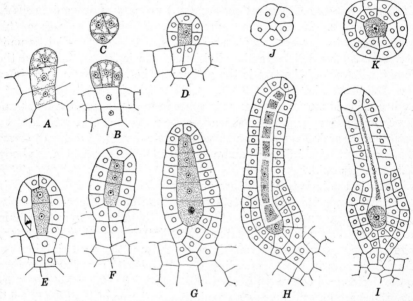

Fig. 28.—Stages in development of archegonia of *Fossombronia augulosa* (Dicks.) Raddi. *A–B, D–I*, in vertical section; *C, J–K*, in transverse section.   (*A–G*, × 325; *H–K*, × 215.)

neck initials and their daughter cells is only in a transverse plane, so that the neck of the archegonium is composed of five rows of cells (Fig. 28*J*).   Occasionally there may be a vertical division at an early or a late stage in neck development that results in the entire neck, or only the lower portion of it, containing more than five vertical rows of cells. The venter developing from the five venter initials is usually only slightly greater in diameter than the base of the neck.   Archegonia of the Jungermanniales also differ from those of other Hepaticae in that previous to fertilization there is often a periclinal division of all venter cells, and sometimes the lower neck cells, to form a tissue of two or more cells in thickness (Fig. 28*K*).

As in other liverworts, the primary axial cell divides transversely into a *primary cover cell* and a *central cell* (Fig. 28*D*); after which the central cell divides transversely into a *primary canal cell* and a *primary ventral cell* (Fig. 28*E*). The extent to which the primary neck canal cell divides and redivides is much more variable in Jungermanniales than in other Hepaticae. According to the genus concerned, there may be a formation of 4, 8, or 16 neck canal cells; or the number may vary from individual to individual in a given species. All species investigated have a division of the primary ventral cell into a *ventral canal cell* and an *egg cell*, but there is great variation from genus to genus both in the time at which this division takes place and in the time at which the ventral cell degenerates (Fig. 28*I–J*). The primary cover cell generally divides to form a cover composed of four cells quite similar in appearance to neck cells. Dehiscence of an archegonium is usually effected by a spreading apart and folding back of the cover cells, but it may be due to an internally developed hydrostatic pressure. Dehiscence due to hydrostatic pressure causes a bursting of the cover cells, or neck cells immediately beneath them.[1]

Entrance of antherozoids into archegonia is undoubtedly in response to chemotactic stimuli, but specific chemical compounds exerting such stimuli have not been determined as they have for Marchantiales (page 34). However, contrary to general opinion, it has been shown[1] that the seat of the chemotactic stimulation is not in the gelatinous slime resulting from disintegration of the neck canal cells.

Antherozoids entering the venter of an archegonium soon penetrate the egg.[2] After penetrating it, they may move immediately to the egg nucleus and become applied to it, or they may remain in the peripheral portion of the cytoplasm of the egg for some time.[3] Fusion of male and female nuclei takes place 24 to 48 hours after the entrance of the antherozoid. *Polyspermy*, the entrance of more than one antherozoid into an egg, is a common phenomenon, but there is rarely a fusion of more than one male nucleus with that of the egg.

The first division of the zygote is transverse and into an upper (*epibasal*) and a lower (*hypobasal*) cell. For certain genera (*Fossombronia*,[2] *Frullania*[4]) it has been shown that the epibasal cell also divides transversely; and that the upper, median, and lower cell of the resultant three-celled embryo develop, respectively, into capsule, seta, and foot of the mature sporophyte. Other genera have been shown to have the hypobasal cell developing into a haustorium and the entire mature sporophyte coming from the epibasal cell (*Riccardia*,[5] *Pallavicinia*,[6] *Symphyogyna*,[7] *Treubia*[8]).

There are no essential differences between foot and seta of mature sporophytes of Jungermanniales and those of sporophytes of other Hepat-

[1] Showalter, 1928.   [2] Showalter, 1926*A*, 1927, 1927*A*.   [3] Chalaud, 1929–1931.
[4] Campbell, 1918.   [5] Clapp, 1912.   [6] Campbell and Williams, 1914.
[7] McCormick, 1914.   [8] Campbell, 1916.

icae, but the capsules differ in several respects. Capsules of Jungermanniales have a jacket layer either two, three, four, or more cells in thickness. There is always a sclerification of cells in the jacket layer, and most genera have the mature capsule dehiscing into four valves at the time when the spores are shed. All genera have a differentiation of the sporogenous tissue into elaters and spore mother cells, and in many genera the elaters are radially oriented either to the base or to the apex of a capsule. The orientation may be centered around a columella-like mass of sterile cells (*elaterophore*), or an elaterophore may be lacking. Another distinctive feature of the sporophyte, although not exclusively restricted to those of the Jungermanniales, is the quadripartition of the spore mother cells to form the spores.

There is so much variation from genus to genus in the method of spore germination that no one method may be considered typical for the Jungermanniales. In one genus (*Pellia*) the spore develops into a six- to nine-celled gametophyte while still within the capsule, but this is not of particular significance since the same precocious germination is also found in one of the Marchantiales. Germinating spores of Jungermanniales may immediately develop into a massive gametophyte, or the first-formed portion may be distinctly protonema-like in structure. Thallose genera usually have the germinating spore developing immediately into a thallose structure, but sometimes[1] there is a small protonemal stage. When the germling is thallose from the beginning, there is an early differentiation of the apical cell, and this may even be recognizable as early as the three-celled stage (*Riccardia*).[2] Germlings of foliose genera usually undergo considerable development before the appearance of a definite organization into stem and leaves. The juvenile phase may be protonemal at first and then thallose (*Fossombronia*),[3] or it may be thallose from the beginning. In certain tropical foliose genera the juvenile phase constitutes the dominant portion of the gametophyte generation, and the adult phase is found only in the erect leafy branches producing the sex organs. The permanent juvenile phases of this type may be thallose structures,[2] or they may be protonemal.[4]

The Jungermanniales are divided into two suborders.

SUBORDER 1. ANACROGYNAE

Typical Anacrogynae do not have the apical cell developing into an archegonium at the time sex organs are formed. Genera with this type of thallus are easily recognizable because the sporophytes lie some distance back from the growing apex. The suborder also includes certain thallose genera in which the formation of archegonia checks apical

[1] Goebel, 1889.   [2] Showalter, 1925.
[3] Chalaud, 1929–1931.   [4] Spruce, 1884.

growth. Some 17 genera containing over 550 species are referred to the Anacrogynae.

The Anacrogynae include some genera in which the gametophyte has a simple undifferentiated dorsiventral thallus (*Riccardia*) and others in which it has a well-marked differentiation into stem and leaves (*Fossombronia, Treubia*). Between these two extreme types there are also genera in which the gametophyte is differentiated into a distinct midrib with a simple longitudinal wing along either side (*Pallavicinia*) and those in which the marginal wings are so deeply lobed that the lobes are almost leaf-like. These various types of gametophyte might be arranged in a single ascending series in which there has been a progressive evolution from a simple leafy thallus to one in which there is a well-marked differentiation into stem and leaves. However, other features in the structure of the gametophyte and certain features in the structure of the sporophyte seem to show that there the foliose gametophyte has been evolved in at least two independent lines among the Anacrogynae. Certain foliose genera seem to have been evolved from simple thallose forms like *Riccardia;* other foliose genera seem to have arisen from simple thallose forms like *Pellia.* In addition to this parallel evolution of foliose gametophytes, there are several independent cases where the gametophyte has evolved from a prostrate to a partially erect structure.

Gametophytes of most Anacrogynae are without an internal differentiation of tissues, but certain genera, as *Pallavicinia*, have a central strand composed of elongate thick-walled cells with simple pits in the walls. There has been experimental demonstration[1] that this central strand functions as a water-conducting tissue. The ventral surface of the gametophyte, or all surfaces when it is rhizome-like in nature, may develop smooth-walled rhizoids. Superficial cells of the thallus may also develop uni- or multicellular mucilage-secreting hairs. These are especially conspicuous near the growing point. They protect the apical cell and its newly formed segments in much the same fashion as do the ventral scales of Marchantiales.

There are so many conflicting features among the Anacrogynae that all systems proposed for classification of the suborder are more or less artificial. The Anacrogynae (exclusive of the Calobryaceae) are sometimes[2] divided into three families, but it is better to recognize only the following two:

FAMILY 1. RICCARDIACEAE

Genera placed in the Riccardiaceae have no one feature in common distinguishing them from other Anacrogynae. Most of the genera have

---

[1] Tansley and Chick, 1901.   [2] Cavers, 1910.

thallose gametophytes and sporophytes with an apical elaterophore; but both of these features are lacking in certain genera. The family has been divided into two families,[1] the Aneuraceae in which the sex organs are borne on special branches and the Blyttiaceae in which they are not on special branches, but recent opinion[2] holds that this is not justifiable. The family includes some 6 genera and 480 species. Of the two genera discussed below, *Riccardia* would belong to the Aneuraceae, and *Pallavicinia* to the Blyttiaceae.

Riccardia (*Aneura*), a genus with over 250 species, has a simple thallose gametophyte (Fig. 29). This thallus is dichotomously branched, but unequal growth of the dichotomies results in a gametophyte in which the branches seem to be lateral appendages.[3] The gametophyte may be wholly prostrate or partially prostrate and partially erect. Species with prostrate gametophytes, among which *R. pinguis* (L.) S. F. Gray is the commonest in the United States, rarely have a differentiation into a midrib and lateral wings. Species with partially erect gametophytes, as *R. eriocaulis* (Hook.), have the prostrate portion rounded, and the erect branches have a well-defined midrib bearing lateral wings one cell in thickness. *R. pinguis* and related species have no internal differentiation of tissues, but several of the partially erect species have a well-defined conducting system in the main branches.

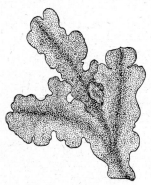

FIG. 29.—Gametophyte of *Riccardia* sp. (Natural size.)

There is also a division of function in gametophytes of the latter type, the ultimate branches being photosynthetic organs, and the main axis a mechanical or a conducting organ. The ventral surface of the thallus bears smooth-walled rhizoids and mucilage hairs. Young rhizoids may contain chloroplasts, old rhizoids always lack them.

Riccardia has a wedge-shaped apical cell with two cutting faces which alternately form primary segments right and left.[4] The apical cell lies in a depression at the anterior end of the thallus, and each depression usually contains two or more apical cells. Primary segments from an apical cell divide in the same manner as a two-faced apical cell, but one which cuts off segments above and below, not right and left. Now and then a segment cut off by an apical cell cuts off three or four derivatives above and below, and then begins to function as a true apical cell cutting off segments right and left. This results in two apical cells in the apical depression and is the beginning of a dichotomy of the branch.

[1] Cavers, 1910.   [2] Campbell and Williams, 1914; Evans, 1921.
[3] Evans, 1921.   [4] Clapp, 1912; Showalter, 1923.

The gametophyte generation may be propagated vegetatively by progressive growth and death. *Riccardia* may also have a formation of two-celled asexual reproductive bodies in any superficial cell of the thallus. There is a rounding up of the protoplast, a secretion of an entirely new wall about the rounded protoplast, followed by a division of this cell into two daughter cells firmly united to each other. The two-celled body thus formed is liberated from the thallus by a gelatinization of the original cell wall. These two-celled structures, peculiar to *Riccardia*, are frequently termed "endogenous gemmae," but they have much more in common with the aplanospores of the Chlorophyceae than with the gemmae of other Hepaticae.

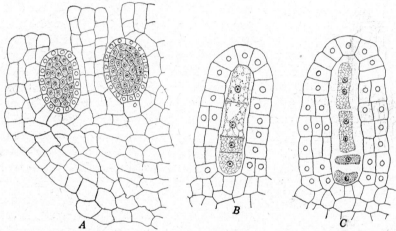

Fig. 30.—*Riccardia pinguis* (L.) S. F. Gray. *A*, vertical section of antheridia embedded in the gametophyte. *B–C*, stages in development of archegonia. (*A*, × 120; *B–C*, × 325.)

Species of *Riccardia* may be heterothallic or homothallic, but in either case the sex organs are borne on short lateral branches. In some species the mature sex organs cover the entire branch; in other species they are restricted to the apex of the branch.

Successive segments cut off by the apical cell may develop into antheridia, and in most species the antheridia lie in a double row on the dorsal side of the branch. In *R. pinguis* the antheridia lie in three or four irregular rows because of displacement during later growth of the branch. Development of an antheridium is according to the type characteristic of the Jungermanniales.[1] Unlike most other Anacrogynae, but similar to most Marchantiales, growth of adjoining vegetative cells keeps pace with development of the antheridium, and results in a sunken antheridial chamber connected with the thallus surface by a narrow canal (Fig. 30*A*).

[1] Clapp, 1912; Florin, 1922.

Archegonial branches are generally shorter than those bearing antheridia. Each successive segment cut off by the apical cell develops into an archegonium, but the arrangement of mature archegonia is much more irregular than that of antheridia. Development of archegonia is according to the manner characteristic of Jungermanniales.[1] Typically, there is a formation of five tiers of neck cells, and a formation of four to six neck canal cells. One minor distinctive feature is the very early division of primary ventral cell into egg and ventral canal cell (Fig. 30*B*). There is also a precocious periclinal division of jacket cells so that mature archegonia have a neck two cells in thickness and a venter two or three

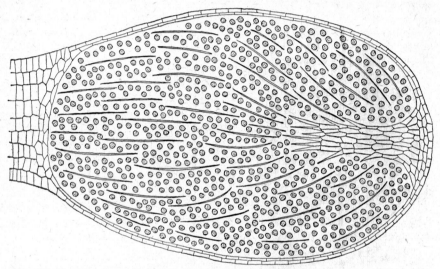

Fig. 31.—Semidiagrammatic longitudinal section of capsule of a sporophyte of *Riccardia pinguis* (L.) S. F. Gray. (× 70.)

cells in thickness. This results in a massive archegonium and one with little external differentiation into neck and venter (Fig. 30*C*).

Fertilization takes place in the usual manner.[2] The first division of the zygote is transverse. The hypobasal cell immediately starts elongating into a haustorium that grows deeper and deeper into the female branch below the archegonium.[3] In many cases there is no division of the haustorial cell. The epibasal cell divides transversely, and the upper daughter cell soon divides transversely. These three superimposed cells derived from the epibasal cell develop, respectively, into foot, seta, and capsule of the mature sporophyte. The cells developing into foot and seta first undergo two successive vertical divisions, after which there are transverse and vertical divisions in irregular sequence. The cell develop-

[1] Clapp, 1912; Florin, 1922; Showalter, 1923.
[2] Showalter, 1926*A*, 1928.   [3] Clapp, 1912; Florin, 1922.

ing into the capsule also undergoes two successive vertical divisions to form a tier of four cells. Each of the four cells then divides periclinally into an outer jacket initial cell and an inner primary sporogenous cell. Divisions of the sporogenous cells are in irregular sequence, but rather early there is a differentiation of an apical mass of cells, the future elaterophore. Later on, the sporogenous cells not developing into the elaterophore become differentiated into spore mother cells and elaters (Fig. 31). Jacket initials divide anticlinally for the first two or three divisions, after which each cell divides periclinally. This results in a sterile jacket layer two cells in thickness. During later stages in development of the jacket layer there is a considerable thickening of the cell walls, except in four vertical rows of cells—the future lines of dehiscence of the mature capsule. Capsule dehiscence begins at the apex and the four valves, each with a portion of the elaterophore, bend back with a jerk. This expels the spores and elaters in a catapult-like manner.

A developing sporophyte is surrounded by a massive sheath of gametophyte tissue. The apical portion of this sheath is derived from the venter of the archegonium; the major portion of it is derived from portions of the female branch immediately below the archegonium. Thus the sheath is more in the nature of a marsupium than a true calyptra.

The spores germinate immediately after they are shed and by a transverse division into two daughter cells of unequal size.[1] The larger daughter cell rarely divides again; the smaller cell divides by a diagonally vertical wall and thus differentiates a wedge-shaped apical cell which begins to function immediately. Rhizoids appear quite early on the germling and are borne toward the posterior end of the young thallus.

Pallavicinia is representative of the Riccardiaceae in which the sex organs are not borne on special branches. *P. Levieri* Schiffn. is typical of the species in which the gametophyte is wholly prostrate and with the entire ventral surface bearing rhizoids. Its thallus has a conspicuous midrib. On either side of the midrib are relatively broad longitudinal wings with undulate margins. The greater portion of the midrib consists of elongate cells whose thick walls have simple pits, and it has been definitely established[2] for certain species that such elongate cells function as a definite water-conducting tissue. *P. Zollingeri* (Gottsch.) Schiffn. (Fig. 32*A–B*) is typical of the species in which the gametophyte is differentiated into a prostrate portion and an erect portion. The prostrate portion, often termed the rhizome, is cylindrical and clothed on all sides with numerous rhizoids. There is a central axis of conducting tissue; between this and the rhizoid-bearing surface layer is a parenchymatous tissue whose cells may contain numerous starch grains (Fig. 32*C*). The rhizome may give rise to adventitious branches from its ventral surface,

[1] Showalter, 1925. [2] Tansley and Chick, 1901.

but the conducting tissue of adventitious branches is not continuous with
that of the main axis. The erect portion of the thallus results from an
upward growth of the distal end of the rhizome. However, a mature
erect branch is not terminal in position because early in its development
it gives rise to an adventitious branch which continues the prostrate
forward growth of the rhizome. The basal portion of an erect branch is
cylindrical and without lateral wings. The upper portion, which has
three to five successive dichotomous forkings, is differentiated into midrib
and lateral wings. The wings are the photosynthetic portion of the

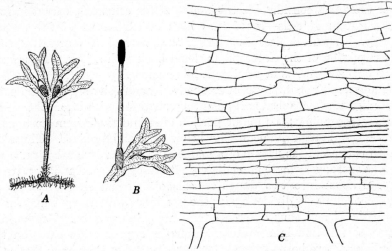

Fig. 32.—*Pallavicinia Zollingeri* (Gottsch) Schiffn. *A*, gametophyte with young
sporophytes. *B*, portion of a gametophyte bearing a mature sporophyte. *C*, longitudinal
vertical section of a gametophyte. (*A–B*, × ¾; *C*, × 100.)

gametophyte; the midrib consists largely of conducting tissue which is in
direct connection with that of the rhizome.

Most species of *Pallavicinia* have a two-faced apical cell which alternately cuts off segments right and left as in *Riccardia*.[1] One species has
been reported[2] as having an apical cell with four cutting faces, three
lateral and one basal.

All species of *Pallavicinia* are heterothallic. Male plants bear their
antheridia along the sides of the midrib, either in continuous series or in
series interrupted here and there by sterile areas. Each antheridium or
group of antheridia is subtended by a scale-like outgrowth from the midrib. Stages in the development of an antheridium are essentially like
those of other Jungermanniales, with the formation of two primary
androgonial cells by diagonal vertical division of the primary antheridial

<hr>

[1] Campbell and Williams, 1914; Haupt, 1918.   [2] Farmer, 1894.

cell.[1] Archegonia are borne in restricted areas (receptacles). In *P. Zollingeri* the receptacles are differentiated near the region where there is a dichotomous forking of the erect branch. In prostrate species, as *P. radiculosa*, they occur at various points along the dorsal surface of the midrib, but there is no correlation between position of the receptacle and dichotomy of the thallus. The receptacle is encircled by an annular upgrowth from the surface of the thallus, the *involucre* (Fig. 33*A*). The receptacle itself, which is not elevated, continues the formation of archegonia up to the time of fertilization. Shortly after the first-formed archegonia are mature, there is the development of an additional ring-like upgrowth, the *perianth*, just inside the involucre. Except for the long

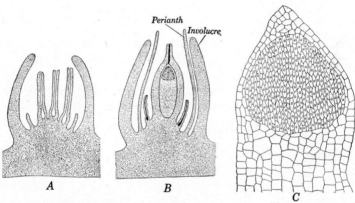

Fig. 33.—*Pallavicinia Zollingeri* (Gottsch) Schiffn. *A*, vertical section through a receptacle with mature archegonia. *B*, a similar section through a receptacle in which one archegonium contains a sporophyte. *C*, longitudinal section through the capsule of a young sporophyte. (*A–B*, × 12; *C*, × 95.)

twisted neck and the formation of a relatively large number of neck canal cells (10 to 18 in one species), there is little distinguishing the development of an archegonium from that of other Jungermanniales.[1]

The first division of the zygote is transverse,[2] and, as in *Riccardia*, the hypobasal cell develops into a haustorium. Different from *Riccardia* the mature haustorium is three- or four-celled. The epibasal cell develops into the sporophyte, but there is not as early a differentiation of the foot, seta, and capsule as in many other Jungermanniales. Differentiation of the sporogenous tissue occurs fairly early in the development of a capsule. At first the jacket layer external to the sporogenous tissue is one cell in thickness; later on it becomes three to five cells in thickness in the apical portion and two cells in thickness elsewhere (Fig. 33*C*). Four vertical lines of dehiscence develop in the maturing jacket, but these are restricted to the apical region. Because of this the apices of the four valves do not

[1] Campbell and Williams, 1914; Haupt, 1918.   [2] Campbell and Williams, 1914.

separate from one another when the capsule opens, and the spores escape through four longitudinal slits in the capsule wall.

The young sporophyte is surrounded by the calyptra, and this is successively ensheathed by the perianth and the involucre (Fig. 33*B*). As the sporophyte and calyptra begin to elongate, there is an upward growth of the perianth but not of the involucre. When the sporophyte has attained about a quarter of its eventual length, it pushes through the apex of the calyptra and grows upward above the perianth (Fig. 32*B*).

Thus only the basal portion of a mature sporophyte is ensheathed by involucre, perianth, and calyptera.

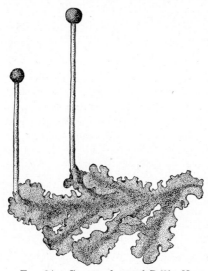

FIG. 34.—Gametophyte of *Pellia Neesiana* (Gottsch) Limpr. with two mature sporophytes. (Natural size.)

FAMILY 2.   CODONIACEAE

Most genera referred to this family have a thallose gametophyte, but there are also those in which it is foliose. The sporophytes have a globose capsule, and in several cases there is a distinct basal elaterophore or a radiate arrangement of the elaters at the base of the capsule. The family includes 9 genera and about 70 species. The two genera described below represent thallose and foliose types, respectively.

Pellia, a genus with two species only, is representative of the Codoniaceae with a thallose gametophyte. Its thallus[1] is dichotomously branched and with the irregularly lobed margins of branches often overlapping one another (Fig. 34). The branches do not have a differentiation into midrib and wings, although the central portion of the branch is thicker than the marginal portions. Aside from a slight elongation of cells near the axial portion of a branch, there is no internal differentiation of tissues. The ventral portion of the "midrib" bears numerous smooth-walled rhizoids. Scales are lacking. The evanescent multicellular mucilage hairs protecting the growing point have been held to be homologous with the ventral scales of other Hepaticae.

Growth is due to a single apical cell. According to the species this has two or four cutting faces.[2] The species in which the apical cell has two cutting faces have the cell cutting off segments dorsally and ventrally, not right and left. During vegetative growth of the thallus this apical

[1] Hutchinson, 1915; Leitgeb, 1877.   [2] Hutchinson, 1915.

cell is distinctly wedge-shaped, but at the time antheridia are formed it becomes lens-shaped and has one cutting face on the posterior side.[1] Each segment from the lenticular apical cell divides into five or six daughter cells before the apical cell cuts off a new segment.

Pellia may be heterothallic or homothallic. In the latter case the antheridia are produced before the archegonia. Mature antheridia lie irregularly scattered along the dorsal surface of the midrib. Each antheridium lies in an antheridial chamber resulting from an upward growth of gametophytic tissue adjacent to the young antheridium (Fig. 35B). Development of antheridia is usually according to the type characteristic of Jungermanniales, with diagonal vertical divisions of the primary antheridial cell producing two primary androgonial cells. Occasional antheridia may have the same differentiation of a single primary androgonial cell as in *Calobryum* (page 69). The first antheridia appearing on a thallus have been described as developing in the manner characteristic of Marchantiales, but this statement has been held[2] to be due to a misinterpretation of the material examined. The antherozoid, which is the largest thus far found in any bryophyte,[3] has the two flagella inserted at different points in the anterior end.

Production of archegonia is accompanied by the formation of a slightly elevated receptacular tissue from the apical cell, which checks further apical growth. Thus, *Pellia*, although placed in the Anacrogynae, is acrogynous. However, the receptacle does not have a truly acrogynous position because there is further forward growth of the thallus by an elongation of cells near the ventral surface (Fig. 35A). After this, the cells encircling the receptacle develop into a diagonally inserted cylindrical involucre which eventually grows up to a height considerably above that of the receptacle and its archegonia. Any superficial cell near the apex of a receptacle may develop into an archegonium. There is not a simultaneous production of archegonia from these archegonial initials, and on a single receptacle one may find all stages of archegonial development from the first initial to the mature archegonium. The development of archegonia is the same as in other Jungermanniales; namely, with a formation of five tiers of neck cells. The number of neck canal cells varies from six to nine or more. The venter becomes two or three cells in thickness before the time of fertilization, and it is usually subtended by a massive stalk (Fig. 35A).

Fertilization is effected in the usual manner[4] and there is a transverse division of the zygote about six days after the gametic union. The hypobasal cell from this first division develops into a haustorium which usually remains one-celled. The haustorium penetrates deeply into the recep-

[1] Hutchinson, 1915.   [2] Chalaud, 1929–1931.
[3] Showalter, 1926.   [4] Showalter, 1927A.

tacle, and the embryo grows downward into the cavity thus formed.
Thus, the protective tissue surrounding a young sporophyte is derived in
part from the archegonium and in part from the receptacle.

It is very probable that early development from the epibasal cell is the
same as in *Riccardia* and that there is a formation of three superimposed

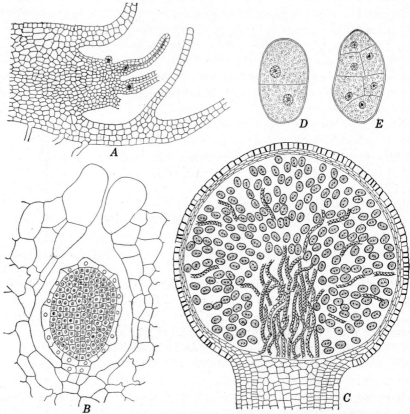

FIG. 35.—*A, C–E, Pellia Fabbroniana* Raddi.   *B, P. Neesiana* (Gottsch) Limpr.   *A*,
longitudinal vertical section through apex of a female gametophyte.   *B*, vertical section
of an antheridium embedded in a gametophyte.   *C*, longitudinal section through the capsule of a mature sporophyte.   *D–E*, young gametophytes before liberation from capsule.
(*A, C,* × 45; *B,* × 220; *D–E,* × 325.)

tiers of cells which eventually become capsule, seta, and foot of the
mature sporophyte.[1]   Mature sporophytes have a spherical capsule in
which the jacket layer is more than two cells in thickness.   Late in
development of a capsule, the sporogenous tissue differentiates into elaters
and spore mother cells.   At the base of the capsule there is also a formation of a mass of 50 to 100 erect elater-like cells whose lower ends are

[1] Kienitz-Gerloff, 1875.

attached to the capsule and whose upper ends are free and intermingled with the spores and true elaters (Fig. 35C). This basal structure is an elaterophore. Division of the four-lobed spore mother cells is as in other Jungermanniales. The jacket of a mature capsule has four vertical rows of thin-walled cells, the lines of dehiscence along which the capsule separates into four valves that bend back upon themselves. The function of the elaterophore is to entrap the "spores" for a time after the capsule opens and thus effect a more gradual shedding of the "spores."

Spore germination takes place within the capsule. Germination begins with two successive transverse divisions of a spore[1] cell. The basal cell of this four-celled stage does not divide again; the other cells divide vertically (Fig. 35D–E). Dehiscence of the capsule takes place when the young gametophytes are six- to nine-celled ovoid masses. These are discharged in the same manner as are the spores of other liverworts, and there is an immediate resumption of growth after these young gametophytes are liberated from the capsule. The basal cell sends out a rhizoid; the other cells begin to divide and oblique divisions at the anterior end of a young germling soon establish a definite apical cell.

Fossombronia, a widely distributed genus with some 50 species, is representative of the Codoniaceae in which the gametophyte is distinctly foliose. The thallus is almost wholly prostrate and with a sparse or profuse dichotomous branching (Fig. 36). A branch consists of a well-defined stem portion which bears a single row of leaves along both lateral margins. The leaves near the growing apex are vertically inserted; those farther back on a branch are *succubous* in insertion, that is, the posterior

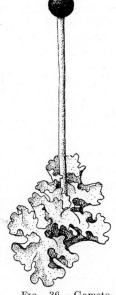

Fig. 36.—Gametophyte and mature sporophyte of *Fossombronia longiseta* Aust. (× 3.)

margin of each leaf overlaps the anterior margin of the next older leaf. The change from a vertical to a succubous insertion of the leaves results from the ventral surface of the thallus elongating at a faster rate than does the dorsal side. The reverse condition of growth, not found in the Codoniaceae, results in an *incubous* insertion in which the posterior margin of each leaf *underlies* the anterior margin of the next older leaf. Leaves of *Fossombronia* are usually irregularly lobed and with each lobe terminating in a small elongate mucilage cell. The basal portion of a leaf is two or three cells in thickness; elsewhere it is but one cell in thickness. The stem of *Fossombronia* is a fairly massive structure, but without any

[1] Showalter, 1925; Wolfson, 1928.

indication of the internal differentiation found in *Pallavicinia* and certain other Anacrogynae. The ventral surface of the stem bears smooth-walled, reddish- to violet-colored rhizoids. Near the growing apex the ventral surface also bears multicellular mucilage hairs which overarch and protect the apical cell, but these are not found on older parts of the stem.

Growth of the main axis and of its branches is by means of an apical cell with two cutting faces that alternately cut off segments right and left. As seen in vertical longitudinal section, the apical cell is semi-circular in outline; as seen in horizontal longitudinal section, it is narrowly triangular. The first division of a segment cut off by the apical cell is in a horizontal plane perpendicular to the free face of a segment. The ventral daughter cell contributes only to the ventral portion of the stem. The dorsal daughter cell contributes to the dorsal portion of the stem and all the leaves. Its first division is horizontal, the upper daughter cell contributing to the dorsal surface of the stem and the lower daughter cell functioning as the initial of a leaf.[1] Unlike most other Jungermanniales, dichotomous branching is not due to a vertical division of the apical cell. Instead, there is the differentiation of a second apical cell in a very young segment cut off from the original apical cell. Combined growth from the original apical cell and the newly formed apical cell bring about what appears to be a true dichotomy, but what is really a false dichotomy.

Fossombronia may be homothallic or heterothallic. The sex organs are borne singly or in small groups along the dorsal surface and near the bases of the leaves. Heterothallic species have the sex organs borne in strict acropetalous succession, and the sex organs begin to develop in segments only once removed from the apical cell. Homothallic species usually have antheridia and archegonia more or less separately grouped, but both kinds of sex organs may be formed in the same leaf axil.

Development of antheridia[2] is according to the manner typical for the Jungermanniales (Fig. 27). There is a sudden bursting of an antheridium when it is mature, but this is not accompanied by an explosive discharge of the antherozoids. The antherozoids are relatively large and have the two flagella inserted at different points near the anterior end.[3] The development of archegonia is also typical (Fig. 28). The mature arche-gonium has six to eight neck canal cells surrounded by five vertical rows of neck cells. The venter is relatively slender and has a jacket layer two cells in thickness.

Fertilization[4] is effected in the usual manner and division of the zygote takes place six to nine days after gametic union. The first division is always transverse, and the hypobasal cell is somewhat smaller than the

---

[1] Chalaud, 1929–1931.　　[2] Chalaud, 1929–1931; Haupt, 1920, 1929*A*.
[3] Showalter, 1926.　　[4] Showalter, 1927.

epibasal. The hypobasal cell eventually develops into the foot of a mature sporophyte. In many cases the first division of the epibasal cell is transverse; the upper cell develops into the capsule and the lower cell into the seta.[1] However, the first divisions of an embryo do not always take place in such regular sequence, and there may be vertical divisions in hypobasal and epibasal cells before there is a transverse division.[2] The periclinal division differentiating the jacket layer and sporogenous tissue of the capsule occurs quite early. Soon afterward the jacket layer becomes two cells in thickness, and there may be further periclinal divisions in the apical portion of the jacket layer. The primary sporogenous cells develop into a sporogenous tissue of many cells. Differentiation of elaters does not take place until the last cell generation of the sporogenous tissue. Cells developing into elaters are homologous with spore mother cells, instead of being homologous with a row of spore mother cells as is usually the case. Elaters of *Fossombronia* are unusual in that the thickenings on their walls are laid down in five to nine transverse rings instead of the usual two or three longitudinal spirals. The elaterophore, when present in *Fossombronia*, is a very indistinct structure.

The young sporophyte is surrounded by a calyptra and this, in turn, is surrounded by a perianth which begins to develop shortly after fertilization. The seta remains relatively short until the spores are mature. Then it begins to elongate rapidly and pushes the capsule through the calyptra and to a considerable distance above the perianth. According to the species, the capsule either dehisces irregularly or dehisces into four valves.

Germination of the spore results in a filamentous protonema of 2 to 12 cells in which those nearest the old spore often bear rhizoids. Termination of the protonemal phase is marked by the distal cell dividing irregularly into a globose mass of cells, one of which soon begins to function as an apical cell with two cutting faces.[1] For some time the segments cut off by the apical cell develop into a distinctly thallose plant body without any differentiation into stem and leaves. This juvenile condition is generally succeeded by the adult condition in which derivatives from segments cut off by the apical cell become differentiated into stem and leaves.

SUBORDER 2. ACROGYNAE

The Acrogynae have the apical cell of a branch or of the main axis developing into an archegonium after it has cut off segments that also develop into archegonia. Because of this, the sporophytes are always terminal in position. Gametophytes are always foliose and generally have the leaves in three vertical rows. There are some 125 genera and 7,250 species in the suborder. The Acrogynae have been evolved from the

[1] Chalaud, 1929–1931.   [2] Showalter, 1927.

Anacrogynae.   Some hepaticologists, as Cavers,[1] derive the Acrogynae immediately from the foliose Anacrogynae and think that *Fossombronia* might be a possible progenitor of the Acrogynae.   However, the Anacrogynae and the Acrogynae have certain fundamental differences in structure of the apical cell and in the method by which its segments differentiate into stem and leaves.   This seems to show that there is a considerable gap between present-day members of the Anacrogynae and Acrogynae.

There are two lines of evidence which tend to show that the Acrogynae are of relatively recent origin.   One is the lack of Acrogynae among the remarkable thallose and foliose Jungermanniales recently discovered in the Palaeozoic.[2]   Negative evidence of this sort cannot be considered conclusive, but it is significant.   The other is the intergrading between the many genera and species of the suborder.   Large groups with many intergrading genera and species are thought to be of recent origin because natural selection has not been in operation for a sufficient length of time to obliterate intermediates between genera and groups of genera.

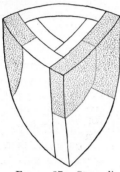

Fig.   37.—Stereodiagram of an apical cell and recently formed segments at the thallus apex of one of the Acrogynae.   Leaf initials of a segment are shaded; the stem initial is unshaded.

The adult portion of the gametophyte among Acrogynae has a well-marked differentiation into stem and leaves.   With very few exceptions, a gametophyte produces leaves in spiral succession and in three vertical rows.   This spiral succession is most clearly evident close to the growing apex.

With one exception[3] all Acrogynae have a pyramidal apical cell with three cutting faces.   The apical cell lies with one cutting face toward the ventral side of the thallus and two cutting faces toward the dorsal. Successive segments may be cut off in clockwise or counter-clockwise sequence.   The first division in a segment does not take place until a new segment has been cut off between it and the apical cell (Fig. 37).   The first division of a dorsal segment is anticlinal and asymmetrical.   The smaller of the two daughter cells is a *segment half cell*.   The larger sister cell immediately divides anticlinally to form another segment half cell and an inner cell.   The two segment half cells jointly give rise to a leaf which is usually bilobed and with each of the lobes derived from a single segment half cell.   The inner cell of the three formed by primary division of a segment develops into a portion of the stem.   Segments cut off from the ventral face on an apical cell may function in the same manner or they may develop only into stem tissue.

[1] Cavers, 1910.   [2] Walton, 1925, 1928.   [3] Goebel, 1893.

Branching of the thallus is never truly dichotomous,[1] that is, the apical cell of a stem never divides vertically into two apical cells which become the initials of a dichotomy. Branches formed at the distal end of a stem originate in a new apical cell differentiated in a segment half cell of a recently formed segment. The new apical cell may be differentiated in a segment half cell either next the dorsal or the ventral face of a branch. In either case its sister cell develops into a leaf somewhat different in appearance from other leaves. According to the position of its initial, this axillating leaf of the branch is dorsal or ventral in position. Equal growth of the main axis and the new branch results in what appears to be a true dichotomy; more vigorous growth in the main axis results in a monopodial type of branching. Apical cells of lateral (intercalary)

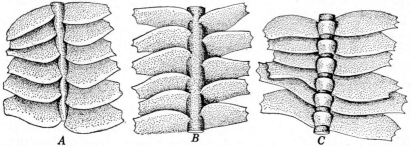

Fig. 38.—*A*, dorsal view of succubous leaves of *Plagiochila*. *B–C*, dorsal and ventral views of incubous leaves of *Bazzania*. (× 12.)

branches may also be differentiated from superficial cells in mature portions of the thallus. Branches developed from these apical cells are essentially adventitious in nature.

Leaves generally lie in three vertical series corresponding to the three cutting faces of the apical cell, two dorsal and one ventral. All leaves are transverse in insertion when first formed, but unequal elongation of dorsal and ventral faces of the stem usually results in a diagonal insertion of the older lateral leaves (Fig. 38). Greater elongation of the ventral side of the stem results in a *succubous* arrangement of lateral leaves, or one in which the posterior margin of each leaf *overlaps* the next older leaf. Greater elongation of the dorsal surface results in an *incubous* arrangement of lateral leaves in which the posterior margin of each leaf *underlies* the next older leaf. The ventral leaves (*amphigastria*) are always transversely inserted.

Lateral leaves of many genera have a well-marked differentiation into two lobes, one toward the dorsal side of the stem, the other toward the ventral side. This formation of two lobes is due to more or less independent growth from the two segment half cells derived from first divisions

[1] Evans, 1912; Leitgeb, 1871.

of a segment. According to the independence of development by the two cells, the two lobes are free from one another or restricted to the apex of a leaf. Among genera in which the lobes are practically independent of each other, the two may be of equal or unequal size. In the latter case the dorsal lobe may be smaller than the ventral lobe, or vice versa. Genera with ventral lobes larger than dorsal lobes, as *Scapania*, seem to have four rows of lateral leaves. Most genera have lateral leaves one cell in thickness, but a few of them have leaves several cells in thickness. Segments from the ventral face of the apical cell may or may not give rise to leaves. When ventral leaves (amphigastria) are formed, they are always smaller than the lateral leaves, different in shape, and without the differentiation into two lobes so characteristic of lateral leaves (Fig. 38*C*). The unusual water sacs found upon both lateral and ventral leaves are formed by an enfolding of the entire leaf or a portion of it.

Stems of Acrogynae have even less internal differentiation of tissue than those of Anacrogynae. In only a very few Acrogynae does the stem show any suggestion of a differentiation of water-conducting tissue. When the ventral surface of a stem is in contact with a substratum, it may produce smooth-walled rhizoids, especially just beneath the amphigastria, but rhizoids are generally lacking on erect branches. Superficial cells of the stem may also give rise to *paraphylls*—filamentous or laminate outgrowths which supplement the photosynthetic activity of the leaves.

Acrogynae may be homothallic or heterothallic and with the sex organs borne upon the main axis or upon short lateral branches. However, many tropical species have never been found in a fruiting condition. The entire sexual branch, or the portion bearing the sex organs, has leaves differing in shape and size from those borne on vegetative portions of the gametophyte. Leaves adjacent to the sex organs are often called bracts, and the antheridial bracts are generally morphologically different from archegonial bracts of the same species. One, two, or a small group of antheridia may be produced in the axil of an antheridial bract. These leaves are usually terminal in position, but they may be in an intercalary series between foliage leaves. The number of successive antheridial bracts upon a branch is usually considerable, and there may be as many as 60 bracts on either side of a branch.[1]

All archegonia of Acrogynae are restricted to the apex of a branch or to the apex of the main axis. Accordingly as the apical cell alone or the apical cell and its recently formed segments develop into archegonia, there is but one archegonium or a group of archegonia. The last three leaves matured before production of archegonia are usually the only ones to develop into female bracts. The group of archegonial bracts is known collectively as the *perianth*, but it should be noted that this structure is

[1] Johnson, 1929.

not homologous with either the perianth of the Anacrogynae or that of other Hepaticae.[1]

There have been but few investigations on development of sex organs among the Acrogynae. So far as reported[2] antheridial development is according to the method typical of Jungermanniales and has a differentiation of two primary androgonial cells. Mature antheridia of Acrogynae are globose and most of them have a long stalk. Archegonia develop in the usual manner and typically have five vertical rows of neck cells. Many Acrogynae have the venter and lower portion of the neck becoming two or more cells in thickness before fertilization.

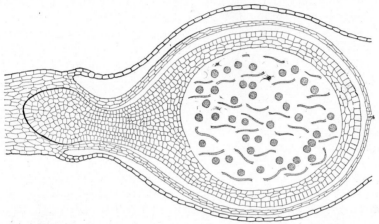

Fig. 39.—Longitudinal section through a nearly mature sporophyte of *Porella*. (× 45.)

The first division of a zygote is transverse. Among some genera, transverse division of the epibasal cell produces three superimposed cells which develop respectively into capsule, seta, and foot of the mature sporophyte (*Frullania*).[3] In other cases (*Porella*)[3] the early cell divisions are in irregular sequence, and there is a rather late differentiation into capsule, seta, and foot (Fig. 39). Capsules of mature sporophytes are usually globose and have a jacket layer two to six cells in thickness.[4] Acrogynae regularly have the capsule dehiscing into four valves at the time when the spores are shed. In most genera all of the sporogenous tissue develops into spores and elaters, but there are certain genera, as *Gottschea*,[5] in which the basal portion of the sporogenous tissue develops into an elaterophore. Differentiation of elaters usually takes several cell generations before division to form spore mother cells. Certain genera have the elater-producing cells alternating with the spore-producing cells[6] in vertically (*Frullania*) or horizontally (*Cephalozia*) parallel series.

[1] Knapp, 1930.   [2] Campbell, 1918; Johnson, 1929; Manning, 1914.
[3] Campbell, 1918.   [4] Andreas, 1899.   [5] Goebel, 1927.   [6] Goebel, 1906.

In addition to being enclosed by a calyptra, the young sporophyte is also ensheathed by protective structures derived from the apex of a gametophyte. In many cases this ensheathing structure is a perianth;[1] in other cases it comprises more than the perianth since other portions of the gametophyte are involved. Apical tissues growing into an ensheathing structure may include only the receptacle (Fig. 40*B*), the entire stem apex (Fig. 40*C*), or only the margin of the stem apex (Fig. 40*D*). Upward growth restricted to the stem margin results in a sac-like structure often

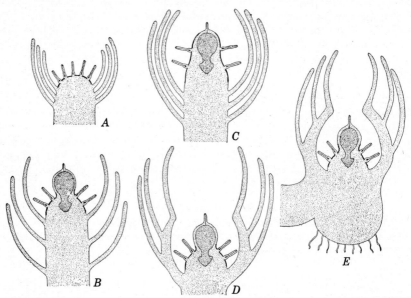

Fig. 40.—Diagrams showing the various types of protection of the sporophyte found in the Acrogynae. The receptacle and the portions derived from it are outlined with a heavy line. *A*, receptacle before development of the sporophyte. *B*, a sporophyte surrounded by a calyptra. *C*, a sporophyte surrounded by the receptacle. *D–E*, marsupia. (*Diagrams based upon Knapp, 1930.*)

called a *marsupium*. The most striking marsupia among the Acrogynae are found in those genera in which the marsupium comes to lie at right angles to the long axis of the gametophyte or becomes bent back upon the stem apex (Fig. 40*E*). The inverted position of the marsupium is due either to a bending of the entire stem apex or to unequal elongation of two sides of the apex.[2] Bending of the marsupium is often accompanied by a considerable growth of the curved portion, and this frequently develops rhizoids when it is in contact with the soil. The older hepaticologists grouped all marsupial genera in a separate family, the Geocalycaceae. Modern hepaticologists hold that this is a wholly artificial family, since

---

[1] Knapp, 1930.   [2] Cavers, 1910; Goebel, 1906; Knapp, 1930.

the ability to produce marsupia has arisen in several unrelated genera of Anacrogynae.

Spores of Acrogynae usually germinate immediately after they are shed from a capsule.[1] The germinating spore first gives rise to a protonemal stage. This may consist of a single cell, but more often the protonema is a multicellular filament, with or without branching. Sooner or later there are cell divisions in all directions at the end of a filament and production of a mass of cells. One of the cells in the mass begins to function as an apical cell, and the plant body resulting from early activity of the apical cell may be distinctly thallose. Eventually the apical cell ceases forming this thallose juvenile phase of the gametophyte and produces the adult phase in which there is a differentiation of stem and leaves. In some genera the protonemal and juvenile phases are reduced to a few cells, and the gametophyte begins to form leaves and stem at a very early stage in its development. Conversely, other genera have protonemal and juvenile phases of long duration and constituting the major portion of the gametophytic cycle. In Acrogynae of this type the adult phase is restricted to branches bearing the sex organs. *Schiffneria*[2] is a good example of permanent retention of the thallose juvenile phase.

The more recent attempts to classify the Acrogynae are largely modifications of the system of Spruce.[3] The characters used to distinguish families include structure of perianth, structure of lateral leaves, and structure and arrangement of elaters. Certain of the eight families generally recognized are natural; others are artificial. These families are:

Lejeuneaceae. A natural family of 60 or more genera distinguishable from all other Acrogynae by the fact that the elaters have a single spiral thickening and the fact that each elater extends from top to bottom of the capsule and has its upper end affixed to the capsule wall.

Porellaceae. A monotypic family distinguished from other families with unequally lobed lateral leaves by the incomplete dehiscence of the capsule.

Pleuroziaceae. A monotypic family distinguishable from other families with unequally lobed lateral leaves by the saccate ventral lobes.

Radulaceae. A monotypic family distinguishable from other families with unequally lobed lateral leaves by the rhizoids on the ventral lobes.

Scapinaceae. A family with about five genera in which the ventral lobes of the lateral leaves are larger than the dorsal lobes.

Ptilidiaceae. A family with about six genera in which the lateral leaves have several apical teeth or lobes, and in which the ventral leaves, although smaller, are similar in form to the lateral leaves.

[1] Chalaud, 1931; Lampa, 1903.   [2] Goebel, 1928.   [3] Spruce, 1884.

Cephaloziaceae. A family with some 30 genera in which the lateral leaves are entire or with lobes of equal size and different in form from the ventral leaves. The perianth is usually triangular in outline and with two angles toward the dorsal side of the thallus.

Lophoziaceae. Differing from the foregoing in that the triangular perianth has a single angle toward the dorsal side.

ORDER 4. CALOBRYALES

The Calobryales have a moss-like gametophyte that is differentiated into stem and leaves. The antheridia are ovoid, stalked, and develop in a typical manner. Archegonia differ from those of other Hepaticae in

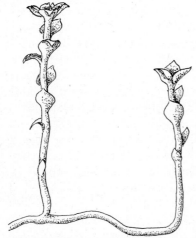

that the jacket portion of a neck has only four vertical rows of cells. The sporophyte has an elongate capsule in which the jacket layer is one cell in thickness except at the apex.

There is but one family, the Calobryaceae. This family is often placed among the Anacrogynae of the Jungermanniales. However, it differs so markedly in external appearance of the gametophyte, early ontogeny of the sex organs, and in structure of the capsule, that it is in a more natural systematic position when placed in a separate order, the Calobryales.

FIG. 41.—Male gametophyte of *Calobryum Blumei* Nees. ($\times 1\frac{1}{2}$.)

There are but two genera in the family. *Calobryum* has three species and grows in Java, Japan, South America, and the West Indies. *Haplomitrium* is monotypic and is known from several localities in northern Europe and from one station[1] in the United States. Both genera have a pale subterranean, sparingly branched rhizome, from which arise erect leafy branches (Fig. 41). The erect branches bear their leaves in three vertical rows, and all leaves may be of the same size, or those of one row may be smaller than those of the other two. The smaller leaves are thought to be homologous with the amphigastria of the Jungermanniales, and the side of the stem bearing them is considered the morphologically ventral side of a branch. Erect branches bearing sex organs have the uppermost leaves close together and in more than three rows. Such branches have a strong superficial resemblance to the erect gametophores of mosses.

[1] Evans, 1917.

Terminal growth in a branch of *Calobryum*[1] is due to a pyramidal apical cell with three cutting faces, one slightly narrower than the other two. It is thought that this narrower face gives rise to the ventral file of leaves. The first division in a segment from the apical cell is transverse and perpendicular to the cutting face of an apical cell. The lower daughter cell develops into the thick leaf base and the portion of a stem between it and the next older leaf. The upper daughter cell develops into the portion of a leaf that is one cell in thickness. Early growth of this portion of a leaf is by means of an apical cell with two cutting faces; later growth is by intercalary cell division in the basal region.

Rhizoids are lacking on both the subterranean and erect portions of the stem. Superficial cells anywhere on the stem may develop into short two- or three-celled mucilage hairs in which the terminal cell is clavate. The axial portion of a stem of *Calobryum* contains a sharply delimited conducting tissue 10 to 15 cells in diameter. External to the conducting tissue are large parenchymatous cells in which there are numerous starch grains. Branches of a rhizome are intercalary in origin. A newly formed branch grows horizontally for a time, then grows upward and develops leaves.

Both genera are heterothallic, and with the sex organs produced in abundance on flattened apices of leafy branches (Fig. 42*A*). Leaves surrounding antheridia of male plants are larger than the others. As a result these fertile branches resemble gametophores of mosses. The details of antheridial development have only been followed in *Calobryum Blumei* Nees.[2] Here, the initial cell of an antheridium divides transversely into a basal cell, embedded in the thallus, and an outer cell, which projects above the thallus. The outer cell then divides transversely into a primary antheridial cell and a primary stalk cell (Fig. 42*B*). In most antheridia there then follow three successive vertical divisions of the primary antheridial cell. The sequence of division is similar to that in an archegonium and results in three jacket initials completely enclosing a single primary androgonial cell (Fig. 42*C*). The first division of the primary androgonial cell is transverse (Fig. 42*D–E*). After this, the two daughter cells divide transversely and longitudinally (Fig. 42*F–G*). The primary stalk cell develops into a stalk composed of several superimposed tiers of four cells each. Occasionally antheridia of *Calobryum* may have the primary antheridial cell dividing vertically and in the same sequence as in the Jungermanniales.

Female plants of *Calobryum* have a development of archegonia from about a half dozen recently formed segments from the apical cell and then the apical cell itself develops into an archegonium. *Calobryum*, therefore,

---

[1] Campbell, 1920; Goebel, 1891.   [2] Campbell, 1920.

is acrogynous. *Haplomitrium* is anacrogynous and without any disappearance of the apical cell when the archegonia are formed. *Calobryum* has the usual three vertical divisions of the primary archegonial cell to form three jacket initials that surround a primary axial cell. In most cases the jacket initials intersect one another to completely enclose the

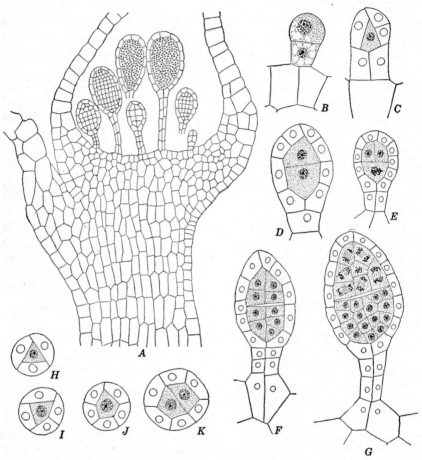

Fig. 42.—*Calobryum Blumei* Nees. *A*, vertical section through fertile apex of a male gametophyte. *B–K*, stages in development of antheridia. *B–G*, in vertical section; *H–K*, in transverse section. (*A*, × 70; *B–D*, *H–K*, × 485; *E–G*, × 325.)

primary axial cell. Consequently the primary axial cell functions directly as a central cell and without cutting off a primary cover cell (Fig. 43*A–B*). Most of the archegonia have a vertical division of only one of the three jacket initials and a resultant development of an archegonial neck composed of only four rows of cells (Fig. 43*J*). The neck of a *Calobryum* archegonium is very long, markedly twisted, and surrounds a vertical row of 16 to 20 canal cells.   The venter is not much broader than the neck, and its jacket is two cells in thickness at maturity (Fig. 43*C–F*).

Except for a massive calyptra there are no protective structures surrounding a developing sporophyte.   Early cell divisions in development of a *Calobryum* embryo are in irregular sequence.   The hypobasal

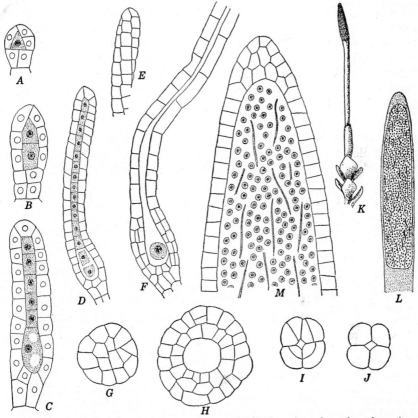

Fig. 43.—*Calobryum Blumei* Nees.   *A–D*, longitudinal sections through archegonia at various stages of development.   *E–F*, surface view of the neck and longitudinal section through the base of a mature archegonium.   *G–J*, transverse sections through the base, venter, and neck of a mature archegonium.   *K*, apex of a female gametophyte bearing a mature sporophyte.   *L–M*, longitudinal sections through the capsule of a nearly mature sporophyte.   (*A–C*, × 325; *D–E*, *F–J*, × 215; *K*, × 1½; *L*, × 18; *M*, × 60.)

portion of the embryo develops into a haustorium; the epibasal portion gives rise to foot, seta, and capsule of the mature sporophyte.   The mature sporophyte has a cylindrical capsule, a long seta, and an acuminate foot.   Except for the apical portion, the jacket layer of the capsule is one cell in thickness, with the thickening of the cell walls localized in a median annular band perpendicular to the surface of the capsule

(Fig. 43*L–M*). Opening of the capsule is by a dehiscence into four valves, which may remain more or less united.[1] Sporogenous tissue within the young capsule does not have a partial sterilization to form an elaterophore, but it does have an early differentiation into elaters and cells that are destined to form the spores.

The Calobryales seem to be a group which arose along the same evolutionary line as the Jungermanniales but which departed quite early from that line. Gametophytes of Calobryales exhibit a strange combination of advanced and primitive features. The gametophyte has attained a degree of differentiation unequaled by any other liverwort as far as external and internal complexity are concerned. However, evolution of these complex vegetative features has not been accompanied by a corresponding evolution of the sex organs. The similarity in early ontogeny of antheridia and archegonia is a decidedly primitive feature, and one giving the best evidence for the theory that antheridia and archegonia are homologous structures. In fact, from the standpoint of early ontogeny, the sex organs of Calobryales are the most primitive of any in the Hepaticae.

Bibliography

ÅKERMAN, Å. **1910.** *Zeitschr. Bot.* **2**: 94–103. [Chemotaxis of antherozoids.]

ALLEN, C. E. **1919.** *Proc. Amer. Phil. Soc.* **58**: 289–316. 28 figs. [Sex inheritance *Sphaerocarpos.*]

ANDERSEN, EMMA N. **1929.** *Bot. Gaz.* **88**: 150–166. 34 figs. [*Marchantia.*]
  1931. *Ibid.* **92**: 66–84. 19 figs. [Discharge of antherozoids.]

ANDREAS, J. **1899.** *Flora* **86**: 161–213. 1 pl. 29 figs. [Sporangial dehiscence, Calobryales.]

BARNES, C. R., and W. J. G. LAND. **1907.** *Bot. Gaz.* **44**: 197–213. 22 figs. [Air chambers.]
  1908. *Ibid.* **46**: 401–409. 14 figs. [Cupule of *Marchantia.*]

BEER, R. **1906.** *Ann. Bot.* **20**: 277–291. 2 pl. [Spores, *Riccia.*]

BERGDOLT, E. **1926.** *Bot. Abhandl.* **10**: 1–86. 121 figs. [Marchantiaceae.]

BLACK, CAROLINA A. **1913.** *Ann. Bot.* **27**: 511–532. 2 pl. [*Riccia.*]

CAMPBELL, D. H. **1896.** *Ibid.* **10**: 489–510. 2 pl. [Sphaerocarpales.]
  1896A. *Erythea* **4**: 73–78. 1 pl. [*Sphaerocarpos.*]
  1898. *Bot. Gaz.* **25**: 272–274. [*Monoclea.*]
  1916. *Amer. Jour. Bot.* **3**: 261–273. 6 figs. [Anacrogynae.]
  1918. The structure and development of mosses and ferns. 3d ed. New York. 708 pp. 322 figs.
  1918A. *Ann. Bot.* **32**: 319–338. 2 pl. 10 figs. [Marchantiaceae.]
  1920. *Ibid.* **34**: 1–12. 1 pl. 6 figs. [*Calobryum.*]

CAMPBELL, D. H., and FLORENCE WILLIAMS. **1914.** *Leland Stanford Junior Univ. Publ.* Univ. Ser. **15**: 1–44. 23 figs. [*Pallavicinia.*]

CAVERS, F. **1903.** *New Phytol.* **2**: 121–133, 155–165. 8 figs. [Asexual reproduction.]
  1903A. *Ann. Bot.* **17**: 270–274. 1 fig. [Discharge of antherozoids.]
  1904. Contributions to the biology of the Hepaticae. Part I. Targionia, Reboulia, Preissia, Monoclea. Leeds. 47 pp. 12 figs.

---

[1] Andreas 1899.

1904A. *Rev. Bryol.* **31**: 69–80. 4 figs. [*Monoclea.*]

1904B. *Ann. Bot.* **18**: 87–120. 2 pl. 5 figs. [Marchantiaceae.]

1910. *New Phytol.* **9**: 81–112, 157–186, 193–196, 197–234, 269–304, 341–353. 54 figs. [Interrelationships, Hepaticae.]

CHALAUD, G. **1929–1931.** *Rev. Gen. Bot.* **41**: 24–34, 95–105, 129–141, 213–236, 293–306, 353–364, 409–423, 474–497, 541–554, 606–621, 676–699. 8 pl. 189 figs. **42**: 31–45, 99–114, 159–163, 219–232, 297–312, 366–377, 429–438, 505–512, 553–588. 61 figs. [*Fossombronia.*]

1931. *Ann. Bryol.* **4**: 49–67. 4 figs. [Gametophyte development, Acrogynae.]

CLAPP, GRACE L. **1912.** *Bot. Gaz.* **54**: 177–193. 4 pl. [*Riccardia.*]

CRIBBS, J. E. **1918.** *Ibid.* **65**: 91–96. 2 pl. [*Marchantia.*]

DEUTSCH, H. **1912.** *Ibid.* **53**: 492–503. 13 figs. [*Targionia.*]

DUPLER, A. W. **1921.** *Bull. Torrey Bot. Club* **48**: 241–252. 22 figs. [Air chambers, Marchantiales.]

DURAND, E. J. **1908.** *Ibid.* **35**: 321–335. 5 pl. [*Marchantia.*]

EVANS, A. W. **1912.** *Ann. Bot.* **26**: 1–37. 36 figs. [Branching of Acrogynae.]

1917. *Rhodora* **19**: 263–272. [*Haplomitrium.*]

1918. *Bull. Torrey Bot. Club* **45**: 235–251. 14 figs. [Air chambers.]

1921. *Trans. Conn. Acad. Arts and Sci.* **25**: 93–209. 13 figs. [*Riccardia.*]

1923. Marchantiales. In North American Flora. Vol. 14. Part 1. New York. Pp. 9–66.

FARMER, J. B. **1894.** *Ann. Bot.* **8**: 35–52. 2 pl. [*Pallavicinia.*]

FLORIN, R. **1922.** *Ark. Bot.* **18**, No. 5: 1–58. 1 pl. 25 figs. [*Riccardia.*]

GARBER, J. F. **1904.** *Bot. Gaz.* **37**: 161–177. 2 pl. 4 figs. [*Riccia.*]

GOEBEL, K. **1889.** *Flora* **72**: 1–45. 2 pl. 6 figs. [Juvenile gametophytes.]

1891. *Ann. Jard. Bot. Buitenzorg.* **9**: 1–40. 4 pl. [*Calobryum.*]

1893. *Flora.* **77**: 423–459. 2 pl. 18 figs. [Leaves of Acrogynae.]

1906. *Ibid.* **96**: 1–202. 144 figs. [Acrogynae.]

1910. *Ibid.* **101**: 43–97. 45 figs. [Marchantiaceae.]

1927. *Ibid.* **122**: 33–56. 11 figs. [Spore formation, Acrogynae.]

1928. *Ann. Jard. Bot. Buitenzorg.* **39**: 1–116. 14 pl. [Acrogynae.]

1930. Organographie der Pflanzen. 2d Teil. Bryophyten-Pteridophyten. Aufl. 3 Jena. 736 pp. 850 figs.

HAUPT, A. W. **1918.** *Bot. Gaz.* **66**: 524–553. 5 pl. [*Pallavicinia.*]

1920. *Ibid.* **69**: 318–331. 6 pl. 1 fig. [*Fossombronia.*]

1926. *Ibid.* **82**: 30–54. 2 pl. 16 figs. [Marchantiaceae.]

1929. *Ibid.* **87**: 302–318. 1 pl. 21 figs. [Marchantiaceae.]

1929A. *Ibid.* **88**: 103–108. 1 pl. [*Fossombronia.*]

HEBERLEIN, ENID A. **1929.** *Ibid.* **88**: 417–429. 21 figs. [*Marchantia.*]

HIRSCH, PAULINE E. **1910.** *Bull. Torrey Bot. Club* **37**: 73–77. 6 figs. [Air chambers, *Riccia.*]

HORNE, A. S. **1909.** *Ann. Bot.* **23**: 159–160. 3 figs. [Discharge of antherozoids.]

HOWE, M. A., and L. M. UNDERWOOD. **1903.** *Bull. Torrey Bot. Club* **30**: 214–224. 2 pl. [*Riella.*]

HUMPHREY, H. B. **1906.** *Ann. Bot.* **20**: 83–108. 2 pl. 8 figs. [*Fossombronia.*]

HUTCHINSON, A. H. **1915.** *Bot. Gaz.* **60**: 134–143. 4 pl. 1 fig. [Gametophyte, *Pellia.*]

JOHNSON, D. S. **1904.** *Ibid.* **38**: 185–205. 2 pl. [*Monoclea.*]

1929. *Ibid.* **88**: 38–62. 3 pl. 4 figs. [Antheridia, Acrogynae.]

JUEL, O. **1910.** *Svensk Bot. Tidskr.* **4**: 160–166. 1 pl. 5 figs. [*Riccia.*]

KIENITZ-GERLOFF, F. **1874.** *Bot. Zeitg.* **32**: 161–172, 193–204, 209–217, 225–235. 2 pl. [Development of sporophytes.]

KNAPP, H.   **1930.**   *Bot. Abhandl.* **16:** 1–168. 214 figs.   [Protection of sporophyte, Acrogynae.]

KURCH, O.   **1890.**   *Malphigia* **4:** 403–423. 2 pl.   [*Riella.*]

LAMPA, EMMA.   **1903.**   *Sitzungsber. Akad. Wiss. Wien* (Math.-Nat.Kl.)   **112¹:** 779–792. 4 pl.   [Spore germination Acrogynae.]

LANG, W. H.   **1905.**   *Ann. Bot.* **19:** 411–426. 2 pl.   [Targioniaceae.]

LEITGEB, H.   **1871.**   *Bot. Zeitg.* **29:** 557–565. 3 figs.   [Branching of Acrogynae.]

1877.   Untersuchungen ueber die Lebermoose. III Heft.   Die frondosen Junge₋ mannieen.   Jena. 144 pp. 9 pl.

1879.   *Ibid.* IV Heft.   Die Riccieen.   Graz. 101 pp. 9 pl.

1881.   *Ibid.* VI Heft.   Die Marchantieen und allgemeine Bemerkungen über Lebermoose.   Graz. 158 pp. 11 pl.

LEWIS, C. E.   **1906.**   *Bot. Gaz.* **41:** 109–138. 5 pl.   [*Riccia.*]

LIDFORSS, B.   **1904.**   *Jahrb. Wiss. Bot.* **41:** 65–87.   [Chemotaxis of antherozoids.]

McALLISTER, F.   **1916.**   *Bull. Torrey Bot. Club* **43:** 117–126. 1 pl.   [Ricciaceae.]

1928.   *Ibid.* **55:** 1–10. 11 figs.   [Sex ratios, *Riccia.*]

McCORMICK, FLORENCE A.   **1914.**   *Bot. Gaz.* **58:** 401–418. 3 pl.   [Anacrogynae.]

McNAUGHT, HELEN L.   **1929.**   *Ibid.* **88:** 400–416. 22 figs.   [Sporophyte, *Marchantia.*]

MANNING, FLORENCE L.   **1914.**   *Ibid.* **57:** 320–323. 2 pl.   [Sex organs, Acrogynae.]

MENGE, F.   **1930.**   *Flora* **124:** 423–476. 5 pl. 7 figs.   [Spore germination, *Marchantia.*]

MEYER, K.   **1912.**   *Bull. Soc. Imp. Nat. Moscou* N.S. **25:** 263–286. 1 pl. 22 figs.   [Sporophyte, Marchantiales.]

1914.   *Ber. Deutsch. Bot. Ges.* **32:** 262–266. 4 figs.   [Sporophyte, *Corsinia.*]

MÜHLDORF, A.   **1931.**   *Ibid.* **49:** 21–28. 1 fig.   [Antherozoids.]

NEVINS, BEATRICE I.   **1933.**   *Cellule* **41:** 293–334. 3 pl.   [Antheridia, *Sphaerocarpos.*]

O'HANLON, SISTER MARY ELLEN.   **1926.**   *Bot. Gaz.* **82:** 215–222. 4 pl.   [Spore germination, *Marchantia.*]

O'KEEFE, LILLIAN.   **1915.**   *New Phytol.* **14:** 105–116. 2 figs.   [*Targionia.*]

ORTH, R.   **1930.**   *Flora* **124:** 152–203. 78 figs.   [Air chambers.]

PAGAN, F. M.   **1932.**   *Bot. Gaz.* **93:** 71–84. 24 figs.   [Sporophyte, *Riccia.*]

PANDE, S. K.   **1933.**   *Jour. Indian Bot. Soc.* **12:** 110–121. 3 pl. 2 figs.   [*Riccia.*]

PEIRCE, G. J.   **1902.**   *Bull. Torrey Bot. Club* **29:** 374–382. 5 figs.   [Discharge of antherozoids.]

PIETSCH, W.   **1911.**   *Flora* **103:** 347–384. 21 figs.   [Air chambers, *Riccia.*]

RICKETT, H. W.   **1920.**   *Amer. Jour. Bot.* **7:** 182–194. 4 pl. 1 fig.   [Thallus, *Sphaerocarpos.*]

1920A.   *Bull. Torrey Bot. Club* **47:** 347–357. 25 figs.   [Regeneration, *Sphaerocarpos.*]

1923.   *Ann. Bot.* **37:** 225–259. 2 pl. 3 figs.   [Fertilization, *Sphaerocarpos.*]

SCHNIFFER, V.   **1893–1895.**   Hepaticae.   In A. Engler and K. Prantl, Die natürlichen Pflanzenfamilien.   Teil. 1. Abt. 3. 1 Hälfte. Pp. 3–141. 73 figs.

1913.   *Oesterr. Bot. Zeitschr.* **63:** 29–33, 75–81, 113–121, 154–159. 1 fig.   [*Monoclea.*]

SEALEY, J. E.   **1930.**   *Amer. Jour. Bot.* **17:** 19–28. 1 pl.   [Ricciaceae.]

SHOWALTER, A. M.   **1923.**   *Ibid.* **10:** 148–166. 4 pl. 3 fig.   [*Riccardia.*]

1925.   *Bull. Torrey Bot. Club* **52:** 157–166. 1 pl. 2 figs.   [Spore germination, *Riccardia, Pellia.*]

1926.   *Ann. Bot.* **40:** 691–707. 1 pl. 3 figs.   [Antherozoids.]

1926A.   *Ibid.* **40:** 713–726. 3 pl. 4 figs.   [Fertilization, *Riccardia.*]

1927.   *Ibid.* **41:** 37–46. 2 pl. 4 figs.   [Fertilization, *Fossombronia.*]

1927A.   *Ibid.* **41:** 409–417. 3 pl.   [Fertilization, *Pellia.*]

1928.   *Cellule* **38:** 295–349. 5 pl. 29 figs.   [Fertilization, *Riccardia.*]

Spruce, R. **1884.** *Trans. and Proc. Bot. Soc. Edinburgh* **15**: 1–588. 22 pl. [South American Hepaticae.]

Steil, W. N. **1923.** *Bull. Torrey Bot. Club* **50**: 197–201. 5 figs. [Antherozoids.]

Stephani, F. **1900–1924.** Species hepaticarum. Geneva. Vol. 1. 413 pp. Vol. 2. 615 pp. Vol. 3. 693 pp. Vol. 4. 824 pp. Vol. 5. 1044 pp. Vol. 6. 763 pp.

Studhalter, R. A. **1931.** *Bot. Gaz.* **92**: 172–191. 25 figs. [*Riella.*]

Tansley, A. G., and Edith Chick. **1901.** *Ann. Bot.* **15**: 1–38. 2 pl. [Conducting tissue.]

Walton, J. **1925.** *Ibid.* **39**: 563–571. 1 pl. 1 fig. [Fossil Hepaticae.]

1928. *Ibid.* **42**: 707–716. 1 pl. 1 fig. [Fossil Hepaticae.]

Wolfson, A. M. **1928.** *Amer. Jour. Bot.* **15**: 179–184. 2 pl. [Spore germination, *Pellia.*]

CHAPTER III

ANTHOCEROTAE

The Anthocerotae have simple thallose gametophytes that are without any internal differentiation of tissues. Antheridia develop from hypodermal cells on the dorsal side of a thallus, and they lie free within roofed-over chambers. The archegonia also lie embedded in the thallus.

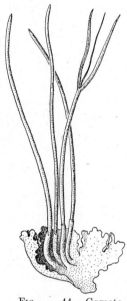

The sporophyte consists of a foot and a capsule in which the lowermost portion is meristematic and continually adding to the upper portion. The sporogenous tissue in a capsule is derived from the outermost layer (amphithecium) of an embryo.

Five genera and 320 species are referred to a single order—the *Anthocerotales*. This order is often placed among the Hepaticae, but members of it differ markedly in position and development of the sex organs, structure of the chloroplasts, and structure of the sporophyte. For these reasons it seems better to follow the suggestion[1] that the order be placed in a special class coordinate with the Hepaticae and the Musci.

The order contains but one family, the Anthocerotaceae. Differences between the various genera are based in large part upon sporophytic structure of the elaters. Two of the genera (*Anthoceros* and *Notothylas*) are cosmopolitan; the remaining three genera are tropical or subtropical in distribution.

Fig. 44.—Gametophyte and sporophytes of *Anthoceros fusiformis* Aust. (× 2.)

The gametophytes of Anthocerotae are thallose, somewhat lobed or radially dissected, and sometimes have a tendency toward dichotomous branching (Fig. 44). Gametophytes are always dorsiventrally differentiated and have numerous smooth-walled rhizoids on the ventral surface. The ventral surface lacks scales or mucilage hairs. One genus (*Dendroceros*) has the gametophyte differentiated into a thick midrib with lateral wings one cell in thickness; the remaining genera have lateral margins of their thalli more than one cell in thickness. Aside from a

[1] Howe, 1899.

76

more regular arrangement of the superficial cells, there is no internal differentiation of tissues.   The ventral portion of the thallus has mucilage-filled intercellular cavities opening to the ventral surface by narrow slits. Very often these cavities contain colonies of *Nostoc*.   As a result the gametophyte has a greasy dark-green color, instead of the bright green characteristic of Hepaticae.   The presence of the endophytic alga is not essential for growth of the gametophyte, and it has been shown[1] that thalli without *Nostoc* grow better than those containing the alga.   Cells of the gametophyte usually contain a single large chloroplast, but deep-lying cells of certain genera[2] may contain two to eight of them.   The chloroplast differs markedly from those of other Bryophyta in that it contains a large pyrenoid.   Pyrenoids of Anthocerotae are not homolo-gous with those of green algae since they consist of a crowded mass of 25 to 300 disk- or spindle-shaped bodies,[3] each of which may be trans-formed into a rudimentary starch grain without changing its form or position.

Growth of a thallus is initiated by a single apical cell.   In most cases the apical cell has two cutting faces which alternately form dorsal and ventral segments, but in *Dendroceros*[4] it has a convex posterior cutting face and two lateral cutting faces.   Segments from the posterior face of an apical cell of *Dendroceros* contribute to the midrib; those from the lateral faces contribute to the wings.   Now and then the apical cell of *Anthoceros* and of other genera gives rise to a transverse row of cells by a series of vertical divisions.   A cell near each end of the row then begins to function as an apical cell, and the two growing points thus initiated separate farther and farther from each other as growth continues.   Con-tinued repetition of this dichotomous branching results in a compact rosette-like thallus.   More active growth of one lobe, as in *Anthoceros Halli* Aust.,[5] results in a long, narrow, pinnately branched thallus.

Vegetative multiplication may take place by progressive growth and death, but this is of much less frequent occurrence than in Marchantiales. In regions with prolonged dry seasons the gametophyte frequently devel-ops marginal thickenings in which the superficial cells of the mass develop into a protective corky layer.   Such "tubers" may develop into new thalli with the return of favorable growing conditions.

All Anthocerotae are homothallic, although they frequently are protandrous.   One can rarely distinguish between fruiting and sterile thalli when specimens are examined with a hand lens because the sex organs are deeply embedded in the thallus and are not borne on special branches.

---

[1] Peirce, 1906.   [2] Campbell, 1907.   [3] McAllister, 1914, 1927.
[4] Campbell, 1898, 1908.   [5] Bartlett, 1928.

One fundamental difference between the Anthocerotae and other Bryophyta is the fact that an antheridial initial is the inner daughter cell produced by a periclinal division of a superficial thallus cell. The discovery of atypical individuals in which the outer daughter cell functions as the antheridial initial[1] suggests that the Anthocerotae are derived from ancestors in which antheridia developed from superficial cells. Immediately after the division into an antheridial initial and an outer sterile cell,

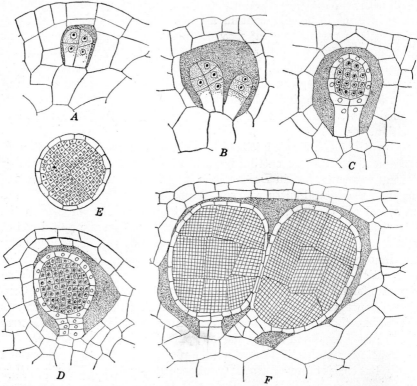

Fig. 45.—Stages in the development of the antheridium of *Anthoceros fusiformis* Aust. *A–D, F*, in vertical section; *E*, in transverse section. (*A–C*, × 485; *D–E*, × 325; *F*, × 215.)

there is a development of a mucilage-filled space between the two that eventually enlarges to form the antheridial chamber. The sterile cell above the antheridial initial divides and redivides to form a sterile layer overroofing the antheridial chamber. This layer may be one or more cells in thickness. In certain genera, including *Anthoceros*, the antheridial initial may divide vertically into two or four daughter cells, each of which develops into an antheridium (Fig. 45*B, F*). Thus the antheridial chamber may contain two or four antheridia. Transverse division of the antheridial

---

[1] Lampa, 1903; Leitgeb, 1879.

initial (or of the daughter cells formed by vertical division of it) is into a *primary antheridial cell* and a *primary stalk cell*. The primary stalk cell develops into a stalk two cells in breadth and several cells in height. Development of the primary antheridial cell into the antheridium proper seems to be according to the same sequence as in the Marchantiales,[1] one or two tiers of four cells each dividing periclinally to form primary andro-

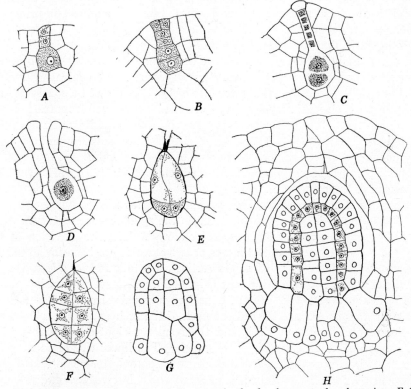

FIG. 46.—*Anthoceros laevis* L. *A–D*, stages in the development of archegonia. *E–G*, early stages in the development of embryos. *H*, an embryo after formation of the arche-sporium from the amphithecium. (× 325.)

gonial cells and primary jacket cells (Fig. 45). Spermatogenesis[2] is much like that of other Bryophyta and involves a metamorphosis of the androcytes into biflagellate antherozoids.

Archegonia of Anthocerotae are embedded in the thallus and in direct contact with vegetative cells lateral to them. In Anthocerotae the archegonial initial functions directly as the primary archegonial cell, instead of dividing into primary archegonial cell and primary stalk cell. Obliteration of this division is the main reason for the embedded arche-

[1] Campbell, 1898.   [2] Bagchee, 1924.

gonium and its direct lateral contact with cells of a thallus.   The first divisions of an archegonial initial are vertical and into three jacket initials surrounding an axial cell.   The axial cell divides transversely into a cover initial and a central cell, after which the central cell divides into a primary canal cell and a primary ventral cell (Fig. 46*A*).   Transverse division and redivision of the primary canal cell results in a vertical row of four to six neck canal cells.   These are much smaller in diameter than are the ventral canal cell and egg formed by transverse division of the primary ventral cell (Fig. 46*B–C*).   Development of this axial row of cells is accompanied by transverse division of the jacket initials.   It is not clear whether the jacket layer of a mature archegonium is lateral to the neck canal cells alone or lateral to all derivatives from the central cell.   In either case the cells next the lower face of the egg cannot be considered a part of the archegonium since they have not been derived from the archegonial initial.   Mature archegonia have the usual gelatinization of neck canal and ventral cells (Fig. 46*D*).   During the development of the archegonium, there is a vertical division of the cover initial into four cover cells, which become separated from the archegonium shortly after gelatinization of the canal cells.

At the time of fertilization, an egg does not fill the venter of an archegonium.   Shortly after fertilization the zygote swells to completely fill the venter, after which it secretes a wall.   The first division of a zygote is usually vertical, but in one or two cases[1] it has been found to be transverse.   If the first division is vertical, it is followed by a transverse division of the two daughter cells (Fig. 46*E*).   Transverse division may be either into daughter cells of equal[2] or unequal[3] size.   In the latter case the larger cells are toward the neck of the archegonium.   The next series of divisions is vertical, and the resultant eight-celled embryo is composed of two tiers of four cells each.   The lower tier of four cells develops into the sterile portion (foot) of a sporophyte.   The first divisions in the foot tier of four cells are transverse, but very soon divisions begin to take place in all planes (Fig. 46*G–H*).   At this time, or even earlier, the superficial cells of the foot grow into short rhizoid-like processes which increase the absorptive surface obtaining food from the adjoining gametophyte tissues.   Eventually the foot becomes a massive inverted cap (Fig. 47*B*).

Development of the capsule from the upper four cells of an eight-celled embryo begins with one or two transverse divisions (Fig. 46*F*).   The periclinal divisions differentiating *amphithecium* and *endothecium* occur at a time when the capsule portion is not more than two or three cells in height (Fig. 46*G*).   In all cases where the capsule has a columella, it is developed from the entire endothecium.   Young embryos have a

[1] Pande, 1932.   [2] Campbell, 1898, 1907.   [3] Campbell, 1918.

columella of four vertical rows of cells (Fig. 46*G–H*). Somewhat older embryos have a columella composed of 16 vertical rows of cells, so arranged that they form a solid square when seen in cross section. Columella cells in the mature portion of a capsule are vertically elongate and have somewhat thickened walls (Fig. 47*A, C*).

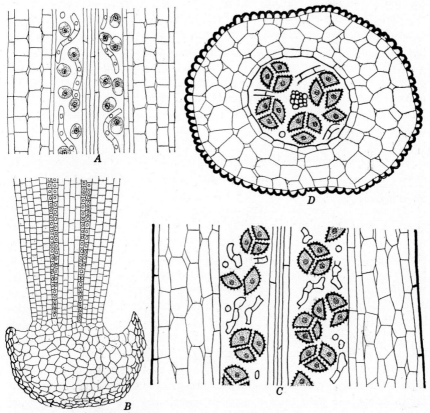

Fig. 47.—*Anthoceros laevis* L. *A–B*, longitudinal section through the upper and the basal portion of an immature sporophyte. *C–D*, vertical and transverse sections through the mature portion of a sporophyte. (× 160.)

The amphithecium typically divides periclinally into a sterile outer layer—the initials of the jacket layer—and an inner sporogenous layer— the archesporium (Fig. 46*H*). Certain species which lack a columella are said to have the sporogenous tissue developing from the endothecium rather than from the amphithecium.[1] Periclinal divisions in the jacket layer eventually make it four to six cells in thickness. The outermost of these jacket cells mature into an epidermal layer in which the cells are vertically elongate and with their walls strongly cutinized (Fig. 47*C–D*).

[1] Pande, 1933.

Certain of the young epidermal cells divide vertically, and the two daughter cells mature into a typical pair of guard cells surrounding a typical stoma. The cells beneath the epidermal layer mature into a parenchymatous tissue with intercellular spaces that are in communication with the exterior through the stomata. Cells in the parenchymatous portion of the jacket contain chloroplasts. If the species is one in which the gametophytic cells contain a single chloroplast, there are two chloroplasts in the sporophytic cells. If the species has more than one chloroplast in gametophytic cells, the number in the sporophyte is greater.

The layer of sporogenous tissue formed by periclinal division of the amphithecium overarches the columella apex. It may extend to the base of a columella or only half way to its base. The sporogenous layer may remain but one cell in thickness throughout its further development (*Anthoceros hawaiensis* Reich); it may become two cells in thickness (*A. Pearsoni* Howe), or it may become three to four cells in thickness.[1] In any case, alternate transverse bands of sporogenous cells develop into spores and into elaters. The cells maturing into elaters are joined in simple or branching filaments of three or four cells (Fig. 47*A*). According to the species, the elaters have smooth walls, irregularly thickened walls, or walls with the spiral thickenings typical of elaters. Sporogenous cells functioning as spore mother cells undergo a typical reduction division, and after this each divides to form four spores. When the spores are mature, there is a dehiscence of the portion of the jacket layer external to them. Dehiscence is usually into two valves that arch away from each other, or twist about each other, but in some cases[1] the capsule opens by a single longitudinal slit.

Early growth of a sporophyte is accompanied by an upward growth of the archegonium and adjoining gametophytic tissue. This surrounding sheath is sometimes called the calyptra, but it really is an involucre rather than a true calyptra. For a time upward growth of involucre and sporophyte keep pace with each other, but eventually the capsule grows the faster and pushes up through the involucre. At this time its uppermost jacket cells are mature, contain chloroplasts, and contribute to the nutrition of the sporophyte. As growth continues, the sporophyte becomes less and less dependent upon the gametophyte for carbohydrates. In most cases it never becomes completely self-sufficient as a producer of carbohydrates, but does become sufficiently independent to remain alive for several months and to show a limited amount of growth when separated from the gametophyte and maintained under suitable conditions.[2]

One unique feature of the Anthocerotae is the fact that cells of a capsule do not mature at the same rate and that cells in the basal portion

[1] Bartlett, 1928. [2] Campbell, 1917, 1924.

remain embryonic even after those in the apical portion are fully mature. The embryonic region thus differentiated at the base of a capsule shows the beginning of a differentiation into columella, archesporium, and jacket layer (Fig. 47*B*). Maturation of derivatives from these three areas of the embryonic region continually add new cells to the corresponding mature portions of the sporophyte. New cells may be matured from the meristematic portion of the capsule even after the apical portion has dehisced and shed its spores. When conditions for growth are unusually favorable, the sporophyte may grow to three or four times its usual length. In such cases[1] there is more or less suppression of sporogenous tissue in later-formed portions of the capsule and a development of the columella into a conspicuous conducting strand. The foot of such sporophytes is larger than normal and is in more or less direct contact with the soil because of semidecay of the gametophyte. Sporophytes of this type are comparable to those of Pteridophyta since they are capable of maintaining themselves without assistance from the gametophyte. The lack of a root is sometimes cited as an argument to show that these bryophytic sporophytes are not comparable to those of Pteridophyta, but this argument is invalidated by the recent discovery of fossil Pteridophyta (Psilophytales) in which the sporophyte has no root.

Bibliography

BAGCHEE, K. **1924.** *Ann. Bot.* **38**: 105–111. 1 pl. [Spermatogenesis, *Anthoceros.*]

BARTLETT, EMILY M. **1928.** *Ibid.* **42**: 409–430. 1 pl. 9 figs. [Sporophytes, *Anthoceros.*]

CAMPBELL, D. H. **1898.** *Jour. Linn. Soc. Bot. London* **33**: 467–478. 2 pl. [*Dendroceros.*]

    1907. *Ann. Bot.* **21**: 467–486. 3 pl. [Structure of Anthocerotae.]

    1908. *Ibid.* **22**: 91–102. 2 pl. 2 figs. [Structure of Anthocerotae.]

    1917. *Proc. Nation. Acad. Sci.* (U.S.) **3**: 494–496. [Self-sustaining sporophytes.]

    1918. The structure and development of mosses and ferns. 3d. ed. New York. 708 pp. 322 figs.

    1924. *Ann. Bot.* **38**: 473–483. 8 figs. [Self-sustaining sporophytes.]

HOWE, M. A. **1899.** *Mem. Torrey Bot. Club* **7**: 1–208. 35 pl. [Anthocerotae of California.]

LAMPA, EMMA. **1903.** *Oesterr. Bot. Zeitsch.* **1903**: 436–438. 5 figs. [Sex organs, *Anthoceros.*]

LEITGEB, H. **1879.** Untersuchungen über die Lebermoose. Heft. V. Die Anthoceroteen. Graz. 60 pp. 5 pl.

McALLISTER, F. **1914.** *Amer. Jour. Bot.* **1**: 79–95. 1 pl. [Pyrenoid.]

    1927. *Ibid.* **14**: 246–257. 2 pl. [Pyrenoid.]

PANDE, S. K. **1932.** *Jour. Indian Bot. Soc.* **11**: 169–177. 5 pl. [*Notothylas.*]

    1933. *Current Sci.* **1**: 272. 3 figs. [Formation of archesporium.]

PEIRCE, G. J. **1906.** *Bot. Gaz.* **42**: 55–59. [*Nostoc* colonies.]

[1] Campbell, 1924.

CHAPTER IV

MUSCI

The Musci are a homogeneous series in which there are no such marked differences between the various orders as there are among Hepaticae. Musci differ from other Bryophyta in the following respects: (1) There are two phases in the development of a gametophyte. The spore germinates to form a filamentous or thallose protonema of simple construction. The protonema gives rise to upright leafy branches (*gametophores*) which bear the sex organs. Typically the protonemata die after the gametophores are formed and each of the latter continues growth as an independent plant. (2) With a few exceptions the gametophores grow by means of a pyramidal apical cell in which the vertical file of segments from each of the three cutting faces develops into a vertical row of leaves and a portion of the stem. The distortion incident to growth usually obliterates all evidence of the three-ranked arrangement of leaves. (3) Rhizoids of the gametophyte are multicellular and with diagonal cross walls. They may be formed directly from superficial stem cells of a gametophyte. (4) Early stages in development of sex organs usually have an apical cell with two cutting faces. Mature sex organs are usually borne on much longer stalks than in other Bryophyta. (5) Although the sporophyte consists of the same parts (foot, seta, capsule) as in many other bryophytes, those of Musci have a greater sterilization of fertile tissue within the capsule and frequently have the sterile portion differentiated into a variety of tissues. Unlike other Bryophyta, the Musci have no elaters. The class includes some 660 genera with approximately 13,900 species. The Musci fall into three groups in which the major differences are in the development and structure of the sporophyte. These differences are of sufficient magnitude to warrant the segregation of the three groups into three subclasses. These subclasses are:

Sphagnobrya in which the young embryo is filamentous and without an apical cell. The sporogenous tissue is formed from the amphithecium. The mature sporophyte has a very short seta and a capsule that becomes elevated above surrounding leaves of the gametophyte by growth of the gametophytic apex into a columnar structure, the *pseudopodium*.

Andreaeobrya in which early growth of the embryo is by means of apical cells and in which the sporogenous tissue is formed from the endothecium. Similar to the preceding subclass there is a development of a *pseudopodium* at the apex of a gametophyte.

84

Eubrya in which early growth of the embryo is by means of an apical cell and in which the sporogenous tissue is derived from a portion of the endothecium. The capsule becomes elevated above surrounding leaves of the gametophyte by an elongation of the seta. Most genera of the subclass have capsules with an elaborate method of dehiscence.

SUBCLASS 1. SPHAGNOBRYA

This subclass differs from other Musci in its broadly thallose protonema, in vegetative structure of the gametophore, and in ontogeny of the sex organs. It is also distinctive in that the sporogenous tissue of a sporophyte develops from the amphithecium of an embryo. Elevation of a sporophyte above the gametophyte is due to elongation of a stalk of gametophytic tissue, the pseudopodium, rather than to an elongation of the seta of the sporophyte. The single order of the subclass, the Sphagnales, contains but one family, the Sphagnaceae, and this, in turn, has but one genus, *Sphagnum*. There are some 320 species.

All species of *Sphagnum* grow in ponds, swamps, or other moist places and usually only in softwater regions where there is but little lime. Growth of the gametophyte is continuous from year to year. *Sphagnum* usually grows in water so acid that there is but little decay of the dead basal portion of gametophytes. The compacted mass of dead gametophytic tissue accumulating as growth continues from year to year, together with the remains of other plants, is *peat*.

Sphagnum is of considerable ecological importance in modifying the landscape in regions with small lakes. When it becomes established on the shore of a morainal lake, it may encroach more and more on the lake and eventually cover its entire surface. The result of this encroachment is a quaking bog. The time interval required for conversion of a lake into a bog may be relatively short. At several localities in the eastern United

Fig. 48.—Gametophyte of *Sphagnum recurvum* Beauv. (Natural size.)

States there are areas where maps made a hundred years ago show lakes and which now are quaking bogs in which there is no open water. The floating mat of vegetation comprising the bog has certain angiosperms in addition to the *Sphagnum*. As the mat becomes dryer, through the accumulation of organic material, the *Sphagnum* eventually disappears and the hydrophytic angiosperms are replaced by those of a more meso-phytic type. Lakes bordered by gently sloping banks may have the *Sphagnum* invading the shore and occupying land several feet above the water. Such "creeping bogs" are due to the extraordinary water-absorbing and water retaining capacity of *Sphagnum*.

The erect perennial portion of the gametophyte, the gametophore, is differentiated into stem and leaves (Fig. 48). Terminal growth of the stem is due to an apical cell with three cutting faces (Fig. 49*A–B*). Each segment cut off by the apical cell eventually gives rise to a single leaf and the subtending portion of the stem. When first formed, the leaves are in three vertical rows, corresponding to the three cutting faces of the

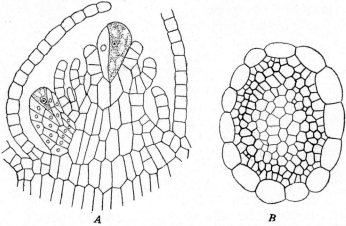

A   *B*

Fig. 49.—*Sphagnum subsecundum* Nees. *A*, longitudinal section through apex of gametophore bearing the primordium of a lateral branch. *B*, transverse section of a lateral branch of a gametophore. (*A*, × 325; *B*, × 215.)

apical cell, but growth of the stem soon displaces this three-ranked arrangement. A young leaf primordium grows by means of an apical cell with two cutting faces that alternately cut off segments right and left (Fig. 50*A*). Maturation of derivatives from the segments sometimes results in a leaf in which all cells are alike, but more often it results in a leaf with two types of cells. In leaves of the latter type each cell of a young leaf divides asymmetrically into a small cell, which lies toward the margin of a leaf, and a large cell (Fig. 50*C*). The large daughter cell then divides asymmetrically into a large cell and a small cell which lies toward the apex of a leaf. The two small cells formed by these divisions mature into long narrow cells which remain alive and which contain chloroplasts. The third cell enlarges in all directions and develops spiral thickenings on its walls (Fig. 49*D–F*). Its protoplast disappears after enlargment is completed and after there has been a development of large circular pores in the walls. The green photosynthetic and the hyaline cells have a regular reticulate arrangement with respect to one another in a mature leaf. The hyaline cells of leaves and similar cells in the cortex of a stem play an important role in the absorption and retention of water. Leaves of *Sphagnum* frequently have one or more axillary glandular hairs, but these disappear as the leaves become mature.

Every fourth leaf of the stem usually bears a group of three to eight lateral branches in its axil. Near the apex of a stem the branches are

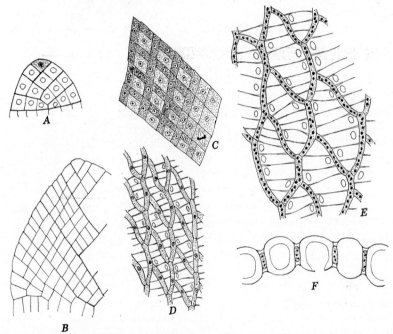

Fig. 50.—Development of leaf of *Sphagnum subsecundum* Nees. *A–B*, surface views of a very young and a slightly older leaf. *C–E*, surface views of portions of leaves at successive stages of development. *F*, transverse section of a mature leaf. (*A, C,* × 650; *B,* × 485; *D–F,* × 325.)

short and densely crowded in a compact head. Lower down on the stem they are in tufts. In many cases, especially when the plant does not grow submerged, the branches comprising a tuft are of two sorts, those which are upwardly divergent, and those which are drooping and lying next the stem. Occasionally one of the branches in a tuft continues upward growth to the same height as the main stem and becomes similar to it in structure. These branches eventually become independent plants through progressive death at the base of the axes bearing them. Vegetative propagation by this method is the main reason for the large number of individuals at any station where *Sphagnum* has become established.

The stem is internally differentiated into a central cylinder and an ensheathing layer, the cortex. When first formed, the cortex is but one cell in thickness. Later on the cortex of the main axis becomes four to five cells in thickness, and, as the cells mature, they may develop spirally thickened walls similar to those in hyaline leaf cells. The cortex of lateral branches never becomes more than one cell in thickness (Fig. 49*B*). Cells toward the exterior of a central cylinder are thick-walled; those at the interior may be thin- or thick-walled.

Mature gametophores have no rhizoids and all intake of water is by direct absorption. Upward movement of water to the apex of a stem is through the cortex in species in which the cortical cells have pores and spirally thickened walls. In species without such cortical cells upward movement of water is by capillarity and in the wick-like system of pendant branches clothing the stem. Proof of this is to be seen in the lack of water movement when stems of such species are denuded of their branches but have their lower ends in water.

According to the species, *Sphagnum* is heterothallic or homothallic. Plants with mature sporophytes are relatively rare, but there does not seem to be a correspondingly infrequent production of sex organs. The sex organs are borne on short lateral branches inserted near the apex of a gametophore. The antheridial branches are spindle-shaped and with the leaves in three rows. They are often distinguishable from other branches by their reddish, purplish, or brownish color. Archegonial branches are also inserted just below the apex of the stem. They are more or less globose and sometimes they are a yellowish to a reddish brown.[1] In the Middle West the sex organs begin to develop in the fall, but they are not mature and fertilization does not take place until the following spring.

Antheridia are produced in acropetalous succession and in the axils of leaves on an antheridial branch. The antheridial initial is a superficial cell of the stem. Although not demonstrated beyond all doubt, there seems to be good reason for believing that initials of antheridia and of leaves are homologous. Successive transverse divisions of an antheridial initial results in a filament of a few cells. As growth continues in the filament the terminal cell functions as an apical cell with two cutting faces (Fig. 51*A*). After a young antheridium has become 12 to 15 cells in height, there are two successive vertical divisions in each of the last two to five derivatives from the apical cell (Fig. 51*B–D*). These divisions[2] are similar to those in antheridia of Jungermanniales. That is, an asymmetrical diagonal vertical division divides each cell into a jacket initial and a larger sister cell which soon divides vertically into a jacket initial and a primary androgonial cell. Thus, the body of a young antheridium consists of two to five primary androgonial cells surrounded

[1] Bryan, 1915.   [2] Melin, 1915.

by a layer of jacket initials. One of these jacket initials is the old apical cell. Further development of the antheridium consists of a division and redivision of the androgonial cells, with compensating divisions in the jacket layer (Fig. 51*E–F*). There may also be vertical division of the stalk cells to form a stalk that is two cells broad. The antherozoids have two flagella of equal length and a structure much the same as in Hepaticae.[1]

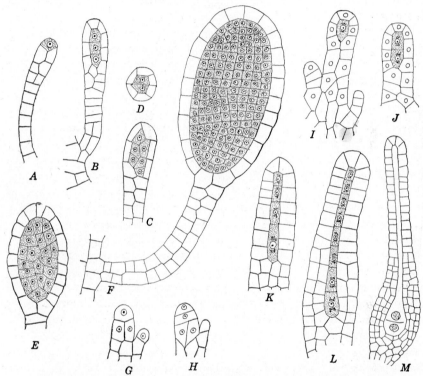

FIG. 51.—*Sphagnum subsecundum* Nees. *A–F*, stages in the development of antheridia. *G–M*, stages in the development of archegonia. (*A–L*, × 325; *M*, × 160.)

Archegonia are borne at the apex of an archegonial branch. Typically there are three of them, a primary archegonium formed from the apical cell of the branch, and two secondary archegonia formed from the last two segments cut off by the apical cell. The first step in development of an archegonium is the production of a short filament of cells (Fig. 51*G–H*). In the primary archegonium this may be by successive transverse divisions, or the terminal cell of the filament may function as an apical cell with two cutting faces.[2] There is no differentiation of an apical cell in the formation of secondary archegonia. No matter how developed, after

[1] Mühldorf, 1930.   [2] Bryan, 1915.

the filament is four to six cells in length, there is a vertical division of the terminal cell to form three jacket initials and an axial cell. Transverse division of the axial cell produces a cover initial and a central cell (Fig. 51*I*). As in archegonia of other Bryophyta, the central cell divides transversely into a primary canal cell and a primary ventral cell (Fig. 51*J*). The primary canal cell ultimately gives rise to a row of eight or nine canal cells (Fig. 51*K–L*). Late in the development of archegonium, there is a transverse division of the primary ventral cell into two cells of approximately the same size—the ventral canal cell and the egg.[1] There is also the usual disintegration of canal cells and ventral canal cell late in development of the archegonium, but the nucleus of the ventral canal cell may persist until just before fertilization (Fig. 51*M*). The jacket portion of the archegonium is derived from the primary cover cell and the three jacket initials. A mature archegonium does not have a well-marked differentiation into neck and venter. The venter and lower portion of the neck are two or three cells in thickness. The upper part of the neck is but one cell in thickness. The terminal portion of the neck is derived from the primary cover cell, but this cover portion is not sharply differentiated as in archegonia of Hepaticae.

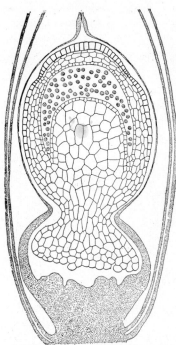

Fig. 52.—*Sphagnum subsecundum* Nees. Longitudinal section of a sporophyte and the surrounding gametophytic tissue. (× 60.)

Usually the zygote is formed by union of an egg and an antherozoid, but under certain conditions there may be a gametic union of egg and ventral canal cell.[2] The first division of a zygote is transverse and transverse division continues until the embryo is a filament 5 to 12 cells in length.[3] The upper half of the filament develops into the capsule of a mature sporophyte; the submedian portion develops into the foot and seta; and the lowermost portion develops into a haustorium which becomes obliterated as the sporophyte approaches maturity. Each cell in the portion destined to become the capsule undergoes two successive vertical divisions. Periclinal division in each tier of four cells thus formed results in the differentiation of an endothecium and an amphithecium. Division

[1] Bryan, 1915; Melin, 1916.   [2] Bryan, 1920*A*.   [3] Bryan, 1920.

and redivision of the endothecium produces the dome of sterile cells (the *columella*) at the center of a capsule. Periclinal division of the amphithecium cuts off an inner fertile layer, the archesporium, and an outer sterile layer. The archesporium gives rise to a sporogenous layer two to four cells in thickness, after which each sporogenous cell undergoes a typical meiosis[1] and forms four spores (Fig. 52). The outer sterile layer derived from the amphithecium eventually becomes three or four cells in thickness. The sterile jacket thus formed is homogeneous, except for the division of certain superficial cells into a pair of guard cells which lack the usual stomatal opening. All cells of the jacket, except the guard cells, contain chloroplasts until the capsule is nearly mature. Thus, the

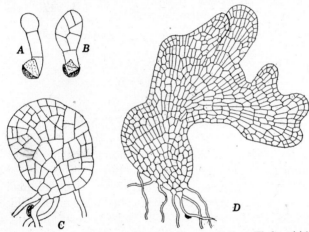

Fig. 53.—Development of protonema of *Sphagnum cymbifolium* Ehrh. (*After Müller in Rhuland*, 1924.)

sporophyte is not wholly dependent upon the gametophyte for its carbohydrate nutrition. During the later stages of capsule development, there is a differentiation of a transverse ring of cells in the upper portion of the jacket that delimits the lid (*operculum*). At the same time there is a pronounced thickening of walls of other superficial cells of the jacket.

Development of the sporophyte is accompanied by a differentiation of the subtending portion of the gametophore into a leafless stalk, the *pseudopodium*. This remains relatively short until the sporophyte is mature, after which it elongates rapidly and pushes the sporophyte above the leaves at the summit of the gametophore. Dehiscence of a capsule is explosive and may hurl the operculum and spores several inches upward. The explosive discharge is due to air pressure developing in the cavity containing the spores.[2]

[1] Melin, 1915.   [2] Nawaschin, 1897.

The germinating spore of *Sphagnum* first gives rise to a short cellular filament (Fig. 53*A*). At the two- to four-celled stage, the terminal cell of the filament begins to function as an apical cell with two cutting faces, which alternately form segments right and left (Fig. 53*B*). The flat plate (*protonema*) thus formed is one cell in thickness. The apical cell functions for a short time only, and it becomes indistinguishable after cutting off six to eight segments. After this certain marginal cells begin to divide anticlinally and periclinally. This results in an irregularly lobed plate, still one cell in thickness, and one in which the cells toward the posterior end may give rise to multicellular rhizoids (Fig. 53*C–D*). Any marginal cell of the protonema may also grow into a filament which, in turn, may develop into a new thallose protonema. Thus there may be considerable vegetative multiplication of the thallose protonemal stage.[1] In general, only one erect leafy branch (gametophore) is formed by a protonema of *Sphagnum*.

SUBCLASS 2. ANDREAEOBRYA

The Andreaeobrya have some features that are characteristic of the Eubrya and others that are characteristic of Sphagnobrya. The gametophores have a vegetative structure similar to those of Eubrya. The sporophytes resemble the Eubrya in that the sporogenous tissue is derived from the endothecium of an embryo. Mature sporophytes are like those of Sphagnobrya in that they are subtended by a pseudopodium. The one unique character of Andreaeobrya is the longitudinal dehiscence of a mature capsule into four valves. This subclass contains but one order (the *Andreaeales*) with a single family (the *Andreaeaceae*) in which there are but two genera, *Andreaea* and *Neuroloma*. The former has about 120 species, the latter a single species.

Andreaea is a genus of small dark-brown to blackish mosses which grow exclusively on rocks. It is usually restricted to regions with a cold climate and grows either in arctic regions or on the tops of high mountains.

The general structure of a gametophore is like that of the Eubrya. The stem grows prostrate along the surface of a rock and with a sympodial branching, in which one fork of the branching grows more strongly than the other (Fig. 54*A*). The stem bears numerous rhizoids, and these are cylindrical or plate-like accordingly as they grow in crevices of the rock or upon its surface. There is not the internal differentiation into cortex and central conducting strand that is found in stems of other mosses, but there may be differences in wall structure of deep-lying and superficial stem cells.[2] Terminal growth of the stem is by means of an apical cell, and the leaves are formed in three rows, corresponding to the three

---

[1] Rhuland, 1924.   [2] Lorch, 1931.

cutting faces of the apical cell.[1] Some species have leaves one cell in thickness; others have the median longitudinal axis of the leaf differentiated into a midrib more than one cell in thickness.[1]

The gametophores are usually homothallic and have the antheridia and archegonia in terminal groups on separate branches. So far as known,[2] the development of sex organs is similar to that of other Musci. Antheridia have an ellipsoidal body subtended by a long stalk either one

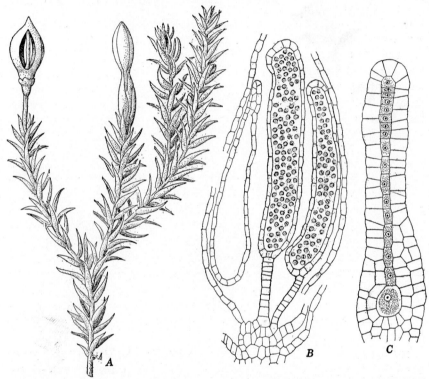

Fig. 54.—*Andreaea petrophila* Ehrb. *A*, gametophyte with mature and immature sporophytes. *B*, longitudinal section through apex of a male plant bearing antheridia. *C*, archegonium. (*A*, × 3; *B*, × 215; *C*, × 430.)

or two cells broad (Fig. 54*B*). Archegonia have a short stalk and a long neck (Fig. 54*C*).

The venter of the archegonium increases somewhat in thickness after fertilization and develops into a calyptra which surrounds the sporophyte until it is nearly mature. *Andreaea* is similar to *Sphagnum* in that there is a differentiation of a pseudopodium at the apex of the gametophyte (Fig. 55*C*).

[1] Pottier, 1921.   [2] Kühn, 1870.

The first division of the zygote is transverse.[1]   The lower daughter cell gives rise to an irregularly arranged mass of cells that is haustorial in nature.   The upper daughter cell functions as an apical cell with two cutting faces.   Each segment from an apical cell divides vertically into two daughter cells that divide periclinally into an amphithecial and an endothecial cell (Fig. 55*A*).   The amphithecial cells develop into the jacket portion of the capsule that eventually becomes three to eight cells in thickness.   Most of the superficial cells of the jacket become thick-

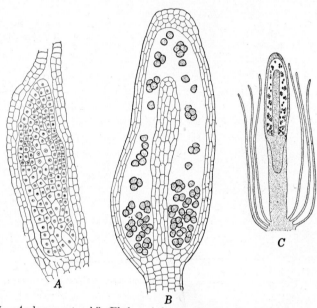

Fig. 55.—*Andreaea petrophila* Ehrb.   *A*, longitudinal section through an embryo.   *B*, semidiagrammatic longitudinal section through the capsule of a nearly mature sporophyte. *C*, longitudinal section through a sporophyte and the apex of a gametophyte.   (*A*, × 215; *B*, × 105; *C*, × 30.)

walled, but there are four vertical rows of cells, the future lines of dehiscence, that remain small and thin-walled (Fig. 55*B*).   Periclinal division of the endothecium results in an outer fertile layer, the archesporium, and an inner sterile portion, the primordium of the columella.   The archesporium is a dome-shaped layer which eventually develops into a sporogenous layer two cells in thickness.

Dehiscence of a mature capsule is longitudinal (Fig. 54*A*).   In most species the four slits formed by rupture of thin-walled jacket cells do not extend to the apex of the capsule.   As in the Eubrya there is an opening and closing of the ruptured capsule wall in response to hygroscopic

[1] Waldner, 1887.

changes, and there is only a liberation of spores at a time favorable for their dispersal.

The protoplast of the *Andreaea* spore divides several times while still surrounded by the spore wall. This is comparable to spore germination in *Pellia* and a few other Hepaticae, except that in *Andreaea* these divisions take place after the spore is shed. Eventually there is a rupture of the outer spore wall layer (*exosporium*) and a development of a short filament from one or more superficial cells of the exposed globular cell mass. A filament becomes three to five cells in length and then its terminal cell begins to function as an apical cell with a single convex posterior cutting face. There is great variation in the structure of the protonema resulting from activity of this apical cell. It may be a much-branched strap-like structure in which certain of the finer branches function as rhizoids; or, it may be a leaf-like plate quite similar to the protonema of *Sphagnum*. Protonemata of *Andreaea* are unusual in that they may enter into a dormant state if conditions for growth are unfavorable. The protonemal stage may develop buds on any portion, center as well as margin. The bud becomes a globose mass of 20 to 30 cells, and then one of them begins to function as an apical cell with three cutting faces. Further growth is apical and similar to that at the apex of a mature gametophore.

SUBCLASS 3. EUBRYA

Gametophores of the Eubrya generally have leaves with a definite midrib more than one cell in thickness. The sporophyte has a capsule in which the sporogenous tissue does not overarch the columella and which develops from the exterior portion of the endothecium. Mature capsules are generally internally differentiated into several tissues and have a complex organization of the opercular region. Elevation of a capsule above the gametophore is by elongation of the seta.

There are some 13,500 species of Eubrya. These are grouped into 14 orders with about 80 families and 655 genera. The separation into orders and families is largely on the basis of leaf structure and on the method by which the capsule opens. These features are of such minor morphological importance that it is not necessary to consider the various orders in detail.

Gametophytes of Eubrya are differentiated into two portions, a prostrate protonema and an upright gametophore. Except for a very few genera, the protonema is a transitory structure, and the adult plant consists only of persistent gametophores (Fig. 56). The gametophore may be branched or unbranched, with all of the branches erect or certain of them erect and others prostrate. In the latter case the prostrate branches may grow above or below the surface of the soil.

Genera with the gametophores independent at maturity always have them differentiated into stem and leaves. Young leaves at the apex of a stem are arranged in a definite manner. Typically, the arrangement is directly correlated with the number of cutting faces of the apical cell of the stem. Most genera have an apical cell with three cutting faces, the young leaves being spirally arranged in three vertical rows. Mature leaves, back from the apex, may not be definitely arranged because of torsions and displacements appearing during the maturation of the stem. Erect branches of a few genera, including *Fissidens*, have an apical cell with two cutting faces, but prostrate branches of these genera generally have apical cells with three cutting faces. Here the leaves on erect branches are in two vertical rows, and this arrangement usually persists in older parts of the stem. However, stems with the young leaves in three rows may have what appears to be a two-ranked arrangement of the older leaves. This bilateral symmetry is usually due to an asymmetric bending of the leaves so that the shoot is distinctly flattened. Many of the creeping mosses growing on trunks of trees have stems of this type. A flattening of the shoot may also be due to the fact that the leaves of two vertical rows become large, whereas those of the third row remain small.

Fig. 56.—Gametophytes and sporophytes of *Funaria hygrometrica* Sibth. (× 4.)

Mosses of this type, as *Cyathophorum*, have a superficial resemblance to acrogynous Jungermanniales.

When the apical cell is three-sided, segments are cut off in regular sequence from the three cutting faces. The first division in a segment is periclinal. The inner daughter cell contributes to the inner portion of the stem; the outer daughter cell develops into a leaf and the subtending outer portion of the stem.[1]

The first division of the outer daughter cell is approximately perpendicular to the preceding plane of division. The superior daughter cell thus formed develops into a leaf; the inferior daughter cell gives rise to the cortical portion of the stem. Very early in development of a leaf there is an establishment of an apical cell whose two cutting faces alternately cut off segments right and left. The leaf thus formed may be but one cell in thickness throughout, but more often the axial portion becomes differentiated into a midrib that is more than one cell in thickness (Fig. 57B). In some genera the midrib extends only part way to the apex of the leaf; in other genera it extends to the apex of the blade; in still other

[1] Lorch, 1931; Rhuland, 1924.

genera it continues as an apical projection beyond the blade. Midribs, when present, are always composed of elongate cells in which the walls are usually conspicuously thickened. Leaves with a midrib have the chloroplasts restricted to the laminate portion one cell in thickness. Some leaves have a supplemental photosynthetic tissue of longitudinal lamellae borne chiefly in the region of the midrib. These lamellae are usually several cells in height and one cell in thickness (Fig. 58). Differences in the structure of the midrib and in the structure of cells at the margin of a blade, together with differences in concavity of the blade and the extent to which it is twisted, are of major taxonomic importance.

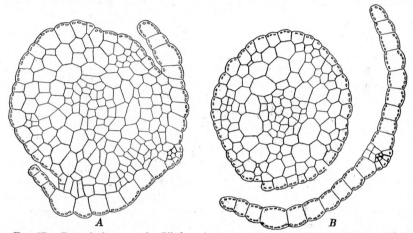

FIG. 57.—*Funaria hygrometrica* Sibth. *A*, transverse section of a gametophore at the level of juncture of a leaf with the stem. *B*, the same leaf and stem cut at a slightly higher level. (× 160.)

Because of this the systematist keeps mounted leaves along with his herbarium material.

Leaves borne on different portions of the gametophore may also differ from one another. Those borne on prostrate branches and on the lower portion of erect branches are often scale-like, nearly colorless, and of simpler construction than those on the upper portion of an erect branch. The *perichaetial leaves* immediately next to the sex organs may also be different in size and shape from the *foliage leaves* lower on the stem. However, in passing down a stem the transition from perichaetial to foliage leaves is gradual, not abrupt.

A mature stem of a moss is differentiated into central cylinder, cortex, and epidermis. Cells of the central cylinder are vertically elongate, are of smaller diameter than those of the cortex, and have greatly thickened or relatively thin walls (Fig. 57). In most cases the central cylinder is a fairly uniform tissue except for differences in thickness of the walls. In certain mosses, as *Polytrichum*,[1] the axial portion of the central cylinder contains thick-walled cells with living protoplasts (*stereids*) and empty thin-walled cells (*hydroids*) intermingled with each other. The outer portion of such cylinders consists of an incomplete pericycle-like sheath of thin-walled living cells.

Cortical cells in young portions of a stem usually contain chloroplasts; those in older portions of the stem lack them. A fully mature cortex usually grades off from thick-walled cells at the exterior to thin-walled cells next the central cylinder. In mosses whose leaves have midribs the cortex usually contains "leaf traces" running diagonally from the leaves to the central cylinder. These traces may be homogeneous in structure

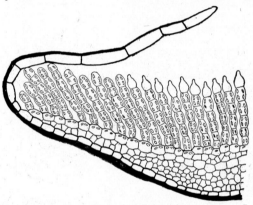

Fig. 58.—Transverse section of a leaf of *Polytrichum commune* L. (× 215.)

or differentiated into stereids and hydroids. The epidermis may be one or more cells in thickness and have thick or thin walls. There is never a differentiation of guard cells in the epidermis.

Although it is gametophytic in nature, the moss stem has an internal differentiation comparable to that of the stem in sporophytes of vascular plants. This resemblance has led to the assumption that conduction of water up the stem of a moss is through the central cylinder and that hydroids, when present, are special water-conducting elements. Recent investigations[2] seem to show that, irrespective of whether a moss is growing in a wet, moist, or dry habitat, only a relatively small amount of water moves up through the central cylinder. Most upward movement is external and by means of capillary films of water between leaves and stem. These experiments seem to show that the major function of the central tissue, and of the midrib of the leaf, is that of a mechanical tissue, but this has been denied by others who hold[3] that internal tissues of stems are also of importance in the conduction of water.

[1] Tansley and Chick, 1901.   [2] Bowen, 1933, 1933*A*, 1933*B*.
[3] Mägdefrau, 1935.

Primordia of branches arise a short distance back from the growing apex of a stem. Each primordium is the result of the differentiation of a superficial stem cell into an apical cell. The cell thus differentiated lies below a young leaf, not axillary to it.[1] Development of a branch is identical with development at a stem apex, the apical cell successively cutting off segments from its cutting faces (Fig. 59).

When mosses grow in favorable habitats, they are usually in dense stands produced by extensive vegetative multiplication. There are certain rather widely distributed mosses which have never been observed with sporophytes and in which all reproduction seems to be by vegetative

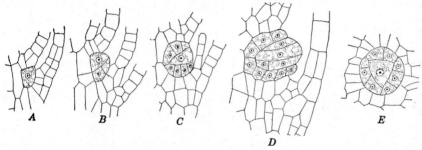

Fig. 59.—*Amblystegium riparium* Bruch. and Schimp. *A–D*, vertical sections of stem showing branch primordia in longitudinal section. *E*, the same with a branch primordium in transverse section. (× 325.)

propagation of the gametophyte. Vegetative multiplication takes place in a variety of ways including:

1. *Progressive growth and death of the gametophore.* This method of asexual reproduction so characteristic of Hepaticae is largely restricted to Eubrya with prostrate rhizomes bearing erect branches. After death of the prostrate branch each erect aerial branch persists as an independent plant. Sometimes separation of erect branches from the parent plant is due to the development of a special abscission layer.

2. *Gemmae.* A rather large number of mosses produce small multicellular gemmae. These are formed in groups and either at the tips of leaves, along the midrib, along the sides of branches, or at the stem apex. Solitary gemmae may be formed on rhizoids, either those of protonemata or those of the leaf shoot. Subterranean gemmae of this type are usually called bulbils.

3. *Primary protonemata.* A protonema developing from a spore usually forms several buds. Development of the buds into leafy shoots, followed by death of the protonema, results in several independent gametophores. The number of gametophores may also be increased by multiplication of the protonemal stage. Death of cells here and there

[1] Rhuland, 1924.

in a protonema results in short fragments, each of which may grow into a new protonema.

4. *Secondary protonemata.* When growing in light, rhizoids of a leafy shoot may become protonemal in nature and produce buds just as do protonemata from germinating spores. Development of the buds into shoots, followed by death of the protonema-like rhizoids, results in new independent gametophores. Secondary protonemata may also be developed from wounded portions of the leafy shoot. The wounded tissue may be that of a leaf or a stem.

5. *Apospory.* Wounding of sporophytic tissue may also result in the production of a protonema. The gametophytes thus developed are aposporous in origin, since they are formed from the sporophyte without a production of spores. Notwithstanding the fact that their cells have the diploid number of chromosomes, the aposporously produced gametophytes are normal in appearance and with fertile gametes. Fertilization may take place between two aposporously produced gametes, or between an aposporously produced and a normal gamete. According to the origin of the gametes, the new sporophyte has $4n$ or $3n$ chromosomes.[1]

Sex organs of most Eubrya are borne on well-developed leafy gametophores. In a few cases, especially in those genera in which the protonema is persistent, the leafy gametophore is but feebly developed. For example, in *Buxbaumia*[2] the male gametophore consists of a single bract-like leaf ensheathing a single antheridium borne directly on a branch of the protonema. Female gametophores of *Buxbaumia* are more elaborate and have a single archegonium borne at the apex of a minute stem bearing a few leaves. Genera with poorly developed gametophores have been considered primitive, but there are equally good reasons for regarding them reduced forms of ancestral types with typical leafy gametophores.

In genera with well-developed leafy gametophores the sex organs are always terminal in position, and there is always a development of more than one of them at the end of a branch. The sex organs may be *acrocarpous* and borne on the main axis or its major branches, or they may be *pleurocarpous* and restricted to the apices of short lateral branches. The leaves adjoining the sex organs are somewhat different from the foliage leaves lower on the stem, and they lie close to one another in a distinct "floral envelope," the *perichaetium.* Plants with sex organs may be homothallic or heterothallic. However, the finding of plants in which antheridia and archegonia are borne on separate individuals is not conclusive proof of heterothallism, since this condition may result from vegetative multiplication of a homothallic species bearing the two types of sex organs on separate branches. Conclusive proof of heterothallism or homothallism can only be established by growing a species in pedigreed

[1] É. Marchal and É. Marchal, 1911; Wettstein, 1923.   [2] Goebel, 1892.

cultures derived from a single spore.[1] Homothallic species bear the sex organs in various ways. Most conspicuous among these are: the *autoicous mosses* in which the antheridia and archegonia are borne on separate branches, the *paroicous mosses* in which the antheridia and archegonia are borne in the same head but in separate groups that are sometimes separated from each other by perichaetial leaves, and the *synoicous mosses* in which antheridia and archegonia are intermingled in the same head.

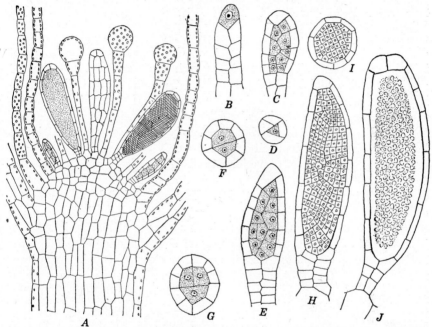

Fig. 60.—*Funaria hygrometrica* Sibth. *A*, vertical section through the apex of a fertile male gametophyte. *B–J*, stages in the development of antheridia. *B–C, E, H, J,* in longitudinal section; *D, F–G, I,* in transverse section. (*A,* × 120; *B–G,* × 485; *H–J,* × 325.)

The production of sex organs at the end of a branch, especially that of antheridia, is not simultaneous, and in actively growing plants all stages in development may be found in the same head. In certain cases the first sex organ to appear comes from the apical cell, and later-formed ones come from segments previously cut off by the apical cell. In other cases this is very doubtful. Many mosses have multicellular hairs (*paraphyses*) intermingled with the sex organs, especially the antheridia (Fig. 60*A*). Paraphyses may be one or more than one cell in breadth and have the apex pointed or capitate. Their function is not definitely known, but it is not improbable that water held between them by capillarity helps prevent undue desiccation.

[1] Brown, 1919.

The initial of an antheridium is a superficial cell at the apex of a stem or branch. This cell soon becomes a papillate projection, after which it divides transversely. The outer daughter cell develops into all of the mature antheridium except the lower embedded portion of the stalk. The outer cell divides transversely to form a filament two or three cells in length and then the terminal cell begins to function as an apical cell with two cutting faces (Fig. 60*B*). Five to fifteen regularly arranged segments are cut off by the apical cell, and the last three to six cut off may have much denser protoplasts than the others. Even before the apical cell has ceased functioning, a segment three or four removed from it divides in a diagonally vertical plane. One daughter cell is a jacket initial. The other cell is one that divides into another jacket initial and a primary androgonial cell (Fig. 60*C–D*). Thus the sequence in division in upper segments from the apical cell resembles that in primary antheridial cells of Jungermanniales.[1] All of the upper segments cut off by the apical cell eventually divide periclinally in this manner. It is not known whether the apical cell contributes only to the antheridial jacket, or divides periclinally to form a jacket cell and a primary androgonial cell. In the case of *Funaria* it seems to contribute only to the opercular portion of the jacket layer (Fig. 60*C, E, H*). Each of the primary androgonial cells divides and redivides to form a large number of androcyte mother cells. These divisions are accompanied by compensating divisions in the jacket layer (Fig. 60*C–H*). The typical club-shaped body of a moss antheridium, as contrasted with the ovoid or globose body in Hepaticae, results from the fact that there are several superimposed elements which give rise to the body of an antheridium. *Funaria* also differs from the Hepaticae in that the division of each androcyte mother cell into two androcytes is not diagonal.[2] Metamorphosis of the androcytes into biflagellate antherozoids is essentially the same as in Hepaticae.[3]

Mature antheridia have the jacket apex differentiated into an *operculum* whose cells are readily distinguished by their larger size, thicker walls, and more hyaline contents (Fig. 60*J*). The operculum may consist of one, two, or several cells.[4] As already indicated, it seems to be derived from the apical cell of a young antheridium. Dehiscence of antheridia does not take place until after they have been moistened and have absorbed considerable water. The intake of water by the jacket cells causes them to become more turgid, and the resultant hydrostatic pressure of the antheridial contents ruptures the operculum and forces out the mass of antherozoids. Except for the lack of an operculum and for their more hyaline appearance, empty antheridia look very much like those which have not discharged their contents.

[1] Campbell, 1918; Rhuland, 1924.   [2] Allen, 1912.
[3] Allen, 1912, 1917.   [4] Goebel, 1898.

The early development of an archegonium is also effected by an apical cell with two cutting faces, but it only cuts off four to eight segments (Fig. 61*A*). Division and redivision of these segments eventually produces the elongate columnar stalk of the mature archegonium. After it has cut off four to eight segments, the apical cell changes abruptly in nature and develops three cutting faces.[1] Only one segment is cut off from each of the three cutting faces. These three segments are the three peripheral initials which encircle the axial cell (the former apical cell).

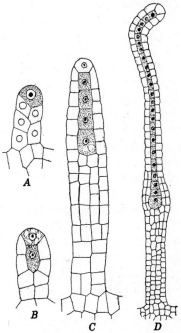

There then follows a vertical division of each peripheral initial, with a resultant formation of six jacket initials. Unlike the Hepaticae there is no transverse division of the jacket initials to form a tier of neck initials and a tier of venter initials. During further development of the archegonium, the jacket portion of the neck may become 40 to 50 cells in height (Fig. 61*C–D*).

Coincident with formation of the jacket initials there is a transverse division of the axial cell into a primary cover cell and a central cell (Fig. 61*B*). The central cell soon divides transversely into a primary canal cell and a ventral cell. In *Catharinea*[2] and *Mnium*,[3] the two genera in which archegonial development has been most thoroughly studied, the neck has a double origin. The upper portion of it is derived from segments cut off from the primary cover cell. Segments cut off laterally from the cover cell contribute to the jacket layer; those cut off posteriorly contribute to the canal row. The median and lower portion of the neck are formed from the primary canal cell and the surrounding jacket initials. During the later stages in archegonial development there is the usual division of the ventral cell into a ventral canal cell and egg. This is followed by the usual disintegration of the canal cells and the ventral canal cell.

Fig. 61.—Stages in the development of archegonia of *Mnium*. (*A–C*, × 325; *D*, × 120.)

Abnormal archegonia are of frequent occurrence among the Eubrya, and it is not at all uncommon to find archegonia in which cells within the neck, venter, or even the stalk divide and redivide to form a mass of

---

[1] Bryan, 1917; Holferty, 1904.   [2] Bryan, 1917.   [3] Holferty, 1904.

androgonial-like cells.[1]   The phylogenetic significance of this has already been noted (page 4).

Fertilization is effected through the agency of water.   All that is necessary in paroicous and synoicous mosses is a connecting film of water between antheridia and archegonia.   Among the autoicous and hetero-thallic species there is generally a transportation of antherozoids to the vicinity of the archegonia.   This may be accomplished by raindrops spattering from heads containing antheridia to those with archegonia, or by antherozoid-containing water trickling down to archegonial branches. In any case, entrance of antherozoids into archegonia is in response to chemical stimulation.[2]   To judge from observations on *Funaria*,[3] where the male and female chromatic masses may become completely inter-mingled within 10 hours, the union of gametes is more rapid than in Hepaticae.

Development of a sporophyte begins with an enlargement of the zygote and transverse division of it.   The upper daughter cell, by two successive diagonal divisions, differentiates an apical cell with two cutting faces.   The lower daughter cell gives rise to an apical cell in a similar manner.   Young embryos of Eubrya differ from those of other Bryophyta in this formation of two growing points.   The upper apical cell alternately cuts off many segments right and left.   These ultimately develop into the capsule and the major portion of the seta.   The lower apical cell also cuts off segments, but these are not formed in such regular sequence.   Seg-ments from the lower apical cell ultimately develop into the foot and the lower portion of the seta.

The embryo of a young sporophyte is long and slender.   Its lower end burrows through the stalk of the archegonium and into the apex of the gametophore.   Early growth of the embryo is accompanied by a corre-sponding growth of the archegonium (calyptra) surrounding it.   Later on, more rapid elongation of the young sporophyte causes a transverse rupture of the archegonial base, and the severed upper portion of the calyptra remains perched upon the sporophyte apex until the latter is nearly mature.   Eubrya, unlike other Musci, do not have the apex of a gameto-phore developing into a pseudopodium.   The sporophytes resemble those of the Hepaticae in that there is a formation of a long seta which elevates the capsule above the surrounding gametophore.   However, elongation of a seta is gradual instead of sudden and just before the capsule is mature as in Hepaticae.   Setae of Eubrya generally have a well-developed central strand.   There has been a general assumption that the chief function of the strand is conduction of food materials to the developing capsule, but there has been no experimental demonstration of this function.   Possibly

---

[1] Bryan, 1927.   [2] Åkerman, 1915.   [3] Beardsley, 1931.

the central strand of a seta is similar to that of the central strand of a leafy gametophore and functions chiefly as a mechanical tissue.

The first division of apical segments developing into the capsule portion of a sporophyte is vertical. A transverse section of a sporophyte apex at this stage shows four quadrately arranged cells, that is, two vertically divided segments apposed to each other. In most genera this is followed by a vertical division of each of the four cells. Since the plane of division is also perpendicular to an internal wall, one daughter cell of each quadrant is approximately triangular when seen in transverse section, and the other approximately rectangular. The eight cells thus formed may or may not be so arranged with respect to one another that there is a regular alternation of triangular and rectangular cells. Periclinal division of the rectangular cells differentiates a symmetrical quadrant of endothecial cells and an encircling layer of eight amphithecial cells. Certain genera, including *Archidium*[1] have a rectangular endothecium containing but two cells.

In *Funaria*, which is representative of genera with eight amphithecial cells, the quadrately arranged endothecial cells divide according to a succession similar to that in the four quadrately arranged cells at the apex of the embryo (Fig. 64*A–D*). Further division of the four cells internal to the eight peripheral cells of the endothecium is not in such regular sequence. The divisions by which the embryonic eight-celled amphithecium becomes an embryonic tissue four or five cells in thickness are also in regular sequence. The first division is periclinal. Each cell of the outer layer thus formed next divides anticlinally. The outer sixteen-celled layer then divides periclinally, after which each of the cells in the outermost layer divides anticlinally. Succeeding development of the amphithecium is by periclinal and anticlinal division although not in such diagrammatic succession.

Since the tissues matured in the operculum and peristome are different from those matured in the fertile region inferior to the peristome, it will be necessary to consider the two regions separately. The archesporium of the capsule is always endothecial in origin and formed from the outermost layer of endothecial cells. Some genera, as *Polytrichum*, have an archesporium extending to the base of the capsule. Other genera, as *Funaria*, do not differentiate an archesporium in the lower portion of the capsule (Fig. 62). In such cases the lower sterile portion of the capsule is an *apophysis*. The archesporium usually develops into a sporogenous layer two cells in thickness. In the Musci all cells of the sporogenous layer function as spore mother cells. Endothecial cells internal to the sporogenous cells mature into the columella. Columella cells immediately internal to the sporogenous cells usually remain small,

[1] Leitgeb, 1880.

and they mature into the *inner spore sac.*　The remainder of the columella may be composed of large colorless cells (*Funaria*) or differentiated into photosynthetic and colorless tissues (*Polytrichum*).　The embryonic amphi-

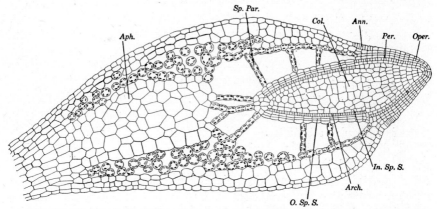

Fig. 62.—Longitudinal section of an immature capsule of a sporophyte of *Funaria hygrometrica* Sibth.　(*Ann.*, annulus; *Aph.*, apophysis; *Arch.*, archesporium; *Col.*, columella; *In. Sp. S.*, inner spore sac; *O. Sp. S.*, outer spore sac; *Oper.*, operculum; *Per.*, peristome; *Sp. Par.*, spongy parenchyma.)　(× 80.)

thecium typically matures into a variety of tissues, and among these there is almost always a spongy tissue in which the cells contain chloroplasts. For example, in *Funaria* the following tissues are matured from the

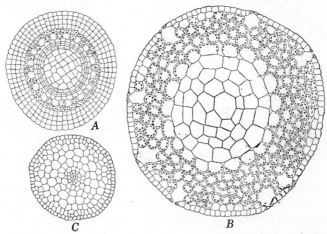

Fig. 63.—Transverse sections of sporophytes of *Funaria hygrometrica* Sibth.　*A*, through the fertile portion of a young capsule.　*B–C*, through the apophysis and stipe of a somewhat older capsule.　(× 140.)

embryonic amphithecium external to the sporogenous tissue.　Immediately outside the sporogenous tissue is the *outer spore sac.*　External to this are successively: a spongy parenchyma in which the cells contain chloroplasts; a layer of colorless cells, two or three cells in thickness; and an epidermis with greatly thickened cell walls (Figs. 62, 63*A*). Here and there in the epidermis are pairs of guard cells surrounding a stomatal opening essentially like those of vascular plants.[1] The amphithecial portion of the apophysis is much the same as the fertile region of a capsule (Fig. 63*B*); the endothecial portion of an apophysis develops into a conducting strand continuous with that of the seta.

Most Eubrya have the apical portion of a capsule differentiated into an operculum which is subtended by a peristome composed of one or two rings of teeth. The number of teeth in a peristome is constant for a genus, and this constancy in number rests upon a regular sequence of development.[2] For example, the apical portion of a capsule of *Funaria hygrometrica* has the usual differentiation into an amphithecial layer of eight cells that surround a rectangle of four endothecial cells (Fig. 64*A*–*C*). Each of the eight amphithecial cells divides periclinally, and the inner daughter cells thus formed eventually develop into the inner cell layer of the peristome, which is 32 cells in perimeter (Fig. 64*H*). The eight outer daughter cells of the peristome then divide anticlinally. Each of the 16 daughter cells then divides periclinally (Fig. 64*D*–*F*). The inner daughter cells of this division mature into the outer cell layer of the peristome without dividing again. The outer peristome, which is 16 cells in perimeter, is so oriented with respect to the inner peristome, 32 cells in perimeter, that one cell of the former lies external to two cells of the latter. There then follows a considerable deposition of wall material on the periclinal walls common to the two layers and on the outer periclinal walls of the outer peristome layer (Fig. 61*I*). There is also some thickening of horizontal anticlinal walls in the outer layer but no thickening of the vertical anticlinal walls (Figs. 64*I*, 65*B*–*C*). When the thickening of the walls is completed, there is a drying out and shriveling up of the peristomial cells and a longitudinal splitting along the unthickened vertical anticlinal walls of the outer layer. Since outer and inner periclinal walls are 16 cells in perimeter, there is a vertical splitting of the peristome into two concentric portions each with 16 teeth. Other genera, as *Ceratodon*, have a thickening of outer tangential walls only in the outer layer of the peristome. When drying and splitting of such a peristome occurs, there is a formation of but a single ring of teeth.[2] Many genera have an outer peristome 32 cells in perimeter and a splitting into 32 teeth.

The operculum develops from the layer, 16 cells in perimeter, that lies external to the one developing into the outer peristome layer. This embryonic operculum becomes three or more cells in thickness, and, when

[1] Haberlandt, 1886; Kuhlbrodt, 1922. [2] Evans and Hooker, 1913.

the cells of an operculum are mature, those of the epidermis have greatly thickened walls (Fig. 64*G–I*, 65*A–C*).   During maturation there is also a radial enlargement of epidermal cells at the opercular base to form an *annulus*.   As the spores approach maturity there is a drying out and shriveling up of the thin-walled cells just below the annulus.   This, together with splitting of the peristome, results in a very loose adhesion between the operculum and underlying tissues.   Shedding of the operculum has been thought to be due to a simple abscission, but it is more

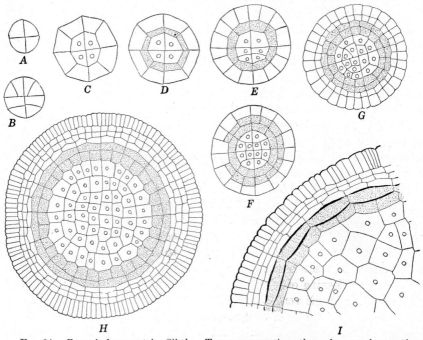

Fig. 64.—*Funaria hygrometrica* Sibth.   Transverse sections through opercular portions of sporophytes at various stages of development.   Nuclei are drawn in cells of the columella and the cells of the inner and outer peristome are shaded.   (× 325.)

probable that the shedding is due to an upward bending of the peristome teeth.   Shedding of the operculum does not result in a liberation of the spores since the interlocked teeth still cover the mouth of the spore sac. The teeth of a peristome are markedly hygroscopic.   In dry air they curve outward and thus make possible a sifting out of spores from the capsule.   In moist weather they bend down over the cavity of the capsule. Thus, the hygroscopic movement of the teeth results in an open capsule at a time favorable for dispersal of spores by wind and a closed one at a time unfavorable for spore dispersal.   Although the foregoing principle of opening and closing applies to all Eubrya with a peristome, there is considerable variation from genus to genus in the manner in which the teeth bend.[1]

There are a few Eubrya, including *Pleuridium*, in which there is no formation of operculum and peristome[2] (Fig. 66) and in which there is an

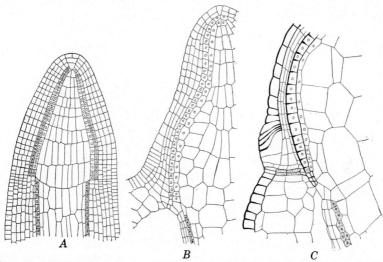

Fig. 65.—*Funaria hygrometrica* Sibth. Longitudinal sections through opercular portions of sporophytes showing successive stages in the development of the peristome. ($\times$ 215.)

irregular rupture of the capsule. Formerly, these *cleistocarpous* genera were grouped in one subclass, and the *stegocarpous* genera (those with a peristome) were placed in another. The present-day practice is to abandon these two subclasses because the ontogeny of a cleistocarpous

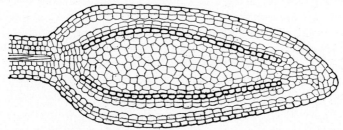

Fig. 66.—Semidiagrammatic longitudinal section of the cleistocarpous capsule of the sporophyte of *Pleuridium subulatum* (L.) Rab. ($\times$ 80.)

capsule is identical with that of a stegocarpous capsule. This practice also denies that cleistocarpous mosses are more primitive than others. Possibly certain of them are primitive; others appear to be reduced forms.

[1] Steinbrinck, 1897. [2] Kienitz-Gerloff, 1878.

There is one anomalous cleistocarpous genus (*Archidium*) in which capsule development is different from other Musci.   Here,[1] all of the endothecium is a potential sporogenous tissue, but only certain isolated endothecial cells function as spore mother cells.   Because of this, *Archidium* has been considered a genus of uncertain systematic position.[2]

Germination of the spore usually does not take place until after it has been shed from the capsule, but in certain exceptional genera, as in certain exceptional Hepaticae, the spore develops into a multicellular structure before it is shed.   A germinating spore increases somewhat in size, ruptures the exospore layer, and then sends out one or two germ tubes in which the wall is continuous with the endospore wall layer of the spore. A germ tube soon forms a cross wall near its point of exit from the spore. The cell cut off by this cross wall soon develops into a branched filament, the *protonema*.   Certain branches of the protonema grow along the surface of the ground or upright in the air for a short distance; others of the branches penetrate the soil.   Those of the latter type are rhizoidal branches and are readily distinguishable from aerial branches by their brown cell walls, diagonal cross walls, and their lack of chloroplasts. Portions of rhizoidal branches growing exposed to light have chloroplasts, colorless cell walls, and cross walls at right angles to the lateral walls. Thus, the differences between rhizoidal and aerial branches are largely due to environmental conditions.   There are a few genera in which the protonema is not a branched filament.   In *Tetraphis*,[3] for example, the protonemal stage is a flat plate much like that of *Sphagnum*.

Sooner or later a filamentous protonema produces buds which develop into erect leafy gametophores.   The buds are usually formed upon the aerial branches, but they may be formed upon rhizoids.   The first few cell divisions in development of a bud are in irregular sequence, but very soon there is an establishment of an apical cell and further growth is similar to that at the apex of a well-developed leafy gametophore.   Most genera have a disappearance of the protonema after the gametophore has formed a few leaves.   Certain genera have a persistence of the protonema. Genera with persistent protonemata may have a feebly developed gametophore or a well-developed one.   Persistence of the protonemata among genera of the latter type is chiefly among species which grow in densely shaded habitats.

As already noted the Eubrya are no longer separated into two subclasses distinguishable from each other by the manner in which the capsule dehisces.   The current practice is to divide the class into a number of orders which differ from one another in structure of the gametophyte, position of the sporophyte, and structure of the peristome. Thus, Brotherus[4] divides the Eubrya into the following orders:

[1] Leitgeb, 1880.   [2] Campbell, 1918.
[3] Rhuland, 1924.   [4] Brotherus, 1924–1925.

Fissidentales, in which all aerial branches have a two-sided apical cell and a consequent development of leaves in two rows.

Dicranales, in which the gametophores are erect, there generally being many-ranked lanceolate leaves that have a blade two or more cells in thickness, with or without a midrib. The sporophytes are generally acrocarpous, and the capsule has a simple peristome of 16 teeth.

Pottiales, in which the gametophores are generally erect and bear many-ranked leaves with midribs. The sporophytes are generally acrocarpous. If the capsule has a peristome, it is simple and with 16 teeth.

Grimmiales, in which the gametophores usually grow upon rocks and have the blackish-green color of Andreaeales. The gametophores have branched stems with densely crowded leaves. The sporophytes are acrocarpous and have symmetrical to ovoid capsules opening by a simple peristome with 16 teeth.

Funariales, in which the gametophores are annual to biennial and erect and have a rosette of leaves at the apex. The sporophytes are mostly acrocarpous and never have cylindrical capsules. The capsules are frequently bent or pendant at maturity. A peristome may be lacking. When present it is double, although sometimes it appears to be simple.

Schizostegiales, in which there is but one genus and species. It grows in dimly illuminated caves and appears to be luminous. The protonema is persistent and has lens-shaped cells. The gametophore has leaves in two rows, and the small capsule of the sporophyte lacks a peristome.

Tetraphidales, in which the peristome of a capsule has but four teeth.

Eubryales, in which the gametophores are perennial and erect, with the stem clothed with many rows of leaves. The sporophytes are mostly acrocarpous and have drooping or pendant capsules. The peristome is double and has well-developed teeth.

Isobryales, in which the gametophores are generally perennial and creeping, with the leaves so twisted on the freely branched stem that they appear to be in two rows. The sporophytes are generally pleurocarpous, and the capsules are generally erect. The peristome is double.

Hookeriales, in which the gametophores are generally prostrate and freely branched, the leaves tending to lie in one plane. The leaves are asymmetrical, frequently having two midribs. The sporophytes are generally pleurocarpous, with a double peristome.

Buxbaumiales, in which there are but two genera. These are unique in their asymmetrical capsules with a peristome composed of three to six cell layers.

Polytrichinales, in which the capsules are angular in cross section, with a peristome several cells in thickness.

Dawsoniales, in which there is but one genus, *Dawsonia*, with gametophores up to 60 cm. in height. The capsule is dorsiventral, and the peristome is subtended by many filamentous hairs.

Bibliography

ÅKERMAN, Å. **1915.** *Bot. Notiser* **1915:** 205–209. [Chemotaxis, antherozoids.]

ALLEN, C. E. **1912.** *Arch. Zellforsch.* **8:** 121–188. 4 pl. [Development of antheridium.]

— **1917.** *Ann. Bot.* **31:** 269–291. 2 pl. [Spermatogenesis.]

BEARDSLEY, MARTHA L. **1931.** *Ann. Missouri Bot. Gard.* **18:** 509–540. 5 pl. [*Funaria.*]

BOWEN, ESTHER J. **1933.** *Ann. Bot.* **47:** 401–422. 20 figs. [Conduction of water.]

— **1933A.** *Ibid.* **47:** 635–661. 41 figs. [Conduction of water.]

— **1933B.** *Ibid.* **47:** 889–912. 23 figs. [Conduction of water.]

BROTHERUS, V. F. **1924–1925.** Bryales. Spezieller Teil. In A. Engler and K. Prantl, Die natürlichen Pflanzenfamilien. 2 Aufl. Bd. 10. Pp. 143–478. 306 figs. Bd. 11. 1–542 pp. 376 figs.

BROWN, MABEL M. **1919.** *Amer. Jour. Bot.* **6:** 387–400. 1 pl. [Gametophyte, *Funaria.*]

BRYAN, G. S. **1915.** *Bot. Gaz.* **59:** 40–56. 4 pl. [Archegonium, *Sphagnum.*]

— **1917.** *Ibid.* **64:** 1–20. 8 pl. 1 fig. [Development of archegonium.]

— **1920.** *Amer. Jour. Bot.* **7:** 296–303. 26 figs. [Embryogeny, *Sphagnum.*]

— **1920A.** *Ibid.* **7:** 223–230. 2 pl. [Archegonium, *Sphagnum.*]

— **1927.** *Bot. Gaz.* **84:** 89–101. 20 figs. [Abnormal archegonia.]

CAMPBELL, D. H. **1918.** The structure and development of mosses and ferns. 3d ed. New York. 708 pp. 322 figs.

EVANS, A. W., and H. D. HOOKER. **1913.** *Bull. Torrey Bot. Club* **40:** 97–109. 26 figs. [Development of peristome.]

GOEBEL, K. **1892.** *Flora* **76:** 92–104. 2 pl. [Persistent protonemata.]

— **1898.** *Ann. Jard. Bot. Buitenzorg* **2.** Suppl. 65–72. [Deshicence of antheridium.]

HABERLANDT, G. **1886.** *Jahrb. Wiss. Bot.* **17:** 359–498. 7 pl. [Anatomy of Eubrya.]

HOLFERTY, G. M. **1904.** *Bot. Gaz.* **37:** 106–126. 2 pl. [Development of archegonium.]

KIENITZ-GERLOFF, F. **1878.** *Bot. Zeitg.* **36:** 33–64. 3 pl. [Development of embryo.]

KÜHN, E. **1870.** *Schenck and Leurssen's Mitt. a. d. Gesammtgebeite d. Bot.* **1:** 1–56. 10 pl. [*Andreaea.*]

KUHLBRODT, H. **1922.** *Beitr. allgemein Bot.* **2:** 363–402. 1 pl. [Stomata.]

LEITGEB, H. **1880.** *Sitzungsber. Akad. Wiss. Wien* (Math.-Nat. Kl.). **80¹:** 447–460. 1 pl. [Sporophyte of *Archidium.*]

LORCH, W. **1931.** Anatomie der Laubmoose. In K. Linsbauer, Handbuch der Pflanzenantomie. 8¹. 358 pp. 230 figs.

MÄGDEFRAU, K. **1935.** *Zeitschr. Bot.* **29:** 337–375. 2 figs. [Water-conducting, tissues.]

MARCHAL, ÉL., and ÉM. MARCHAL. **1911.** *Bull. Cl. Sci. Acad. Roy. Belgique* **1911:** 750–782. 1 pl. [Apospory.]

MELIN, E. **1915.** *Svensk Bot. Tidskr.* **9:** 261–293. 1 pl. 2 figs. [Antheridium, sporogenesis, *Sphagnum.*]

— **1916.** *Ibid.* **10:** 289–311. 6 figs. [Archegonium, *Sphagnum.*]

MÜHLDORF, A. **1930.** *Beih. Bot. Centralbl.* 1 Abt. **47:** 169–191. 1 pl. [Antherozoids, *Sphagnum.*]

NAWASCHIN, S. **1897.** *Flora* **83:** 151–159. 1 pl. [Spore liberation, *Sphagnum.*]

POTTIER, J. **1921.** *Ann. Sci. Nat. Bot.* 10 ser., **3:** 1–144. 32 pl. [Leaf, *Andreaea.*]

RHULAND, W. **1924.** Musci. Allgemeiner Teil. In A. Engler and K. Prantl, Die natürlichen Pflanzenfamilien. 2 Aufl. Bd. 10. 1–100. 90 figs.

STEINBRINCK, C. **1897.** *Flora* **84** : 131–158. 13 figs. [Peristome.]

TANSLEY, A. G., and E. CHICK. **1901.** *Ann. Bot.* **15** : 1–38. 2 pl. [Water-conducting tissues.]

WALDNER, M. **1887.** Die Entwickelung der Sporogone von Andreaea und Sphagnum. Leipzig. 25 pp. 4 pl.

WETTSTEIN, F. VON. **1923.** *Biol. Centralbl.* **43** : 71–83. [Apospory.]

CHAPTER V

PTERIDOPHYTA—INTRODUCTION

The Pteridophyta stand intermediate between the Bryophyta and the Spermatophyta. They are to be distinguished from the Bryophyta by the fact that the sporophyte is independent of the gametophyte at maturity. They differ from the Spermatophyta in the liberation of the spore, or the gametophyte developed from it, from the sporangium.[1] Mature sporophytes of Pteridophytes have an internal conducting system composed of xylem and phloem. Generally, although not always, the plant body is differentiated into stem, leaf, and root. The sporangia may be borne upon the leaves or at the tips of modified or unmodified branches. A plant may be homosporous (with all spores the same size) or heterosporous (with spores of two sizes). The gametophyte is always smaller than the sporophyte and simpler in structure. Gametophytes of homosporous Pteridophyta are wholly independent of the sporophyte in their nutrition; those of heterosporous Pteridophyta are partially or entirely dependent upon the sporophyte.

Origin of the Pteridophyta. The origin of the Pteridophyta is a question that has been debated at length. The geological record shows that it is a series of great antiquity and that certain primitive fossil pteridophytes, the Psilophytales, were widespread during the Middle and Early Devonian, that is, some 350,000,000 years ago. Fossil Psilophytales discovered during the past two decades have revealed a simpler type of pteridophyte than any previously known, but even these do not bridge the gap between Pteridophyta and plants lower in the evolutionary scale. Thus, theories concerning the origin of the Pteridophyta still must be based upon the comparative morphology of living and fossil plants. These theories fall into two general categories: those which postulate a direct origin from algae, and those which consider the Pteridophyta directly or indirectly related to the Bryophyta.

Although a majority vote has no bearing on the correctness or incorrectness of any theory, it is interesting to note that those adhering to a direct origin of Pteridophyta from algae far outnumber those advocating a phylogenetic connection between Bryophyta and Pteridophyta. Support of the direct origin from algae may be based upon a negative or a

---

[1] This is not true of the Lepidocarpales (p. 203), here included among the Pteridophyta.

positive line of reasoning.   Negative proponents of algal origin[1] take the stand that similarities in such structures as sexual organs and similarity in alternation of generations of Bryophyta and Pteridophyta are due to a parallel evolution, not to a relationship between the two.   The lack of any geological proof that the Bryophyta are an ancient group of plants has also been cited as evidence showing that they are not the forerunners of the pteridophytes.   This argument has lost much of its value with the recent demonstration (page 2) that bryophytes existed as far back as the Carboniferous.

Most of those who hold that there has been a direct origin from algae are more concerned with the particular algal progenitors of the Pteridophyta than with the manner in which Pteridophyta have been evolved from algae.   A monophyletic algal ancestry has been sought both in the Chlorophyceae[2] and in the Phaeophyceae.[3]   Others maintain that the origin has been polyphyletic, either in divergent evolutionary lines among the Chlorophyceae alone[4] or in algae of various classes.[5]   In most cases these ancestral algae are thought to have been of a branching filamentous type, but one proponent of algal origin assumes[6] a sudden appearance of complex land plants by "transmigration" from ocean to land of complex algae with a plant body as highly differentiated as that of Laminariales or Fucales.

Bryophytes and pteridophytes are alike in so many respects (dissimilar alternating generations, general similarity in structure of the gametophyte, similarity in ontogeny and mature structure of antheridia, similarity in ontogeny and mature structure of archegonia, encapsulation of the embryo in the archegonium, and partial or complete parasitism of sporophyte upon gametophyte) that there is good reason to think that there is a phylogenetic relationship between the two.   Some of those who believe that there is a phylogenetic connection think that the Bryophyta and Pteridophyta represent two divergent evolutionary lines from hypothetical land plants of a very primitive type.[7]   These have been called the Protohepaticae.[8]   Others think that the Pteridophyta have diverged from true Bryophyta of a type more or less like the Anthocerotae.   The theory that the Pteridophyta have arisen from an anthocerotean type of bryophyte is based upon the idea that

The unlimited growth of the sporophyte . . . in connection with the highly developed assimilative tissue, makes the sporophyte of this plant the nearest approach to the entirely independent sporophyte of the ferns.   Were the foot of the sporophyte in *Anthoceros* prolonged into a root penetrating the earth, it would become quite independent of the gametophyte, and were a special

[1] Bower, 1908, 1935; Scott, 1900.   [2] Fritsch, 1916.   [3] Schenck, 1908.
[4] Bohlin, 1901; Lotsy, 1909.   [5] Arber, 1921.   [6] Church, 1919.
[7] Lignier, 1903; Zimmermann, 1930.   [8] Lignier, 1903.

assimilative organ or leaf developed, a condition directly comparable to the sporophyte of the lower Pteridophytes or ferns would result.[1]

The theory[2] of the anthocerotean origin of Pteridophyta received but little support when first promulgated. Opponents of the theory held that it left too many gaps between the anthocerotean type of sporophyte and the root-bearing, leafy, free-living sporophyte typical of Pteridophyta. The discovery of Psilophytales, in which the sporophyte was a rootless, leafless, dichotomously branched shoot, invalidates much of this objection. If an anthocerotean type of sporophyte had a shifting of the

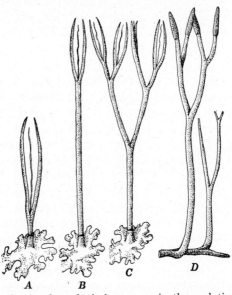

Fig. 67.—Diagrams showing hypothetical sequence in the evolution of a semiparasitic anthocerotean type of sporophyte into a free-living psilophytan type of sporophyte.

meristematic region from base to apex, a dichotomous branching of the apical meristem, and a restriction of spore formation to the branch apices, it would resemble very closely the sporophyte of certain Psilophytales (Fig. 67). Such sporophytes might have the columella metamorphosed into a conducting tissue (central cylinder).

When *Anthoceros* grows in an unusually favorable habitat, it may show the beginnings of an approach toward the conditions described above. Sporophytes have been found[3] in which there was a restriction of spore production to the distal end and in which the columella was differentiated into a conducting tissue in the sterile lower portion. The change from a bryophytic condition, where the sporophyte is parasitic upon the gametophyte, to the pteridophytic condition, where the sporophyte is independ-

[1] Campbell, 1899 (p. 120).   [2] Campbell, 1895.   [3] Campbell, 1924.

ent at maturity, seems to be a long jump. The demonstration that *Anthoceros* sporophytes severed from the gametophyte can remain alive for months and show a limited amount of growth[1] and the demonstration that this obtains in nature[2] show that this change is a short step, not a long jump.

Discussion of the anthocerotean origin of Pteridophyta has centered around the sporophyte generation and has overlooked the fact that sex organs of Pteridophyta have more in common with those of Anthocerotae than with those of other Bryophyta. In Anthocerotae, as in Pteridophyta, the sex organs are embedded in the gametophyte; in all other Bryophyta the sex organs, although sometimes lying in a chamber, stand

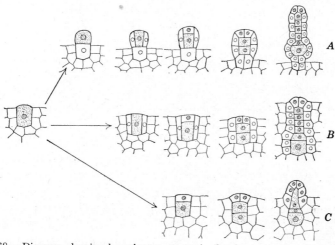

Fig. 68.—Diagram showing homologous stages in development of archegonia of (*A*) Hepaticae, (*B*) Anthocerotae, and (*C*) Pteridophyta. Homologous stages of development stand one above the other.

above the level of gametophytic cells next to the antheridial and archegonial stalks.

Archegonia of Anthocerotae are more reduced than those of other Hepaticae in that they have no stalk. This is due to an obliteration of division of an archegonial initial into a primary archegonial cell and a primary stalk cell (page 79). Direct functioning of the archegonial cell as the primary archegonial cell results in an embedded archegonium, but one which is surrounded by a jacket layer because the initial divides into an axial cell and three jacket initials. Evolution of the pteridophytan archegonium has been accompanied by a further reduction in the early ontogeny. Here, the archegonial initial functions directly as the axial cell and does not form jacket initials. Thus, the entire pterido-

[1] Campbell, 1917.   [2] Campbell, 1924.

phytan archegonium is homologous with the axial row and the cover cells of the anthocerotean archegonium (Fig. 68).

The primitive type of antheridium of Pteridophyta, the so-called eusporangiate type, is found in *Lycopodium, Equisetum,* the eusporangiate ferns, and, in a modified form, in the Psilotales. It consists of a large number of fertile cells, which lie embedded in the gametophyte, and a sterile layer external to the fertile cells. The superficial cell of a gametophyte that gives rise to the sterile and fertile cells is usually considered homologous with an antheridial initial in gametophytes of Hepaticae. The two daughter cells formed by periclinal division of this gametophytic cell of pteridophytes are usually called the primary jacket cell and the

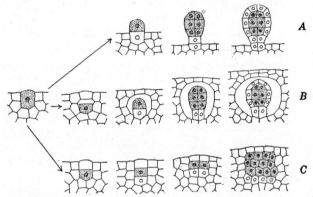

Fig. 69.—Diagram showing the homologies in development of the marchantiaceous (*A*) and anthocerotean (*B*) types of antheridium and (*C*) their possible homologies with the eusporangiate antheridium of Pteridophyta. Homologous stages of development stand one above the other.

primary androgonial cell. The antheridial initial of Anthocerotae is the inner daughter cell from periclinal division of a superficial gametophytic cell, and the sister cell of this initial develops into the cover roofing over the chamber in which the antheridium lies (Fig. 69). In view of the suggested origin of Pteridophyta from an anthocerotean ancestry, is there not a possibility that the fertile portion of a "eusporangiate antheridium" corresponds to the whole anthocerotean antheridium and that its so-called jacket layer is homologous with the cover of an antheridial chamber in Anthocerotae? One of the theories on the evolution of the antheridium of archegoniates holds that its jacket layer arose by a sterilization of the outermost fertile cells (page 3). May not embedding of the anthocerotean antheridium have resulted in a return to the original condition where all cells in the antheridium were fertile?

Embryological data have also been used to shed light upon the phylogeny of the Pteridophyta. We know nothing concerning the embryology of the most primitive fossil forms, the Psilophytales, but it is probably more than a mere coincidence that embryos of their nearest living relatives, the Psilotales, show a remarkable superficial resemblance to those of Anthocerotae. (Compare Figs. 46*H* and 90*B*.)

Evolution of the Plant Body among Pteridophyta. Until some twenty years ago, there was an almost universal belief that evolution of a root preceded,[1] or followed very closely upon,[2] establishment of the independent, self-sustaining, sporophyte characteristic of Pteridophyta. Attention, therefore, centered around the nature of the shoot in primitive Pteridophytes. There were three general theories concerning its nature:[3] (1) that it consisted solely of leaves, or the prototypes of leaves, and that the leaf-bearing axis appeared later in the phylogeny of the shoot; (2) that it was wholly axial in nature and that appendages of the axis (leaves and sporangiophores) were evolved from local superficial areas on the axis; (3) that it was wholly axial in nature and that leaves were evolved by a modification of branches.

The great extension of our knowledge of the Psilophytales during the past decade shows that many of these primitive pteridophytes were rootless, leafless, free-living plants consisting only of a dichotomously branched axis. Demonstration of the stem-like nature of these primitive Pteridophyta invalidates the theory that leaves preceded the axis. The theory that leaves were evolved from local emergences of the axis need not be considered since it has been abandoned by its chief proponent.[4]

Any consideration of the theory, first suggested by Bower,[5] that leaves are modified branches must take into consideration the fact that foliage leaves are of two distinct types—microphyllous and macrophyllous. Microphyllous leaves, even when of large size, have a single unbranched vein.[6] Macrophyllous leaves always have a blade with many veins or a single much-branched vein.

There is a quite general belief that the macrophyllous leaf of the ferns arose through modification of a lateral dichotomous branch system in which the tips of the branchlets were fertile. The primitive leaf thus evolved may have been radial in organization, but it soon became a flattened bifacial structure in which the fertile tips of the branchlets (the sporangia) were marginal in position. From this was evolved a condition in which the sporangia came to lie inward from the leaf margin.

Various opinions have been expressed concerning the origin of the microphyllous leaf of the lycopods. It has been held[7] that leaves in this group of plants are in an entirely different category from macrophyllous

---

[1] Campbell, 1905.   [2] Bower, 1908.
[3] See Bower, 1908, especially Chap. XI, for an extended discussion of these theories.
[4] Bower, 1908, 1923, 1935.   [5] Bower, 1884.
[6] Certain fossil lycopods are an exception in that they have two veins.
[7] Lignier, 1903.

leaves since they arose through a modification of hair-like outgrowths on an axis. It has also been suggested[1] that all microphyllous leaves are reduced forms of macrophyllous leaves. However, there is equal justification for holding that the psilophytan type of plant gave rise to the lycopodian type of leaf through modification of an unforked branchlet.

Certain primitive members of the equisetaceous series (as *Calamophyton*, Fig. 126) have an axis that bears small, forked, lateral branches. Some of these branches are sterile; others are fertile. Metamorphosis of a sterile branch into a leaf would result in one of the macrophyllous type. This macrophyllous leaf, well exemplified by *Sphenophyllum* (Fig. 127), differs from that of ferns in that it is purely vegetative in function. The single-veined, sterile leaf found in so many members of the equisetaceous series may be a reductional form of a sterile macrophyllous leaf.

There remains for consideration the structure evolved from the small fertile branches of the primitive equisetaceous plant. In *Calamophyton* the fertile branches were dichotomously forked and had their apices recurved and terminating in sporangia. Evolution of the fertile branch of *Calamophyton* into the fertile appendage found in *Equisetum* involves but little change. The fertile appendage in *Equisetum* has been thought to be leaf-like in nature and therefore has been called a *sporophyll*. A better name for this structure is *sporangiophore*,[2] since this term is noncommital as to whether or not it is leaf-like in nature. Many members of the equisetaceous series have each sporangiophore subtended by a sterile leaf that is generally called a *bract*. A bract may be free from the sporangiophore or united with it. However, when the two are fused with each other, there is usually a separate vascular supply to bract and sporangiophore. Sporangiophore and subtending bract may have been evolved by a metamorphosis of two branches borne one above the other, one fertile, the other sterile. There is an equal possibility that they were evolved from a single branch in which one arm of the first dichotomy was sterile and the other fertile.

The equisetaceous sporangiophore and bract give a basis for interpreting the nature of the fertile leaf in the lycopods. The fertile lycopodian leaf is usually considered a sporophyll but one which bears only a single sporangium and this near the base of the adaxial face. As will be shown on a later page (page 162), there is some reason for thinking that the so-called lycopodian sporangium is in reality a sporangiophore terminating in a single sporangium. If this is true the "fertile leaf" of the lycopod is to be compared with the united bract and sporangiophore found in the equisetaceous series rather than with the sporangium-bearing leaf (sporophyll) found in the ferns. The same interpretation applies with even greater force to the "sporophyll" of the Psilotales.

[1] Zimmermann, 1930.   [2] Scott, 1900.

The origin of the root system of the pteridophytan sporophyte is obscure. The prototype of a root system is to be seen in the dimorphism among the branches arising from the rhizome of *Asteroxylon* (page 148). Here certain of the branches were aerial and leafy, whereas others were subterranean and leafless. The general restriction of roots to special, prostrate, leafless branches (rhizophores) among the lycopods and the general similarity in vascular organization of root and branch among all primitive root-bearing Pteridophyta indicate that roots are modified branches. However, this does not explain how the root acquired its deep-seated (endogenous) origin within tissues of a stem, its distinctive caps, and its lack of appendages.

The Vascular Elements of Pteridophyta. The free-living, relatively large, sporophyte characteristic of pteridophytes was made possible by an evolution of adequate tissues for the upward and downward conduction of materials. All pteridophytes have two general types of conducting tissue, the xylem and the phloem. The chief function of the former is the upward conduction of water, that of the latter is the upward and downward conduction of foods. Together they constitute the chief elements in the *vascular system* of the sporophyte. The origin of the vascular system is wholly unknown. If one believes in the anthocerotean origin of the Pteridophyta, there is a strong temptation to homologize the columella of an antocerotean sporophyte with the vascular cylinder of a pteridophyte. However, such a hypothesis is purely speculative.

The *tracheid* is the fundamental element of the xylem and is matured from a single embryonic cell. An embryonic cell destined to mature into a tracheid elongates greatly and deposits additional wall material upon limited portions of the inner face of the cell wall (Fig. 70*A*–*C*). Sooner or later there is a disappearance of the cytoplasm and nucleus. A mature tracheid, therefore, is an elongate dead cell consisting only of a cell wall. The first tracheids mature in the xylem have the additional wall material deposited in transverse rings. Because of this they are called *annular tracheids*. Instead of being deposited in transverse rings, the additional wall material may be deposited in a continuous spiral. The result of this is a *spiral tracheid* (Fig. 70*D*). These two types of tracheid are not always distinct from each other and sometimes a tracheid has an annular thickening in one portion of the lateral wall and a spiral thickening in another portion. Both types of tracheid are matured in regions of stem, root, or leaf that are still elongating. In all cases there is considerable passive longitudinal stretching of these tracheids after they are mature and after their protoplasts have disappeared. Thus, the rings or successive spiral turns that were close together when first deposited eventually come to lie some distance from one another. The portion of the xylem containing these tracheids, which may be elongated after maturation, is called the *protoxylem.* This name is based upon the fact that it is always the first-matured portion of the xylem. The portion of the xylem matured after elongation has ceased is the *metaxylem.* The xylem may consist wholly of protoxylem or, as in certain slowly growing organs, wholly of metaxylem. Generally, however, both proto- and metaxylem are present in the vascular tissue of a root, leaf, or stem. Tracheids of the protoxylem are smaller in diameter than those of the metaxylem. This is quite evident

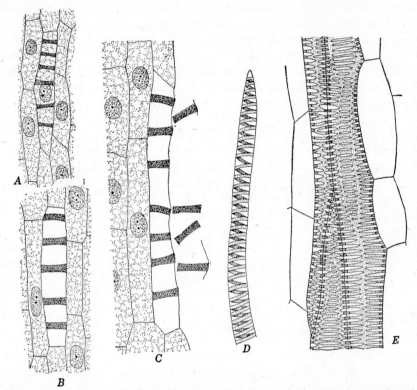

Fig. 70.—*A–C*, stages in the development of annular tracheids of *Equisetum telmateia* Ehrh. *D*, spiral tracheid of *Azolla filiculoides* Lam. *E*, scalariform tracheid of *Marsilea vestita* Hook. and Grev. (× 650.)

when an organ is seen in transverse section, but the real determination of the protoxylem portion of any vascular strand rests upon the demonstration of annular and spiral tracheids from a study of longitudinal sections.

Tracheids of the metaxylem are structurally incapable of a longitudinal stretching after they are mature. The earliest tracheids matured in the metaxylem are the *scalariform tracheids* (Fig. 70*E*). These may be looked upon as spiral tracheids in which there are vertical bands of additional wall material connecting successive spirals one with another. There is the same lack of a hard and fast distinction between spiral and scalariform tracheids that there is between annular and spiral ones. This means that there may be no sharp line of demarcation between the first-matured (protoxylem) and later-matured (metaxylem) portions of the xylem. The type of tracheid most characteristic of older portions of the metaxylem is the *pitted tracheid,* in which there is a deposition of additional wall material on all but limited portions of the tracheid wall. The thin areas (pits) are usually transversely elongate, but in some cases they are circular. Pits of the Ophioglossaceae are unusual in that they are of the bordered type[1] usually found in seed plants.

If a *vessel* is defined as a vertical series of water-conducting elements with open perforations in the end walls, one may say that there are vessels in the Pteridophyta. Unlike the angiosperms, the vessels of pteridophytes are of about the same diameter as tracheids. There are two types of vessel among the Pteridophyta. Several members of the lycopodian

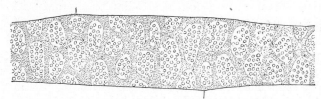

Fig. 71.—Portion of a sieve tube of *Pteridium aquilinum* (L.) Kuhn. (× 650.)

series have vessels in which there has been a complete obliteration of cross walls between successive units.[2] Among the ferns, vessels have only been found in *Pteridium aquilinum* (L.) Kuhn. and the root of *Nephrodium Filix-mas* Rich.[3] Here there are no cross walls (closing membranes) in pits on the end walls between successive vertical elements. Pits on the side walls have been described as being perforated,[4] but this has been denied.[5]

In addition to containing tracheids and vessels, the xylem may contain parenchyma. In some cases the parenchyma lies in a belt between the phloem and tracheids; in other cases, as in *Lycopodium cernuum* L. (Fig. 95C), there is an intermingling of parenchymatous and water-conducting elements.

The phloem of pteridophytes is composed of *sieve tubes* and *phloem parenchyma.* A sieve tube consists of a series of elongate living cells in which the protoplasts are connected to one another through perforations in the walls (Fig. 71). These perforations are of larger diameter than are the perforations (*plasmadesmen*) in walls of embryonic cells. The walls of each cell (*sieve-tube segment*) in a sieve tube are relatively thin and have the perforations in restricted areas, known as *sieve plates.* Sieve plates

[1] Loughridge, 1932.   [2] Duerden, 1933, 1934; Harvey-Gibson, 1894.
[3] Bancroft, 1911.   [4] Gwynne-Vaughan, 1908.   [5] Bancroft, 1911; Wright, 1920.

occur throughout the length of sieve-tube segments wherever they are in lateral contact with other segments.   There may also be connections between the sieve tubes and the abutting phloem parenchyma cells.[1] Sometimes a distinction is made between *protophloem* and *metaphloem*, but, unlike the xylem, there are no pronounced morphological differences between the first-formed and later-formed elements in the phloem.   A sieve tube remains functional until pads of callus are deposited on the sieve plates.   Old sieve tubes of certain ferns regularly have callus pads, those of other ferns have no callus pads.[2]   In some ferns, as *Pteridium aquilinum* L., callus pads may be formed and then resorbed.[1]   If there is no permanent formation of callus, a sieve tube may remain functional for years.

Secondary thickening of the vascular tissue by means of a cambium is of very rare occurrence among living pteridophytes, but it was quite common among equisetaceous and lycopodian plants that existed during the Carboniferous.   *Botrychium* (page 264) and *Isoetes* (page 209) are the only living pteridophytes in which all stems regularly have a secondary thickening.   In *Botrychium*, as in seed plants, the secondary xylem lies internal to and the secondary phloem external to the cambium. Tracheids of the secondary xylem are similar to those of seed plants in that they have bordered pits.[3]   Secondary xylem and phloem in stems of *Isoetes* both lie internal to the cambium.   Occasional individuals of one or two other living Pteridophyta, as *Ophioglossum* (page 265),[4] may produce a very limited amount of secondary tissue.

Evolution of the Vascular System.   The older plant anatomists held that the vascular bundle is the fundamental unit in the vascular system of pteridophytes and higher plants.   In 1886 Van Tieghem and Douliot[5] proposed an entirely different interpretation of the body of a vascular plant.   They held that the fundamental parts of a shoot are the cortex and a central cylinder, which they called the *stele*, and that the two are delimited from each other by the *endodermis*.   They recognized three types of stelar construction and thought that shoots with a single stele (*monosteles*) were rarer than those containing more than one stele (*polysteles*).   We now know that practically all shoots are monostelic and that a polystelic condition (Figs. 72*D*, 102) is of rare occurrence.

Jeffrey was the first to interpret the stelar theory from the phylogenetic standpoint.[6]   He held that the primitive type of stelar construction is that in which the vascular tissue is a solid mass and one in which a central core of xylem is completely ensheathed by a layer of phloem.   There has been a very general acceptance of this concept and of the name (*protostele*) that he proposed for this type of stele.   Proto-

---

[1] Hume, 1912.   [2] Boodle, 1901.   [3] Wright, 1920.   [4] Boodle, 1899.
[5] Van Tieghem and Douliot, 1886.   [6] Jeffrey, 1898.

steles with a smooth core of xylem are generally considered more primitive than those in which the xylem core has radiating ribs. The former type of protostele has been called[1] a *haplostele* (Figs. 72A, 178), the latter an *actinostele* (Figs. 72B, 95A). The most advanced type of

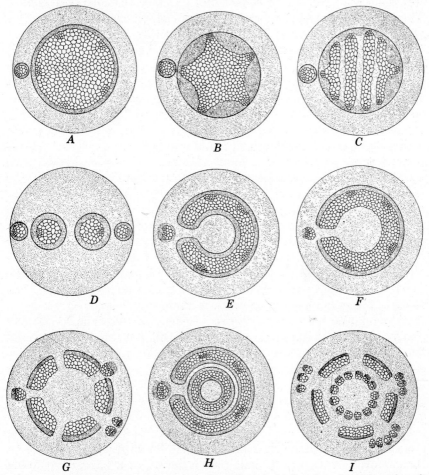

Fig. 72.—Diagrams of various types of stele. *A*, haplostele. *B*, actinostele. *C*, plectostele. *D*, polystele. *E*, ampliphloic solenostele. *F*, ectophloic solenostele. *G*, dictyostele. *H*, polycyclic solenostele. *I*, polycyclic dictyostele.

actinostele is that in which the xylem is divided into a number of separate plates that lie parallel to, or radiate to, one another. Such actinosteles have been called *plectosteles*[2] (Figs. 72C, 95B).

Evolutionary changes among protosteles have involved shifts in the relative position of the protoxylem and metaxylem. The significance of

---

[1] Brebner, 1902.   [2] Zimmermann, 1930.

the relative position of the xylem elements was recognized by palaeo-botanists before shoots were interpreted according to the stelar theory. Vascular strands with the protoxylem developing at the outer face were called[1] *exarch;* those with protoxylem at the middle of the metaxylem were called *mesarch;* and those with protoxylem at the inner face, *endarch.* There was an early incorporation of this concept in the stelar theory,[2] with an interpretation of the exarch condition as more primitive than the mesarch and the latter as more primitive than the endarch.

The vascular connection between the stele and the base of a leaf is called the *leaf supply.* The leaf supply in the cortex of protostelic stems always consists of but one vascular strand or *leaf trace.* Stems with a more elaborate type of stelar construction may have more than one leaf trace connecting with each leaf. A leaf trace is often described as departing from the stele and running through the cortex. This somewhat misleading since it infers that a trace is an outgrowth from the stele that has pushed through the cortex. Actually, of course, a trace is a vascular strand matured from embryonic cortical cells. *Branch traces* are similar to leaf traces, except that they connect with branches, not leaves. Leaf traces of protostelic stems are often similar in structure to the steles from which they depart.

Protosteles are generally encircled by an *endodermis,* a layer one cell in thickness. An endodermis may be recognized by means of the peculiar thickenings (*Casparian strips*) on radial walls of its cells (Fig. 135*B*). Sometimes, also, endodermal cells have suberin lamellae on the inner tangential or on all walls. Sometimes endodermal cells may also be recognized because of their brownish color and their tannin-filled content. It has been held[3] that the endodermis is always differentiated in the innermost layer of the cortex. Hence it affords a criterion for distinguishing between tissues of cortical and of stelar origin. This generalization is open to question since the endodermis may be differentiated from cells of the stele (*Selaginella*)[4] or from a layer that contributes to both the cortex and the stele (*Schizaea*).[5] Furthermore, there is considerable evidence showing that the primary function of an endodermis is physiological and that it serves as a barrier regulating lateral flow of water and dissolved substances between stele and cortex.[6] Thus, the development or nondevelopment of an endodermis external to the vascular cylinder may rest upon physiological causes rather than the specific nature of the innermost cortical cells.

There is a general acceptance of the theory[7] that the stele with a tubular vascular region and a parenchymatous central region was evolved

[1] Scott, 1900.   [2] Wordsell, 1902.   [3] Jeffrey, 1917.
[4] Barclay, 1931.   [5] Bartoo, 1930.
[6] Priestley and North, 1922; Priestley and Radcliffe, 1924.   [7] Jeffrey, 1898.

from a protostele. In the vascular portion of such *siphonosteles*[1] there are parenchymatous areas (*gaps*) immediately above the branch traces only or immediately above each leaf and branch trace (Fig. 73). There are never any gaps above departing roots.

The method by which a protostele evolved into a siphonostele has been a subject of acrimonious debate. According to one theory,[2] the parenchymatous tissue internal to the phloem and xylem is cortical in origin. Adherents of this theory hold that the presence of an endodermis at the inner face of the vascular tissue proves that the parenchymatous cells encircled by this endodermis are cortical in origin. They hold that siphonosteles with an internal endodermis are more primitive than those without an inner endodermis. Siphonosteles of the latter type are thought to have arisen by an obliteration of the inner endodermis during the course of evolution. The chief basis of this theory is the specific nature of the endodermis. However, as already noted, this is open to question. Thus, instead of representing an invasion of cortical tissue, the inner endodermis may merely represent the differentiation of a physiological barrier between vascular tissue and the pith. It is also extremely difficult to interpret certain types of siphonostele on the basis of an invasion of cortical tissue. For example, it is practically impossible to visualize the type of cortical invasion that would produce polycyclic siphonosteles (Fig. 72*H*).

According to another theory, a siphonostele was evolved from a protostele by a metamorphosis of the inner vascular elements into parenchyma.[3] The chief argument in favor of the intraxylic origin of the pith, and one unanswered by proponents of the invasion theory, is the repeatedly described occurrence of siphonosteles[4] in which tracheids are intermingled with the parenchymatous cells of the pith (Fig. 173). The "mixed pith" just described is found only in relatively primitive fossil and living ferns. Steles in which there is a regular occurrence of a mixed pith may be looked upon as transitional types between true protosteles and true siphonosteles.

A siphonostele may be *amphiphloic*[1] with phloem both external and internal to the xylem (Fig. 72*E*), or it may be *ectophloic*[1] with phloem restricted to the external face of the xylem (Fig. 72*F*). Adherents of the intrusion theory of the origin of pith think that the internal phloem also arose by intrusion. Thus an amphiphloic siphonostele is more primitive than an ectophloic one. Some adherents of the intraxylic origin of the pith hold[5] that the internal phloem is intraxylic in origin.

[1] Jeffrey, 1898.   [2] Jeffrey, 1902, 1910, 1917.

[3] Boodle, 1901; Gwynne-Vaughan, 1903.

[4] Bower, 1911; Gwynne-Vaughan, 1914; Petry, 1914; Thompson, 1920.

[5] Thompson, 1920.

Whatever its origin, the evolution of siphonostele has been accompanied by an appearance of parenchymatous areas (gaps) in the vascular cylinder. Steles with gaps fall into two categories;[1] those in which there are gaps axillary to both the leaf and branch traces and those in which there are gaps axillary to branches only (Fig. 73). Steles with leaf gaps always have macrophyllous leaves; those without leaf gaps always have microphyllous leaves.[1] According to the presence or absence of leaf gaps, the vascular plants are divided into two groups, the Pteropsida and the Lycopsida.[1] The Pteropsida include the ferns, gymnosperms, and angiosperms; the Lycopsida include the lycopods, horsetails, and the psilotaceous series. Among the simpler siphono-

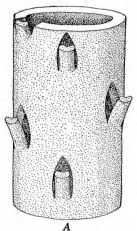 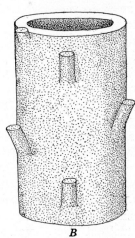

A   *B*

FIG. 73.—Stereodiagrams of steles.   *A*, pteropsidan solenostele.   *B*, lycopsidan solenostele.

stelic Pteropsida and almost always among the siphonostelic Lycopsida, successive gaps in the stele are a considerable distance above one another (Figs. 72*E*, 173). Such siphonosteles without an overlapping of gaps are *solenosteles.*[2] In the more advanced siphonostelic Pteropsida, successive gaps may overlap one another (Figs. 72*G*, 168). Siphonosteles with overlapping gaps are *dictyosteles,*[3] and the intervening portion of the vascular tissue lateral to two overlapping gaps is a *meristele.*[3] When there are numerous meristeles, the dictyostele looks like a cylindrical meshwork. The meristeles of such a dictyostele correspond to the vascular bundles of the older plant anatomists. A dictyostelic condition may be due in part to openings in the vascular cylinder that are not gaps. Lacunae in the vascular cylinder that are not gap-like in nature are called *perforations.*[4] These are sometimes present in solenosteles,[5] but

[1] Jeffrey, 1902.   [2] Brebner, 1902; Gwynne-Vaughan, 1901.
[3] Brebner, 1902.   [4] Bower, 1923.   [5] Gwynne-Vaughan, 1903.

they are of much more frequent occurrence in dictyosteles. Primitive siphonosteles have but one undivided leaf trace departing at each node. More advanced siphonosteles have the distal end of the trace divided into more than one strand (Fig. 72*G*) or have a leaf supply consisting of more than one trace (Fig. 72*I*).

The polycyclic condition[1] is the most complex type of stelar organization found among the Pteridophyta. Polycyclic steles are always siphonostelic and have an internal vascular system connected with an outer siphonostele. This internal connection is always at a node. In most cases the vascular supply to a leaf departs from both the outer and inner portions of a polycyclic stele. Typical polycyclic steles have two or more concentric cylinders of vascular tissue. In some cases the outer cylinder is a solenostele (Figs. 72*H*, 183); in others it is a dictyostele (Figs. 72*I*, 207). The vascular system internal to the outer siphonostele may be protostelic or siphonostelic. Siphonostelic internal cylinders generally, if not always, have perforations. Sometimes, as in *Matonia* (page 308), the internal perforated siphonostele is of a solenostelic type; in other cases, as in *Cyathea* (page 322), it is of a much-dissected dictyostelic type.

The data that have accumulated during the past 30 years tend to confirm the modified stelar theory postulated in the years immediately following 1900. During the past two decades there has been the discovery of a group of fossil Pteridophyta, the Psilophytales, of a much more primitive type than was known at the time the stelar theory was developed in its present form. Without exception, all of the known Psilophytales had a type of vascular organization that the stelar theory postulates as the most primitive, that is, the protostelic central cylinder. During the past quarter century there has also been a discovery that the steles of many stems recapitulate the stelar theory during their early ontogeny. Thus, many stems are protostelic in the first-formed portion and siphonostelic in later-formed portions. *Matonia pectinata* R. Br. affords the best example of recapitulation. Here, as development progresses, there is a transition from protostely to solenostely, and then a transition to a polycyclic condition in which the internal vascular tissue is at first protostelic and then siphonostelic.

On the other hand, the stelar theory has not proved of much service in establishing phylogenetic relationships among the ferns. This is due to the fact that an evolution from protostely to siphonostely and an evolution from solenostely to dictyostely has taken place in several independent lines and at different rates. These evolutionary changes in the stelar organization may be found within the limits of a single family or even a single genus. For example, certain species of *Gleichenia*

[1] Tansley, 1907–1908.

are protostelic; others are siphonostelic; and in the Schizaeaceae, the vascular organization may range from protostely to dictyostely.

Bower and his students are the only ones who have attempted to analyze the factors causing changes from the primitive protostelic organization. They find[1] that actinosteles and siphonosteles are almost always larger in diameter than are haplosteles. This comes out most strikingly when a stem is at first haplostelic and then actinostelic, plectostelic, siphonostelic, or polycyclic.[2] The same is true of haplostelic and actinostelic portions of roots.[3] These stems and roots show that the stelar construction in regions of larger diameter is not a magnified image of the stelar construction in regions of smaller diameter (Fig. 74). Increase in stelar complexity with an increase in size has

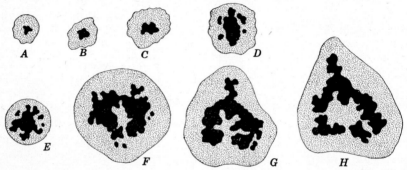

Fig. 74.—*Psilotum triquetrum* Sw. Sections of a stem from base to apex showing the increased complexity of the xylem which accompanies an increase in size. ($\times$ 46.) (*After Wardlaw*, 1924.)

been considered an attempt to maintain physiological interrelationships within a stem or root.[4] In the xylem of a small haplostele the proportion of surface to volume is relatively high. If the size of a haplostele were to be increased, the surface would increase as the square of the linear dimensions, and the volume as the cube of the dimensions. Thus, trebling the size of a haplostele would result in one with a markedly different proportion of surface to volume. This would affect both the surface relationships of xylem and phloem and the relationships between the vascular system and other parts of the shoot. On the other hand, as actual computations show,[5] if increase in diameter of stem or root is accompanied by a change in complexity of outline of the vascular system, there is an approximate maintenance of original proportions between surface and volume of the vascular tissue. Increase of stelar complexity with increase in size also affords certain physical advantage since, in

[1] Bower, 1920, 1923, 1923*A*; Wardlaw, 1924, 1925, 1928.
[2] Wardlaw, 1924, 1925.   [3] Wardlaw, 1928.
[4] Bower, 1920, 1923; Wardlaw, 1924, 1925.   [5] Wardlaw, 1924.

proportion to its volume, a tubular or a radiate mass of xylem is a more efficient mechanical support than a solid cylindrical mass.

Gametophytes of Pteridophyta. Except for a few heterosporous lycopods, nothing is known concerning the gametophyte generation of the fossil Pteridophyta. Hence all inferences concerning the structure of the primitive pteridophytan gametophyte must be based upon data derived from a comparison of those of living homosporous genera. A majority of these have green, dorsiventrally differentiated, thallose gametophytes with sex organs restricted to the ventral surface. In some cases (as in the Psilotales, the Ophioglossales, and certain species of *Lycopodium*) the gametophyte is devoid of chlorophyll, subterranean in habit, and nourished through the agency of a mycorhizal fungus. These gametophytes are almost always interpreted as being derived from a thallose green type. The filamentous green prothallus found in a few ferns, as *Schizaea* (Fig. 176), is also considered a derived rather than a primitive type.

Gametophytes of *Equisetum* and of the more primitive living ferns seem to show that the primitive pteridophytic gametophyte was thallose, more or less elongate, and more than one cell in thickness except along the lateral margins. Such a gametophyte may be compared with those of the Anthocerotae and of the thallose Jungermanniales. It is uncertain whether the sex organs were borne on the dorsal or the ventral side of the primitive gametophyte. They are regularly dorsal in *Equisetum*. Most ferns have sex organs on the ventral side only, but occasional individuals may have a few antheridia on the dorsal side. Thus, there is a certain amount of justification for assuming that the sex organs were dorsal in position and that there has been a shifting of them to a ventral position during evolution of the filicinean series. The structure of the archegonium is so standardized throughout the Pteridophyta that one is justified in believing that those on archaic gametophytes differed but little from those on present-day ones. The theory[1] that the primitive gametophyte had an embedded antheridium is widely accepted. A hypothesis deriving this embedded antheridium from that of Anthocerotae has been given on page 118.

Gametophytes of many homosporous ferns show certain changes from the theoretical primitive type. As far as vegetative structure is concerned, there is a marked tendency toward a thallus one cell in thickness, except immediately posterior to the growing point. This is accompanied by a restriction of growth in length but not in breadth. The result is the heart-shaped thallus typical of so many fern gametophytes. Sometimes, as in *Schizaea* and the Hymenophyllaceae, changes in the game-

[1] Campbell, 1894.

tophyte have been retrogressive and to a filamentous or a strap-shaped type of plant body. The simpler ferns have embedded antheridia; more advanced ferns have emergent antheridia that project beyond the surface of a gametophyte. Emergent antheridia show evolutionary changes in the structure of the jacket layer. In the primitive type of emergent antheridium there is an indefinite number (10 to 20) of irregularly arranged jacket cells; in advanced antheridia there are 3 (sometimes 4) regularly arranged jacket cells.

Evolution of heterospory in the sporophytic generation involved marked changes in the succeeding gametophytic generation. Heterospory has been independently evolved in the lycopodian, the equisetaceous, and the filicinean series of Pteridophyta. Sometimes, as among the giant horsetails, the heterospory is not pronounced. Generally, as in the ferns and the lycopods, the macrospores are many times larger than the microspores. Gametophytes of heterosporous genera differ markedly from those of homosporous genera. Unfortunately there are no living genera of an intermediate type showing steps in this modification of the gametophyte. All heterosporous genera show a very great reduction in the male gametophyte developed from the microspore. In some cases, as *Isoetes* (page 214), it is quite evident that there has been a reduction to a single vegetative cell and a single antheridium. Microgametophytes of other genera also have but one vegetative cell, but there is a possibility that they may have more than one antheridium. Female gametophytes developed from macrospores generally have more than one archegonium and many vegetative cells. Reduction of the female gametophyte has been the most extensive in *Marsilea* (page 336). Here there is but one archegonium and only a few vegetative cells.

Life Cycle of Pteridophyta. The typical life cycle of a pteridophyte consists of an alternate succession of sporophytic and gametophytic generations. However, the alternate succession may be accompanied by a vegetative multiplication of either generation. When there is an alternation of the two generations, the sporophyte generally results from a union of gametes produced by the gametophyte, and the gametophyte results from a spore produced by the sporophyte. In such an alternation, the number of chromosomes is doubled at the time of gametic union and halved at the time of spore formation.

More than half a century ago there was the discovery that a gametophyte might give rise to a sporophyte without gametic union[1] and that a sporophyte might give rise to a gametophyte without a production of spores.[2] The first-named phenomenon has been called *apogamy*,[3] the second, *apospory*.[4] Apogamy and apospory are now known to be very widespread among ferns, and frequently a plant is both apogamous and

[1] Farlow, 1874.   [2] Druery, 1885.   [3] DeBary, 1878.   [4] Bower, 1885.

aposporous. Apogamy has also been reported for one of the lycopods (*Selaginella*).

Aposporously produced gametophytes grow directly out of the leaf of a sporophyte. In some cases certain of the sporangia in a sorus develop into aposporous gametophytes; in other cases the aposporous gametophytes are developed along the margins of or at the tips of leaves (Fig. 75). Apospory has been experimentally induced in several species that are not normally aposporous. This is generally induced[1] by cutting off a leaf from a very young sporophyte and maintaining it under conditions favorable for the formation of regenerative outgrowths.

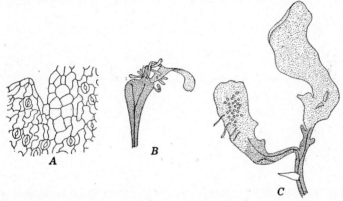

FIG. 75.—Aposporous development of gametophytes from a leaf apex of a sporophyte. *A*, primordium of gametophyte. *B–C*, developing and mature gametophytes. (*A*, × 160; *B–C*, × 15.) (*After Steil, 1919A*.)

Except for their permanent attachment to the sporophyte, aposporous gametophytes resemble those developed from spores. They are frequently typical in shape and have numerous rhizoids. Many aposporous gametophytes bear antheridia and archegonia that are normal in appearance. However, nuclei in cells of aposporous gametophytes contain the same number of chromosomes as those in cells of the sporophyte. In the cases where apospory is induced in a normal sporophyte, this is obviously $2n$. This is also presumably true in species that are naturally aposporous. Sometimes aposporous gametophytes show certain sporophytic characters. Not infrequently, tracheids, a purely sporophytic element, are present in gametophytic tissue back of the apical notch. Very rarely an aposporous gametophyte may have such sporophytic structures as stomata[2] or sporangia.[3]

Although most aposporous gametophytes only produce new sporophytes by apogamy, certain of them may produce sporophytes through

[1] Lawton, 1932.   [2] Goebel, 1908.
[3] Lang, 1898; Lawton, 1932; Pace, 1910.

a union of gametes.   In the case of one fern[1] there has been a demonstration that the sporophyte resulting from such a gametic union contained 4n chromosomes.   The resultant tetraploid sporophyte has been induced to form tetraploid aposporous gametophytes.   In this same fern there has also been a demonstration that a gamete from a diploid gametophyte may also unite with one from a haploid gametophyte and produce a sporophyte with a triploid (3n) number of chromosomes.[1]

Apogamy is found both in aposporous gametophytes and in those developing from spores.   In certain species the spores giving rise to apogamous gametophytes have a diploid number of chromosomes.[2]   In other species[3] the spore has the haploid number of chromosomes, and

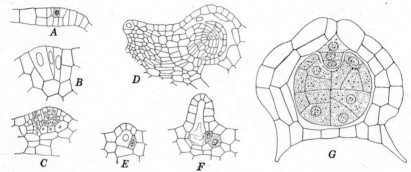

FIG. 76.—Apogamous production of sporophytes.   *A–D*, stages in apogamous production of a sporophyte from a vegetative cell of the gametophyte of *Nephrodium molle* Desv.   *E–F*, from a vegetative cell adjoining the archegonium of *Cyathea Tussacii* Desv.   *G*, by a parthenogenetic germination of the egg of *Marsilea Drummondii* A. Br.   (*A–D, after Yamanouchi*, 1908; *E–F, after Stokey*, 1918; *G, after Strasburger*, 1907.)

this number is retained in the cells of both the gametophyte and the apogamously developed sporophyte.   Such haploid sporophytes may have a doubling and halving of the chromosome in sporogenous tissue within the sporangium.[4]

An apogamously produced sporophyte may be derived from a single cell of the gametophyte.   This cell (Fig. 76*A–D*) may be a vegetative one;[5] it may be one (Fig. 76*E–F*) adjacent to or a component of an archegonium;[6] or it may be the egg (Fig. 76*G*) of an archegonium. Apogamous development of an egg into a sporophyte is generally called *parthenogenesis*.   The discovery of embryos beneath intact canal and ventral canal cells of unopened archegonia of *Marsilea* demonstrates parthenogenesis beyond all doubt.   There are also apogamously produced sporophytes that are not referable to a single cell of the game-

[1] Lawton, 1932.   [2] Strasburger, 1907.

[3] Allen, 1911; Döpp, 1932; Steil, 1919; Yamanouchi, 1908.

[4] Allen, 1911; Döpp, 1932; Steil, 1919.   [5] Yamanouchi, 1908.   [6] Stokey, 1918.

tophyte. Here[1] the young sporophyte is first evident as a compact mass of cells on the ventral side of a gametophyte and posterior to the apical notch. As development continues there is a differentiation of the apical cell of the cotyledon, then of that of the root, and finally of that of the stem.

A gametophyte has also been described as giving rise to a new sporophyte by means of a process that is neither apogamy nor true gametic union. In *Lastrea pseudo-mas.* var *polydactyla* Wills, a nucleus from a vegetative gametophytic cell was thought to migrate through the cell wall into an adjoining cell and there fuse with its nucleus.[2] The cell with the fused nucleus then developed into a sporophyte with a diploid number of chromosomes. This gamete-like fusion of vegetative cells has not been rediscovered since it was described some 30 years ago.

Evolution among the Pteridophyta. The Pteridophyta have been traced with certainty back to the Silurian.[3] These earliest-known pteridophytes belong to the Psilophytales, a series that was widespread during the Devonian and disappeared toward the end of that epoch. In addition to being the oldest, the Psilophytales are also the most primitive of any known pteridophytes. Their rootless plant body consisted of branches only or of branches and small leaves. Their sporangia were like those of bryophytes, and they were borne singly at the tips of branches. Evolution from the Psilophytales proceeded in three divergent directions and primitive representatives of all three lines (the lycopods, the horsetails, and the ferns) are known from the Middle Devonian (Fig. 77).

Pteridophytes belonging to the lycopodian series have microphyllous sporophytes in which the vascular system is without leaf gaps. Sporangia of the lycopods are always borne singly on the adaxial face of a leaf and near its base. Phylogenetic progress within the lycopodian series was at a rapid rate, and there was an early evolution of a tree-like plant body with a true secondary thickening of the vascular system. These "giant lycopods," which were an important element in the flora of the Carboniferous, disappeared shortly after the succeeding era, the Permian. Evolution of a complex type of plant body was accompanied by an evolution of heterospory which, in turn, lead to an almost seed-like mode of reproduction in one fossil group, the Lepidocarpales. Four genera of living plants belong to the lycopodian series. Three of these (*Lycopodium, Phylloglossum,* and *Selaginella*) are obviously related to the carboniferous lycopods; the relationship of the fourth genus (*Isoetes*) is less pronounced. *Lycopodium* and *Selaginella* are frequently considered degenerate relics of the giant lycopods. This is open to question since

---

[1] Steil, 1919.   [2] Farmer and Digby, 1907.   [3] Lang and Cookson, 1935.

there is evidence showing that they are descended from the precursors of the tree-like lycopods.

Another evolutionary line from the Psilophytales leads to the equisetaceous series. Members of this series are microphyllous or macrophyllous and generally with a whorl of leaves at each node. There are no leaf gaps in the vascular system. The sporangia are borne on a distinctive type of appendage, the sporangiophore, and a sporangiophore

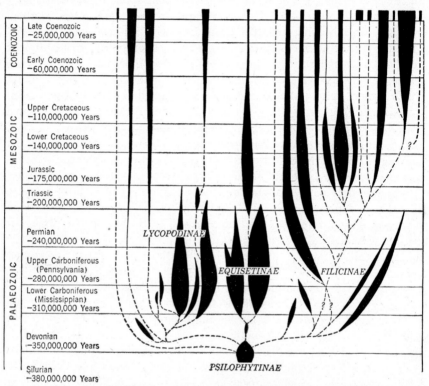

Fig. 77.—Diagram showing the geological range and the suggested interrelationships among the Pteridophyta. For further details see Figs. 91, 125, and 142.

generally has more than one sporangium. Evolution of the plant body also proceeded at a rapid rate in this series and by the beginning of the Carboniferous there had been an evolution of a tree-like plant with a conspicuous secondary thickening of the stem and branches. These "giant horsetails" disappeared about the same time as did the giant lycopods. Sporangial evolution was not as great as in the lycopods and no member of the equisetaceous series progressed beyond an incipient heterospory. *Equisetum* is the only living representative of the series. It is probably a degenerate representative of the giant horsetails.

The ferns, the third evolutionary line from the Psilophytales, differ from the two foregoing series both in their macrophyllous fertile leaves and in that they have leaf gaps in the vascular cylinder. Sporangia of ferns are borne marginally or abaxially on the leaves, and there are always many of them on a leaf. Evolution of the filicinean series was at a relatively slow rate, and the ferns comprised an inconspicuous element in the Carboniferous flora as compared with the lycopods and horsetails. These early ferns had a plant body more or less like that of present-day ones, but their sporangia frequently resembled those of Psilophytales. With a few exceptions, ferns with a typical filicinean sporangium are post-Carboniferous in origin. A majority of present-day ferns are tropical or subtropical in distribution. There are more than 4,100 species of them and about 142 genera. Some of the families of living ferns arose immediately after the Carboniferous, others arose considerably later. Certain families, as the Matoniaceae and the Dipteridaceae, now include only a few vestigial species of limited geographical distribution. Other families, as the Polypodiaceae, are widely distributed and appear to include more species than at any time in their past history.

The relationships of two unusual living Pteridophyta, *Psilotum* and *Tmesipteris*, have been much debated. As will be shown later on (page 142), they appear to be more closely related to the Psilophytales than to any other Pteridophyta.

Classification of the Pteridophyta. Differences between the ferns, lycopods, and horsetails are widely recognized as being of a sufficient magnitude to place each of them in a separate class. During the past decade the psilophytan group has also been recognized as an equally distinct series. There is considerable confusion in the class names applied to the ferns, lycopods, and horsetails. Sometimes the three living classes of Pteridophyta are called[1] the Filicales, the Equisetales, and the Lycopodiales. An obvious objection to this terminology is the use of the ordinary suffix -*ales*. This is especially confusing where authors[1] apply the same name to both a class and an order. An example of this is the recognition of the Equisetales as an order in the class Equisetales. There is a widespread usage[2] of the names Filicinae, Equisetinae, and Lycopodinae for the three classes of living pteridophytes. The psilophytan series has recently been given the class name Psilophytinae.[3] These names are open to objection because the suffix *inae* is one that the international rules of botanical nomenclature[4] reserve for subtribes, a

---

[1] Engler and Gilg, 1924; Engler and Prantl, 1890–1902.

[2] For example, Bessey, 1892, Strausburger, Noll, Schenck and Schimper, 1921; Warming, 1895; Wettstein, 1903–1908.

[3] Wettstein, 1933–1935.   [4] Briquet, 1906.

group of lower rank than a family.   However, this objection is more fancied than real since nobody has recognized subtribes in families where these names would apply.   Certainly, an acceptance of these names for the various classes is preferable to the other alternative, the proposal of an entirely new nomenclature.[1]

The Pteridophyta include the following classes:

Psilophytinae, in which the sporophyte is rootless and has a shoot composed of branches only or of branches and leaves.   The sporangia are borne singly at the tips of elongate branches or at the tips of very much reduced branches.

Lycopodinae, in which the sporophyte is differentiated into root, stem, and leaf.   The leaves are microphyllous and generally spirally arranged. There are no leaf gaps in the vascular cylinder.   Sporangia are borne on the adaxial face of leaves and toward the base.   A leaf bears but one sporangium.

Equisetinae, in which the sporophyte is differentiated into root, stem, and leaf.   The sterile leaves are microphyllous or macrophyllous and are usually in whorls.   There are no leaf gaps in the vascular cylinder. The sporangia are borne on a distinctive type of appendage, the sporangiophore.

Filicinae, in which the sporophyte is differentiated into root, stem, and leaf.   In one or two exceptional genera, roots are lacking on mature plants.   The leaves are macrophyllous and spirally arranged.   The vascular cylinder has leaf gaps.   Sporangia are borne on the margin or the abaxial face of leaves.   A leaf bears many sporangia, and these are generally in clusters (sori).

Bibliography

ALLEN, RUTH F.   **1911.**   *Trans. Wis. Acad.* **17:** 1–56. 6 pl.   [Apogamy.]
ARBER, E. A. N.   **1921.**   Devonian floras.   Cambridge. 100 pp. 47 figs.
BANCROFT, NELLIE.   **1911.**   *Ann. Bot.* **25:** 745–759. 1 pl. 3 figs.   [Vessels.]
BARCLAY, B. D.   **1931.**   *Bot. Gaz.* **91:** 452–461. 19 figs.   [Ontogeny of endodermis.]
BARTOO, D. R.   **1930.**   *Ibid.* **89:** 137–153. 27 figs.   [Ontogeny of endodermis.]
BESSEY, C. E.   **1892.**   Botany. 7th ed.   New York. 611 pp. 573 figs.
BOHLIN, K.   **1901.**   Utkast till de gröna algernas och arkegoniaternas fylogeni. Upsala. 43 pp.
BOODLE, L. A.   **1899.**   *Ann. Bot.* **13:** 377–394. 1 pl.   [Secondary thickening.]
   1901.   *Ibid.* **15:** 359–421. 3 pl.   [Sieve tubes, origin of pith.]
BOWER, F. O.   **1884.**   *Phil. Trans. Roy. Soc. London* **175,** Part 2: 565–615. 4 pl. [Phylogeny of Pteridophyta.]
   1885.   *Jour. Linn. Soc. Bot. London* **21:** 360–368. 2 pl. 6 figs.   [Apospory.]
   1908.   The origin of a land flora.   London. 727 pp. 361 figs.

---

[1] Lycopsida, Sphenopsida, and Pteridopsida are inappropriate for names of classes in the Pteridophyta because they have been used as names of divisions by those who do not separate the vascular plants into Pteridophyta and Spermatophyta.

1911. *Ann. Bot.* **25**: 537–553. 2 pl. [Origin of pith.]

1920. *Proc. Roy. Soc. Edinburgh* **41**: 1–25. 19 figs. [Size and stelar morphology.]

1923. The ferns. Vol. 1. Cambridge. 359 pp. 309 figs.

1923A. *Proc. Roy. Soc. Edinburgh* **43**: 117–126. [Size and stelar morphology.]

1935. Primitive land plants. London. 658 pp. 449 figs.

BREBNER, G. **1902.** *Ann. Bot.* **16**: 517–552. 2 pl. 2 figs. [Stelar theory.]

BRIQUET, J. **1906.** Règles internationales de la nomenclature botanique. Jena. 99 pp.

CAMPBELL, D. H. **1894.** *Ann. Bot.* **8**: 1–20. 2 pl. [Primitive gametophytes.]

1895. The structure and development of the mosses and ferns. 1st ed. New York. 544 pp. 266 figs.

1899. Lectures on the evolution of plants. New York. 319 pp. 60 figs.

1905. The structure and development of mosses and ferns. 2d ed. New York. 657 pp. 322 figs.

1917. *Proc. Nation. Acad. Sci.* (U.S.) **3**: 494–496. [Self-sustaining sporophytes of Bryophyta.]

1924. *Ann. Bot.* **38**: 473–483. 8 figs. [Self-sustaining sporophytes of Bryophyta.]

CHURCH, A. H. **1919.** Thalassiophyta and the subaerial transmigration. Oxford. 95 pp.

DEBARY, A. **1878.** *Bot. Zeitg.* **36**: 449–487. 1 pl. [Apogamy.]

DÖPP, W. **1932.** *Planta* **17**: 86–152. 10 pl. 2 figs. [Apogamy.]

DRUERY, C. T. **1885.** *Jour. Linn. Soc. Bot. London* **21**: 354–357. [Discovery of apospory.]

DUERDEN, H. **1933.** *Ann. Bot.* **47**: 187–195. 1 pl. [Vessels.]

1934. *Ibid.* **48**: 459–465. 1 pl. [Vessels.]

ENGLER, A., and E. GILG. **1924.** Syllabus der Pflanzenfamilien. 10th ed. Berlin. 420 pp. 462 figs.

ENGLER, A., and K. PRANTL. **1898–1902.** Die natürlichen Pflanzenfamilien. I Teil. Abt. 4. Pteridophyta. Leipzig. 808 pp. 481 figs.

FARLOW, W. G. **1874.** *Quart. Jour. Microsc. Sci.* N.S. **14**: 266–272. 2 pl. [Discovery of apogamy.]

FARMER, J. B. and L. DIGBY. **1907.** *Ann. Bot.* **21**: 161–199. 5 pl. [Apospory and apogamy.]

FRITSCH, F. E. **1916.** *New Phytol.* **15**: 233–250. 2 figs. [Origin of Pteridophyta.]

GOEBEL, K. **1908.** Einleitung in die experimentelle Morphologie der Pflanzen. Leipzig. 260 pp. 135 figs.

GWYNNE-VAUGHAN, D. T. **1901.** *Ann. Bot.* **15**: 71–98. 1 pl. [Stelar theory.]

1903. *Ibid.* **17**: 689–742. 3 pl. [Stelar theory.]

1908. *Ibid.* **22**: 517–523. 1 pl. [Vessels.]

1914. *Ibid.* **28**: 351–354. 1 pl. [Origin of pith.]

HARVEY-GIBSON, R. J. **1894.** *Ibid.* **8**: 133–206. 4 pl. [Vessels.]

HUME, E. M. MARGARET. **1912.** *Ibid.* **26**: 573–587. 2 pl. [Sieve tubes.]

JEFFREY, E. C. **1898.** *British Assn. Adv. Sci. Rept. 67th Meeting, Toronto* **1897**: 869–870. [Stelar theory.]

1902. *Phil. Trans. Roy. Soc. London.* Ser. B. **195**: 119–146. 6 pl. [Stelar theory.]

1910. *Bot. Gaz.* **50**: 401–414. 1 pl. [Stelar theory.]

1917. The anatomy of woody plants. Chicago. 478 pp. 306 figs.

LANG, W. H. **1898.** *Phil. Trans. Roy. Soc. London.* Ser. B. **190**: 189–238. 5 pl. [Sporangia on gametophytes.]

LANG, W. H., and ISABEL C. COOKSON. **1935.** *Phil. Trans. Roy. Soc. London.* Ser. B, **224**: 421–449. 4 pl. [Silurian pteridophytes.]

LAWTON, ELVA. **1932.** *Amer. Jour. Bot.* **19**: 303–333. 22 figs. [Apospory.]

LIGNIER, O. **1903.** *Bull. Soc. Linn. Normandie.* 5 ser., **7**: 93. (Cited by Arber, 1921.) [Origin of Pteridophyta.]

LOTSY, J. P. **1909.** Vorträge über botanische Stammesgeschichte. Bd. 2. Jena. 901 pp. 553 figs.

LOUGHRIDGE, G. A. **1932.** *Bot. Gaz.* **93**: 188–196. 24 figs. [Tracheids.]

PACE, LULA. **1910.** *Ibid.* **50**: 49–58. 11 figs. [Sporangia on gametophytes.]

PETRY, L. C. **1914.** *Ibid.* **57**: 169–192. 16 figs. [Origin of pith.]

PRIESTLEY, J. H., and EDITH E. NORTH. **1922.** *New Phytol.* **21**: 113–139. 5 figs. [Endodermis.]

PRIESTLEY, J. H., and FRANCES M. RADCLIFFE. **1924.** *Ibid.* **23**: 161–193. 12 figs. [Endodermis.]

SCHENCK, H. **1908.** *Bot. Jahrb.* **42**: 1–37. 25 figs. [Origin of Pteridophyta.]

SCOTT, D. H. **1900.** Studies in fossil botany. 1st ed. London. 533 pp. 151 figs.

STEIL, W. N. **1919.** *Ann. Bot.* **33**: 109–132. 3 pl. [Apogamy.]

1919A. *Bot. Gaz.* **67**: 469–482. 2 pl. 4 figs. [Apospory.]

STOKEY, ALMA G. **1918.** *Ibid.* **65**: 97–102. 10 figs. [Apogamy.]

STRASBURGER, E. **1907.** *Flora* **97**: 123–191. 6 pl. [Apogamy.]

STRASBURGER, E., F. NOLL, H. SCHENCK, and A. F. W. SCHIMPER. **1921.** Lehrbuch der Botanik. 15th ed. Jena. 701 pp. 849 figs.

TANSLEY, A. G. **1907–1908.** *New Phytol.* **6**: 25–35, 53–68, 109–120, 135–155, 187–203, 219–238, 253–269. 75 figs. **7**: 1–16, 29–40. 5 figs. [Stelar theory.]

THOMPSON, J. McL. **1920.** *Trans. Roy. Soc. Edinburgh* **52**: 715–735. 4 pl. 9 figs. [Stelar theory.]

VAN TIEGHEM, P., and H. DOULIOT. **1886.** *Ann. Sci. Nat. Bot.* 7 ser. **3**: 275–322. 3 pl. [Stelar theory.]

WARDLAW, C. W. **1924.** *Trans. Roy. Soc. Edinburgh* **53**: 503–532. 18 figs. [Size and stelar morphology.]

1925. *Ibid.* **54**: 281–308. 17 figs. [Size and stelar morphology.]

1928. *Ibid.* **56**: 19–56. 22 figs. [Size and stelar morphology.]

WARMING, E. **1895.** A handbook of systematic botany. Translated by M. C. Potter. London. 620 pp. 610 figs.

WETTSTEIN, R. VON. **1903–1908.** Handbuch der Systematischen Botanik. 2d ed. Bd. 2. Leipzig. 577 pp. 365 figs.

1933–1935. *Ibid.* 4th ed. Leipzig. 1149 pp. 709 figs.

WORDSELL, W. C. **1902.** *Bot. Gaz.* **34**: 216–223. 7 figs. [Stelar theory.]

WRIGHT, GERTRUDE. **1920.** *Ibid.* **69**: 237–247. 2 pl. 6 figs. [Vessels.]

YAMANOUCHI, S. **1908.** *Ibid.* **45**: 289–318. 2 pl. 3 figs. [Apogamy.]

ZIMMERMANN, W. **1930.** Die Phylogenie der Pflanzen. Jena. 452 pp. 250 figs.

CHAPTER VI

PSILOPHYTINAE

Sporophytes of Psilophytinae are rootless and have a shoot composed of branches alone or of branches and leaves. The sporangia are borne singly and either at the tips of elongate branches or at the tips of very much reduced branches. The gametophytes (known only from the two living genera) are subterranean and colorless.

For over half a century paleobotanists considered *Psilophyton*[1] a genus of questionable validity. This was due not so much to an incomplete description of the plant as to the fact that it was so unlike any other known plant, living or fossil. The significance of this peculiar plant became apparent some 20 years ago with the discovery[2] of well-petrified remains of other plants of a similar nature.[3] There was soon a realization that the land flora of the early Devonian was of a distinctive type[4] and composed of plants unlike those found in later geological ages. The presence of these fossil plants in such widely separated localities as Eastern Canada,[1] Wyoming,[5] Scotland,[2] Western Europe,[6] and Australia[7] shows that they must have been widespread during the period that they lived. Plants of a similar type have recently been discovered[7] in the Silurian.

Members of the psilophytan flora were vascular plants containing a distinct central axis of xylem with typical tracheids. They differed from other vascular plants in that they were rootless. The plant body was generally differentiated into a subterranean and an aerial portion. In most cases the subterranean portion was rhizome-like with elongate unicellular rhizoids. The aerial portion was sparingly to profusely branched. Most genera had leafless aerial shoots but some of them had the shoots closely beset with small leaves. The sporangia were always strictly terminal in position and borne singly at the tips of branches.

The occurrence of spores in tetrads within sporangia of certain of these fossil plants shows that the plant body was a sporophyte. Since the sporophyte was a vascular plant independent from the gametophyte at maturity, these plants are to be placed among the Pteridophyta. In

[1] Dawson, 1859.   [2] Kidston and Lang, 1917.

[3] The changed attitude toward *Psilophyton* before and after Kidston and Lang's discoveries is well illustrated by Scott (1900, 1920) and by Seward (1910, 1933).

[4] Arber, 1921.   [5] Dorf, 1933.

[6] Halle, 1916; Kräusel and Weyland, 1926.   [7] Lang and Cookson, 1930.

spite of the diversity of external form of the plant body all of the Early and Middle Devonian plants related to *Psilophyton* are referred to a single order, the Psilophytales. This order in turn is placed in a special class, the Psilophytinae. The only other Pteridophyta with a claim for inclusion in the Psilophytinae are two living genera, *Psilotum* and *Tmesipteris*, the only members of the Psilotales. The systematic position of the Psilotales was a troublesome question before it was realized that the Psilophytinae are a class distinct from other Pteridophyta. Before the Psilophytinae were recognized, the Psilotales were variously placed in the lycopodian series,[1] in the equisetaceous series,[2] and in a series independent from other Pteridophyta.[3] Since the recognition of the distinctiveness of the Psilophytales, the Psilotales have either been considered more or less closely related to them[4] or have been placed in a special class.[5] Among the reasons for including the Psilotales in the Psilophytinae are the rootless plant body and the simple vascular system. The lack of roots among the Psilotales is thought to be due to the primitiveness of the sporophyte and not to the evolutionary obliteration of roots that is found in certain ferns, notably *Salvinia* (page 353).

According to the manner in which they are interpreted, the sporangia furnish evidence for or against including the Psilotales in the Psilophytinae. If, as seems to be the case, they are borne terminally on branches, it is another reason for considering the Psilotales related to the Psilophytales.

The Psilophytinae are the simplest of the Pteridophyta. Furthermore, the simplicity is of a fundamentally primitive type, and, irrespective of whether they were derived from the Bryophyta or from the algae (page 114), there is good reason for considering them the basic stock from which all other classes of Pteridophyta have been evolved.

As noted above the living Psilophytinae and the fossil genera of the Devonian are placed in separate orders.

ORDER 1.   PSILOPHYTALES

The Psilophytales had a rootless dichotomously branched plant body that was generally differentiated into a subterranean and an aerial portion. The aerial portion was leafless or with numerous small leaves. The sporangia were borne singly and at the tips of all aerial branches or at the ends of certain branches only. All genera are fossil and most of them are known only from the Early and Middle Devonian.

[1] Campbell, 1918; Jeffrey, 1917.
[2] Bower, 1908; Scott, 1900; Thomas, 1902.   [3] Seward, 1910.
[4] Kidston and Lang, 1920*A*; Kräusel and Weyland, 1923; Zimmermann, 1930.
[5] Hirmer, 1927; Seward, 1933; Wettstein, 1933–1935.

Psilophytales have been found in the Silurian,[1] and there is a possibility that they arose in earlier geological periods. They were widespread during the first half of the Devonian and seem to have been the sole vascular plants during the early part of this era. The type of plant thus evolved was well adapted to a terrestrial mode of life, and the geological record shows that they inhabited many of the land areas of that geological period. Equally striking is the sudden disappearance of this primitive type of plant from the land flora after the Middle Devonian. Thus far we have no record of a typical member of the Psilophytales after the Middle Devonian. The obvious answer for this sudden disappearance of the Psilophytales from the land flora is their being crowded out by other plants that were better suited to land conditions of the time. However, this is too glib an answer, and, despite the negative geological record, it is much more probable that remnants of this flora were present in the Later Devonian and Early Carboniferous.

At the present time new genera are being discovered so rapidly that any scheme of classification of the Psilophytales is tentative. The order has been divided into five[2] and into three[3] families. The former seems to be the more logical, except for the division of the Rhyniaceae into two families.

FAMILY 1. RHYNIACEAE

Members of the Rhyniaceae had a plant body that was small and differentiated into a subterranean and an aerial portion. The subterranean portion was rhizome- or corm-like and with numerous unicellular rhizoids.

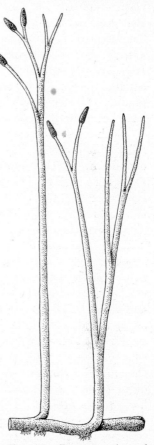

Fig. 78.—Reconstruction of *Rhynia major* Kidston and Lang. (*Based upon Kidston and Lang,* 1921.)

The aerial portion was leafless and with dichotomously forked cylindrical branches. The sporangia, which were indehiscent and had a jacket layer several cells in thickness, were borne terminally on the branch apices.

[1] Lang and Cookson, 1935.   [2] Hirmer, 1927; Kräusel and Weyland, 1929.
[3] Wettstein, 1933–1935.

Rhynia, the type genus of this family, is known only from a single Middle Devonian deposit in Scotland.   However, the numerous specimens of the two species that have been found at this station[1] are so excellently preserved that they give considerable information concerning the form and structure of this very primitive vascular plant.   *Rhynia* was a rootless vascular plant (with a maximum height of about 20 cm.) that grew in swampy marshes comparable to the peat marshes of today.[2] The plant body consisted of a horizontal rhizome whose branches turned gradually or abruptly upward and became leafless aerial shoots (Fig. 78). Rhizoids were borne in patches on the underside of the rhizome.   The aerial branches were dichotomously forked, cylindrical, and tapered gradually.   Elongate sporangia, resembling those of certain Hepaticae, were borne at the tips of the ultimate dichotomies of the aerial branches.

Both the subterranean and the aerial portions of the plant were internally differentiated into epidermis, cortex, and stele, but there was no endodermal layer separating the latter two.   The stele was protostelic and with a cylindrical mass of xylem completely ensheathed by a phloem layer several cells in thickness (Fig. 79*A*).   The xylem contained tracheids only.   The preservation of tracheids is imperfect in most specimens but in certain cases they show an annular thickening on their walls.[3]   Some specimens have all tracheids of the same diameter, other specimens have the peripheral tracheids greater in diameter than those at the center of the xylem.[4]   The phloem layer was generally four to five cells in thickness and composed of elongate thin-walled cells with diagonal end walls.   The cortex, which had a diameter about tenfold that of the stele, was differentiated into an inner and an outer portion.   The inner cortex was much thicker than the outer and consisted of spherical cells separated from one another by fairly large intercellular spaces.   It is thought that this was the chief photosynthetic tissue of the plant.   The outer cortex, which was one to four cells in thickness, was composed of large angular cells without conspicuous intercellular spaces except immediately internal to the stomata.   The epidermal layer was one cell in thickness and with a conspicuous cuticle on the free face.   As seen in surface view, the epidermal cells were broadly fusiform and in more or less regular transverse series.   Here and there in the epidermis of aerial branches were pairs of guard cells surrounding a stoma.

Numerous detached sporangia of *Rhynia* have been found, but it is not known whether these were borne on all or only on certain of the aerial branches.   The sporangia were always borne singly and at the terminus of a branch.   They were cylindrical and with a diameter somewhat greater than that of the subtending branch tip (Fig. 79*B*).   A sporangium

---

[1] Kidston and Lang, 1917, 1920*A*, 1921.   [2] Kidston and Lang, 1921*A*.
[3] Kidston and Lang, 1917.   [4] Kidston and Lang, 1920.

had a jacket layer several cells in thickness in which the cells of the outermost layer were thick-walled and had a heavy cuticle. The sporangia were indehiscent, and liberation of spores seems to have taken place by a decay of the jacket layer. The sporangial cavity, which was without a columella, contained many spores, all of which were of the same size. In some specimens the spores within the sporangium are united in tetrads, in other specimens they lie free from one another.

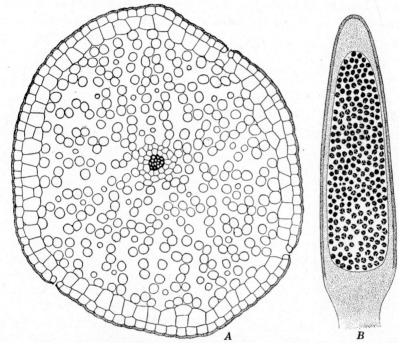

Fig. 79.—*Rhynia Gwynne-Vaughani* Kidston and Lang. *A*, semidiagrammatic transverse section of an aerial branch. *B*, longitudinal section of a capsule. (*A*, × 60; *B*, × 6.)

If the sporangia and fragments of the subtending branch were the only known portions of the plant body, one would unquestionably assign *Rhynia* to the Bryophyta. The resemblance of these sporangia to those of Bryophyta is even more marked in *Hornea*, a genus belonging to the Rhyniaceae and discovered in the deposits containing *Rhynia*. Sporangia of *Hornea*[1] resemble those of *Rhynia* in general appearance but differ in that they contain a well-defined columella that extends nearly to the apex of the sporangial cavity.

FAMILY 2. PSEUDOSPOROCHNACEAE

The Pseudosporochnaceae were relatively large, rootless shrubs with a conspicuous main trunk terminating in several dichotomously forked

[1] Kidston and Lang, 1920.

main branches. These, in turn, bore many leafless branchlets, the ultimate dichotomies of which terminated in sporangia.

The single genus of this family, *Pseudosporochnus*, is known from the Middle Devonian of Bohemia, Scotland, and the eastern part of the United States.[1] Reconstructions based upon fragments seem to show that

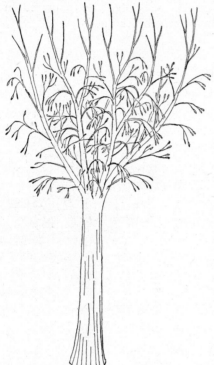

it was tree-like in habit and some three meters tall when conditions for development were favorable.

The tree-like plant body had a conspicuous, longitudinally fluted trunk with a bulbous base that was without roots or root-like branches (Fig. 80). The trunk was unbranched for a considerable distance and then forked rather abruptly into several large branches. It is uncertain[1] whether the trunk and its main branches were woody and with secondary thickening or were herbaceous in nature. Each of the main branches was leafless and with a repeated dichotomous branching. The ultimate branchlets were of a hair-like fineness, and many of them were swollen at their tips. These swellings have been thought to be leaves, but maceration of fossilized swollen branch tips shows that they were sporangia containing spores 4 to 7μ in diameter.[1]

F<small>IG.</small> 80.—Reconstruction of *Pseudosporochnus Krejcii* Potonié and Bernard. (*After Krausel and Weyland, 1933.*)

FAMILY 3. PSILOPHYTACEAE

The Psilophytaceae had a plant body that was relatively small and differentiated into a rhizome and aerial branches. The aerial branches were dichotomously forked, flattened or cylindrical, and sometimes beset with spines. The sporangia had a jacket layer several cells in thickness and were borne terminally at the tips of certain branches.

Among the several genera of the family is *Psilophyton*, the first-discovered member of the order. This genus has been found in Lower Devonian deposits[2] at several widely separated stations in both the

---

[1] Kräusel and Weyland, 1933.   [2] Dorf, 1933.

Eastern and Western Hemispheres. *Psilophyton* has not been found in as well-preserved a condition as has *Rhynia*, but the degree of preservation is sufficient to give some idea of the internal structure. The plants appear to have been gregarious in habit and to have grown on swampy ground. The plant body had a prostrate rhizome that bore erect branches (Fig. 81). The rhizome was rootless but with numerous rhizoids. The

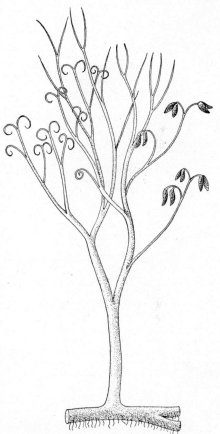

erect branches were dichotomously forked, and their growing tips sometimes had the spiral uncoiling (circinate vernation) found in growing tips of fern leaves. Some species had smooth branches, others had the branches beset with spiny outgrowths.[1] Careful study of these spine-like outgrowths shows[2] that they were neither leaf-like nor branch-like but were excrescent outgrowths. The suggestion has been made that they were glandular in function. At the center of a branch was a central cylinder composed of annular tracheids. External to this was a cortex, parenchymatous in the inner portion and with elongate thick-walled cells in the outer portion. The epidermal layer of the stem contained stomata.

As is the case with other Psilophytales, the sporangia were borne at the tips of branches. Frequently they were in pairs because of a forking of the branch just back of the sporangial region. The sporangia were obovoid in shape, had a blunt or an acute apex, and were considerably

Fig. 81.—Reconstruction of *Psilophyton princeps* Dawson. (*Based upon Dawson,* 1859, 1888.)

broader than the subtending branch. The sporangial jacket, several cells in thickness, opened at maturity. Spores within the same sporangium were somewhat variable in size,[2] but this is not to be taken as an incipient heterospory.

[1] Dawson, 1859; Dorf, 1933. [2] Lang, 1931.

FAMILY 4. ASTEROXYLACEAE

The Asteroxylaceae had a plant body with a prostrate rhizome bearing two kinds of branches: one leafless and subterranean, the other erect and having many small leaves. The sporangia were dehiscent and had a jacket layer several cells in thickness. It is very probable that they were borne at the tips of leafless branchlets.

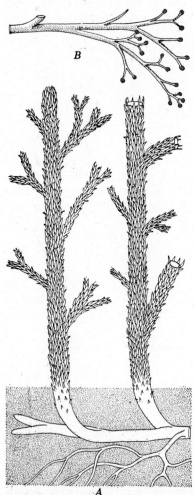

The Asteroxylaceae, with the single genus *Asteroxylon*, differ so markedly from other Psilophytales that they might well be placed in a separate order. There are two species of *Asteroxylon*: *A. Mackiei* Kidston and Lang, found in Middle Devonian deposits at Rhynie, Scotland;[1] and *A. elberfeldense* Kräusel and Weyland, found in Middle Devonian deposits near Elberfeld, Germany.[2] Although differing somewhat in appearance the two obviously belong to the same genus.

Asteroxylon had a horizontal, subterranean, leafless, dichotomously branched rhizome. The tips of certain dichotomies of the rhizome grew upward toward the air and developed into branched aerial shoots that were closely beset with small leaves (Fig. 82*A*). Tips of other dichotomies developed into slender, leafless, repeatedly forked, subterranean branches that resemble the rhizophores of the Lycopidinae (page 182). These branches probably functioned in a root-like manner. According to the species, the leafy shoots had a pronounced or an obscure dichotomous branching. One species had the branch tips clothed with leaves,[1] the other had naked, circinately vernate, branch apices. Although it is known that the sporangia were borne at the tips of leafless aerial branches, it is uncertain

Fig. 82.—Reconstruction of *Asteroxylon Mackiei* Kidston and Lang. *A*, rhizome and vegetative branches. *B*, a fertile branch. (*Based upon* Kidston and Lang, 1921.)

[1] Kidston and Lang, 1920*A*; 1921.   [2] Kräusel and Weyland, 1926.

whether these dichotomously forked branches (Fig. 82*B*) were borne terminally or laterally on the leafy shoots.

The rhizome portion of the plant body was cylindrical and had a structure similar to that of *Rhynia* when seen in cross section. The leafy branches had a more complex internal organization. Similar to the rhizome, they were internally differentiated into central cylinder and cortex (Fig. 83). The central cylinder was a mesarch actinostele. The xylem was 4- to 10-rayed and had a small mass of protoxylem a short distance inward from the outer face of each ray. Except for occasional

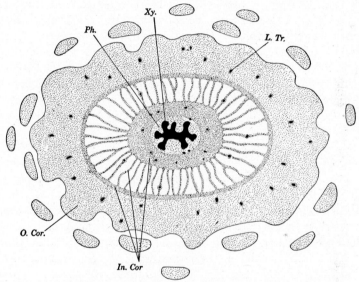

Fig. 83.—Transverse section of a leafy shoot of *Asteroxylon Mackiei* Kidston and Lang. (*In. Cor.*, inner cortex; *L. Tr.*, leaf traces; *O. Cor.*, outer cortex; *Ph.*, phloem; *Xy.*, xylem.) (× 6.)

annular tracheids in the protoxylem, the entire xylem mass was composed of spiral tracheids. The xylem was encircled by a layer of phloem that was thin external to the xylem rays and thick between them. It is thought[1] that the phloem was composed of long, thin-walled, tubular cells with pointed or with transverse end walls. Small leaf traces were given off from the arms of the xylem. A leaf trace extended diagonally upward through the phloem to the base of a veinless leaf. Leaf traces were concentric in organization and had a layer of phloem completely ensheathing an endarch cylinder of xylem. Aerial shoots had their cortices differentiated into an outer and an inner portion. The outer cortex, except for the leaf traces, was a more or less homogeneous parenchymatous tissue. The inner cortex consisted of three concentric regions: an outer

[1] Kidston and Lang, 1920*A*.

layer of tangentially compressed cells, a middle radially septate layer with conspicuous radially elongate intercellular spaces, and a broad homogeneous inner layer. The epidermal layer of the shoot was one cell in thickness and contained stomata.

Fragments of slender, leafless, dichotomously forked branches with sporangia at their tips have been found intermingled with *Asteroxylon*.[1] These are generally considered the fruiting portion of the plant, but their connection with leafy shoots has not been established beyond all doubt. The sporangia were pear-shaped with the narrow end attached to the branch tip. The sporangia had a jacket several cells in thickness, in which the epidermal cells over the sporangial apex had thickened radial and inner tangential walls. The apical dehiscence of mature sporangia seems to have been due to hygroscopic changes in these annulus-like cells. The sporangial cavity was without a columella and contained a considerable number of spores. These were developed in tetrads and were about 65μ in diameter when mature.

ORDER 2. PSILOTALES

The Psilotales have a rootless, dichotomously branched, sporophyte that is generally differentiated into a rhizome and an aerial shoot. The aerial shoots may be leafless or may bear many small leaves. The sporangia are borne in diads or triads and directly upon the stem or at the bases of leaves. The gametophytes are subterranean and without chlorophyll. The antheridia lie partially embedded in the gametophyte.

This order contains but two rather closely related genera, *Psilotum* and *Tmesipteris*, both of which are known only in the living condition. They are placed in a single family, the Psilotaceae. *Tmesipteris*, found in Australia, New Zealand, and certain smaller Pacific Ocean islands, is generally regarded as having but one species, *T. tannensis* Bernh. (Fig. 84*C*). Several species have been described for *Psilotum*, but these are usually reduced to two, *P. triquetrum* Sw. (Fig. 84*A*) and *P. flaccidum* Wall. The two species of *Psilotum* are widespread in tropical and subtropical regions of both hemispheres, but *P. triquetrum* is the commoner of the two. Both genera are usually epiphytic in habit and grow upon tree ferns, but all species may also be terrestrial and grow in soil or in the crevices of rocks.

Both genera have rootless brown rhizomes with a repeated dichotomous branching in which the tip of any dichotomy may develop into a green aerial shoot. The rhizome generally contains a mycorhizal fungus.

Aerial shoots of epiphytic individuals are usually pendant, those of terrestrial individuals are frequently erect. The aerial shoots are quite different in the two genera. In *Tmesipteris* the shoot is generally

[1] Kidston and Lang, 1920*A*.

unbranched and only rarely has a single dichotomy. Near its attachment to the rhizome, the shoot has minute, scale-like leaves; farther up a shoot the leaves are progressively larger and more broadly lanceolate. Most of the leaves toward the distal end of a shoot are bifurcate and have a pair of sporangia in their axils (Fig. 84*D–E*). This fertile portion of the plant is sometimes called a "strobilus," but it is a very lax structure as compared with strobili of lycopods. The aerial shoot of *Psilotum*

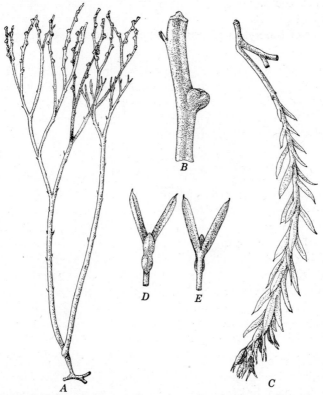

Fig. 84.—*A–B, Psilotum triquetrum* Sw. *A*, portion of a shoot. *B*, portion of a shoot with a sporangium in the axil of a leaf. *C–E, Tmesipteris tannensis* Bernh. *C*, portion of a pendant shoot. *D–E*, ventral and dorsal view of leaf and sporangia. (*A*, × ½; *B*, × 4; *C*, × ⅘; *D–E*, × 2½.)

regularly has several dichotomous branchings. The basal portion of the shoot is cylindrical; the distal green portion may be radially symmetrical and longitudinally ribbed (*P. triquetrum*), or it may be markedly flattened (*P. flaccidum*). Leaves on aerial branches of *Psilotum* are small, scale-like, and more or less irregular in distribution. The sporangia are borne in triads on very short stalks and in the axils of minute bifid leaves. Most of them lie toward the apices of aerial branches, but occasional ones may be relatively low on a branch.

Apices of rhizomes and aerial branches in both genera have a single apical cell with three cutting faces.[1] Mature portions of rhizomes of both genera are actinostelic and have a relatively simple cortex surrounding the stele.

Aerial branches of *Psilotum*[2] are also actinostelic. In these branches the boundaries between stele and cortex are sharply delimited by an endodermal layer with distinct Casparian strips in the radial walls (Fig. 85). The xylem is actinostelic, generally with six rays. It is exarch in arrangement and has a few protoxylem elements at the tip of each ray. The center of the xylem mass is composed of thick-walled sclerenchyma

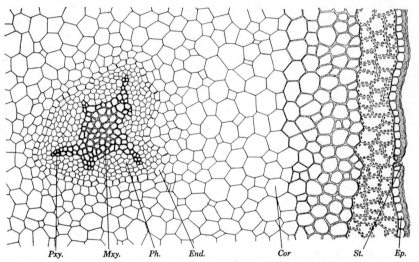

Pxy.   Mxy.   Ph.   End.   Cor   St.   Ep.

FIG. 85.—Transverse section of stele and portion of the cortex of *Psilotum triquetrum* Sw. (*Cor.*, cortex; *End.*, endodermis; *Ep.*, epidermis; *Mxy.*, metaxylem; *Ph.*, phloem; *Pxy*, protoxylem; *St.*, stoma.) (× 80.)

fibers with simple pits in their walls.[3] The thin-walled elements between endodermis and xylem are vertically elongate cells. This tissue is usually called the phloem, but typical sieve tubes have not been demonstrated in it.[2] In some cases there are a few secondary xylem elements between the phloem and the primary xylem.[4] The cortex in aerial branches of *P. triquetrum* is thin-walled and without intercellular spaces for a considerable distance external to the endodermis; outward from this the cells have thicker and thicker walls. The sclerenchymatous portion of the cortex is abruptly succeeded by thin-walled cells with numerous chloroplasts. This photosynthetic portion of the branch is two to five cells in breadth and composed of vertically elongate cells with small

---

[1] Ford, 1904; Holloway, 1918.   [2] Ford, 1904; Stiles, 1910.
[3] Ford, 1904.   [4] Boodle, 1904; Stiles, 1910.

intercellular spaces between the vertical walls. The epidermis is one cell in thickness and heavily cutinized. Stomata are found chiefly in the grooves between longitudinal ridges of the stem.

Aerial branches of *Tmesipteris* have no well-defined endodermal layer.[1] The vascular cylinder is solenostelic and has a small mass of thin-walled parenchyma (*pith*) internal to the tracheids (Fig. 86). Vigorously growing branches have the xylem in a definite cylinder and five small groups of

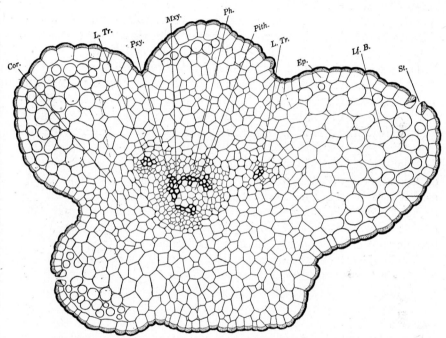

FIG. 86.—Transverse section of shoot of *Tmesipteris tannensis* Bernh. (*Cor.*, cortex; *Ep.*, epidermis; *L. Tr.*, leaf trace; *Lf. B.*, leaf base; *Mxy.*, metaxylem; *Ph.*, phloem; *Pxy.*, protoxylem; *St.*, stoma.) (× 80.)

mesarch protoxylem in the cylinder. The xylem of the stele becomes inconspicuous toward the apices of branches and consists largely of traces departing to the leaves. The major portion of the phloem is composed of sieve tubes with sieve plates on their lateral walls. These sieve tubes are atypical in that they have lignified walls. Leaf traces have their xylem mesarch in arrangement and ensheathed by a layer of phloem after the leaves have departed from the stele. The cortex is composed of angular cells without intercellular spaces, and the epidermis is one cell in thickness, heavily cutinized, and without stomata. Outer portions of branches that belong more to the leaf base than to the cortex have stomata in the

[1] Sykes, 1908.

epidermal layer and conspicuous intercellular spaces in the subepidermal tissue.

Leaves of *Tmesipteris* have a single vascular bundle, continuous with the trace from the stele.   As seen in cross section, a leaf bundle has four or five scalariform tracheids surrounding one or two narrow protoxylem elements.   The xylem is surrounded by phloem, and this, in turn, is ensheathed by a poorly defined endodermal layer.[1]   All mesophyll cells in the flattened blade are angular in outline and have small intercellular spaces.   The epidermal layer has its stomata somewhat sunken below the surface of the blade.   One form of *T. tannensis* has stomata on both faces of the blade; the other form has them only on the adaxial face.   Leaves of *Psilotum* are always small and simple in structure.   The surface layer of the leaf is a cutinized epidermis without stomata.   The interior of the leaf consists entirely of a parenchyma similar in appearance to the photosynthetic tissue of the branch.[2]   The leaves are without a vein, but in *P. flaccidum*[3] there is a leaf trace which terminates just below the leaf base.

Sporangia of *Tmesipteris* are borne in pairs at the bases of large bifid appendages (Fig. 84*D–E*); those of *Psilotum* are in triads on minute bifid appendages (Fig. 84*B*).   Because they are fused with one another, the group of sporangia is sometimes called a *synangium*, but the application of this term to the Psilotales is misleading since the structure is not homologous with the synangium of marattiaceous ferns (page 279).

Three views have been expressed concerning the nature of the fructification in the Psilotales: (1) it is a small branch bearing two leaves and a plurilocular sporangium;[4] (2) it is a bifid sporophyll with a di- or trilocular sporangium;[5] (3) the so-called synangium is a sporangiophore and one that is fused with a subtending bifid bract.[6]   The available evidence seems to indicate that the last named of the three is the most probable.   First of all, stages in the early ontogeny show that there are separate sporangia, not one septate sporangium.   The regular occurrence of a vascular supply in the short pedicel subtending the two (or three) sporangia and the occurrence of occasional individuals with elongate pedicels seem to show that the pedicels are homologous with those in equisetaceous sporangiophores (page 223).   Additional evidence that the "synangia" are sporangiophores is seen in aberrant fructifications. These include repeatedly forked "sporophylls" bearing two or three synangia, and cases in which the synangium is replaced by a leaf lobe of normal appearance.   If the paired sporangia of *Tmesipteris* are in reality a sporangiophore, it is one with a single dichotomy in which the end of

[1] Sykes, 1908.   [2] Ford, 1904.   [3] Stiles, 1910.   [4] Juränyi, 1871.
[5] Bower, 1894; Solms-Laubach, 1884.
[6] Bower, 1935; Eames, 1936; Scott, 1900; Sykes, 1908; Thomas, 1902.

each fork develops into a sporangium; that of *Psilotum* has the end of one arm of the first dichotomy developing into a sporangium and the other arm forking again and both tips developing into sporangia. Union between the subtending bract and the sporangiophore is more complete in Psilotales than it is in Equisetinae. In the Psilotales the vascular supply of bract and sporangiophore are united, not independent as in the Equisetinae.

There are evident homologies between the fructifications of Psilotales and plant bodies of Psilophytales in which one dichotomy of a branch system is fertile and the other sterile. A condensation of a fertile psilo-

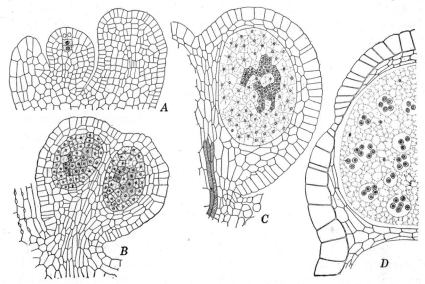

Fig. 87.—*Psilotum triquetrum* Sw. *A*, vertical section of a stem apex bearing a young leaf and a sporangiophore. *B–C*, vertical sections of sporangiophores at later stages of development. *D*, transverse section of an older sporangiophore. (× 50.)

phytan dichotomy to a condition where there are very short branches terminating in sporangia would result in a psilotan sporangiophore; flattening and reduction of the sterile portion of a psilophytan shoot would result in the bract (or pair of bracts) subtending the psilotan sporangiophore.

In very early stages of development it is impossible to tell whether a meristematic lateral outgrowth just back from a stem apex will develop into a fructification or into a foliage leaf.[1] In the case of *Psilotum* the bract subtending a sporangiophore is well along toward maturity before the sporangiophore begins to develop. A sporangiophore of *Psilotum* is first recognizable as a small meristematic hump on the adaxial face of a bract and near its base. Growth of a sporangiophore is said[1] to be due

[1] Bower, 1894.

to an apical cell with three cutting faces, but this cell, if present, is not generally recognizable. The sporangia are differentiated early in the ontogeny of a sporangiophore. Judging from very early stages in sporangial development (Fig. 87A), each of the three sporangia is developed from a single epidermal cell of the sporangiophore. Irrespective of whether formed from one or more than one cell, the first plane of division is periclinal. The outer daughter cell is the *jacket initial;* the inner cell is the *archesporial (primary sporogenous) cell.* Repeated periclinal and anticlinal division of the jacket initial results in a jacket layer four to five cells in thickness (Fig. 87B–D). Division and redivision of the archesporial cell produces a large number of sporogenous cells. Unlike most other Pteridophyta, neither the outermost sporogenous cells nor the

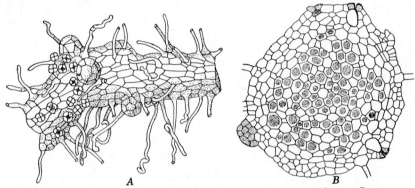

FIG. 88.—*Tmesipteris tannensis* Bernh. *A*, surface view of a gametophyte. *B*, transverse section of a gametophyte. (*A, after Lawson, 1917A; B, after Holloway, 1918.*)

innermost jacket cells develops into a tapetum. As the sporangium approaches maturity, irregular groups of cells in the sporogenous tissue become densely filled with cytoplasm, divide repeatedly, and ultimately give rise to the spore mother cells (Fig. 87B–C). The remaining sporogenous cells, whose protoplasts are watery, divide slowly and disintegrate into a plasmodial mass as the spores are being formed (Fig. 87B–D). Spore formation is accompanied by a thickening of cell walls in the epidermal layer of the jacket except in a small vertical row. This row, running from base to apex of the sporangium, is the future line of longitudinal dehiscence of the sporangium (Fig. 87D).

Gametophytes of Psilotales are subterranean in habit, devoid of chlorophyll, and saprophytic in nutrition through the agency of symbiotic phycomycetous fungi in their cells. This mycorhizal mode of nutrition is not peculiar to the order since it is also found in *Lycopodium* and in certain eusporangiate ferns. The gametophytes are irregularly cylindrical in shape with one or two irregular dichotomous branchings (Fig. 88A). The entire surface of the thallus is covered with long unicellular rhizoids.

Each branch is meristematic at its apex and a definite apical cell has been reported for *Tmesipteris*.[1] There is little internal differentiation of tissues within a gametophyte. The epidermis and a subepidermal layer three to four cells in breadth are rich in starch, free from fungi, and composed of relatively small cells (Fig. 88*B*). The remaining internal cells of a gametophyte are larger and densely packed with the mycorhizal fungus. Antheridia and archegonia are borne on the same gametophyte and indiscriminately intermingled with one another. Sex organs usually begin to develop in the region immediately posterior to the growing apex,

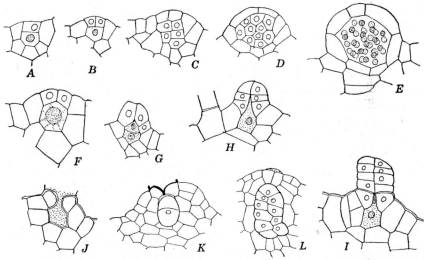

FIG. 89.—*Tmesipteris tannensis* Bernh. *A–E*, vertical sections of antheridia at various stages of development. *F–J*, vertical sections of archegonia at various stages of development. *K–L*, vertical sections of young embryos. (*A–J*, × 115; *K–L*, × 75.) (*A–J*, after *Holloway*, 1918; *K–L*, after *Holloway*, 1921.)

but young developing organs may also be found intermingled with mature ones.

In *Tmesipteris*[2] where the development of sex organs has been studied more fully than in *Psilotum*,[3] an antheridial initial is a superficial cell of the gametophyte. It divides periclinally into an outer cell, the *jacket initial*, and an inner cell, the *primary androgonial cell* (Fig. 89*A*). Division and redivision of the primary androgonial cell results in a large number of androgonial cells, the last cell generation of which are the *androcytes* (Fig. 89*C–E*). The presence of a blepharoplast during the metamorphosis of androcytes into antherozoids has not been established with certainty,[4] but it is known that the antherozoids of both genera are

[1] Holloway, 1918.   [2] Holloway, 1918; 1921; Lawson, 1917, 1917*A*.
[3] Darnell-Smith, 1917; Lawson. 1917*A*.   [4] Lawson, 1917*A*.

multiflagellate and spirally coiled.[1] Development of the androgonial tissue is accompanied by an anticlinal division and redivision of the jacket initial to form a jacket layer one cell in thickness (Fig. 89*B–E*). At the center of a mature jacket layer is a triangular *opercular cell* whose eventual disintegration provides an opening for escape of the antherozoids. Mature antheridia of Psilotales project in a dome-like manner above the gametophyte. They appear to be of an emergent type, but in reality they are of the same embedded type as those of *Lycopodium, Equisetum,* and the eusporangiate ferns.

The archegonial initial of *Tmesipteris* is also a superficial cell of the gametophyte. The first division of this initial is periclinal and into a *primary cover cell* and a *central cell*. By two successive anticlinal divisions the primary cover cell gives rise to four quadrately arranged *neck initials* (Fig. 89*F*). Periclinal division of each of the neck initials results in an archegonial neck four or five cells in height (Fig. 89*G–I*). Development of neck initials into a neck is accompanied by a periclinal division of the central cell into a *primary canal cell* and a *primary ventral cell* (Fig. 89*G*). The primary canal cell elongates vertically as the neck develops, but it is uncertain[2] whether or not it divides to form two canal cells. The behavior of the primary ventral cell is also in doubt. The scanty data at hand seem to show that it functions directly as the egg and does not undergo the usual division into ventral canal cell and egg. As the archegonia approach maturity, there is a cutinization of cell walls in the lowermost tier of neck cells (Fig. 89*I*) and a sloughing off of all neck cells above them. Sloughing off of the upper portion of the neck, together with disintegration of the canal cell (or cells), leaves a passageway for entrance of antherozoids into the venter of the archegonium (Fig. 89*J*).

Development of the sporophyte[3] begins with a division of the zygote in a plane at right angles to the long axis of the archegonium (Fig. 89*K*). The lower daughter cell, that farthest from the archegonial neck, develops into the *foot*. This portion of the embryo is sharply distinguishable through all developmental stages until the young sporophyte becomes an independent plant. The upper daughter cell of the zygote develops into the shoot portion of the sporophyte. Unlike other Pteridophyta, there is no formation of a root, a primary leaf, or a suspensor during embryonal stages. The first division of the cell developing into the foot is in a plane perpendicular to the preceding plane of division. Subsequent divisions in the two halves of the foot are in irregular sequence (Figs. 89*K*, 90*A–C*). As the foot develops, it becomes cylindrical in shape and about as broad as long. Superficial cells on free faces of the foot elongate into short haustoria that burrow into abutting gametophytic tissue. The *Antho-*

---

[1] Darnell-Smith, 1917; Lawson, 1917, 1917*A*.

[2] Holloway, 1918; Lawson, 1917*A*.   [3] Holloway, 1918, 1921.

ceros-like foot functions as an absorptive organ until the shoot portion of the embryo becomes a self-sustaining plant.

Development of the shoot from the upper daughter cell of the zygote begins with a vertical division. The two daughter cells thus formed divide transversely. Subsequent divisions are in a more or less irregular sequence (Figs. 89K, 90A–C). The shoot portion of a young embryo is hemispherical in shape and vertically differentiable into two halves, derived, respectively, from the first two cells of the shoot. There is an early differentiation of an apical cell in one or in both halves of the young shoot. In either case the apical cell lies midway between base and apex of the half in which it is formed. Further development of the shoot is due in large part to activity of the apical cell or cells. If one of these is present the shoot tends to elongate vertically; if two are present it has

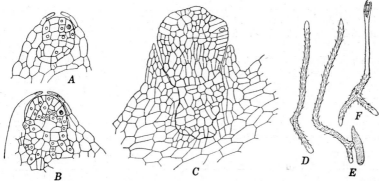

Fig. 90.—*Tmesipteris tannensis* Bernh. *A–C*, stages in the development of embryos. *D–F*, sporophytes after emergence from gametophyte. (*A–C*, × 50; *D–E*, × 3; *F*, × 1½.) (*After Holloway*, 1921.)

two horizontal branches that grow in opposite directions. Early stages in embryonal development are accompanied by growth of adjacent gametophytic tissue into a calyptra-like structure that overarches the upper portion of the embryo (Fig. 90A–C). After the apical cell begins to function, the developing shoot grows through the calyptra and projects beyond the gametophyte. The protruding portion of the sporophyte soon develops rhizoids here and there on its surface and becomes infected with a mycorhizal fungus. A developing shoot is capable of nourishing itself after it has a mycorhizal fungus, and it may become an independent plant (the young rhizome) any time after infection takes place (Fig. 90D–F). Separation from the gametophyte is due to an abscission layer formed in the region where shoot and foot adjoin each other. When abscission does take place, the foot usually remains embedded in the gametophyte. The young rhizome thus separated from the gametophyte has an embryonic stele a short distance back from the growing point, and posterior to this a mature stele with xylem and phloem. Young rhizomes growing through the soil frequently have lateral branches. Sometimes these are due to a dichotomy of the growing point, but more often they are due to a formation of adventitious branch apices in older portions of the rhizome. The original branch, or certain of the adventitious branches, eventually grow above the soil and develop into typical aerial shoots.

Bibliography

ARBER, E. A. NEWELL. **1921.** Devonian floras. Cambridge. 100 pp. 47 figs.

BOODLE, L. A. **1904.** *Ann. Bot.* **18:** 505–517. 1 pl. 7 figs. [Secondary xylem, *Psilotum.*]

BOWER, F. O. **1894.** *Phil. Trans. Roy. Soc. London,* Ser. *B.* **185:** 473–572. 11 pl. [Sporangia; *Psilotum, Tmesipteris.*]

    1908. The origin of a land flora. London. 727 pp. 359 figs.

    1935. Primitive land plants. London. 658 pp. 449 figs.

CAMPBELL, D. H. **1918.** The structure and development of mosses and ferns. 3d ed. New York. 708 pp. 322 figs.

DARNELL-SMITH, G. P. **1917.** *Trans. Roy. Soc. Edinburgh* **52:** 79–91. 2 pl. [Gametophyte, *Psilotum.*]

DAWSON, J. W. **1859.** *Quart. Jour. Geol. Soc.* **15:** 477–488. 6 figs. [*Psilophyton.*]

    1888. The geological history of plants. New York. 290 pp. 79 figs.

DORF, E. **1933.** *Bot. Gaz.* **95:** 240–257. 2 pl. [Psilophytales.]

EAMES, A. J. **1936.** Morphology of vascular plants. Lower groups (Psilophytales to Filicales). New York. 433 pp. 215 figs.

FORD, SIBILLE O. **1904.** *Ann. Bot.* **18:** 589–605. 1 pl. [Anatomy of *Psilotum.*]

HALLE, T. G. **1916.** *Kgl. Svensk Videnskab.-Ak. Handl.* **57,** No. 1: 1–46. 4 pl. [Psilophyales.]

HIRMER, M. **1927.** Handbuch der Paläobotanik. Bd. 1. Berlin. 708 pp. 817 figs.

HOLLOWAY, J. E. **1918.** *Trans. New Zealand Inst.* **50:** 1–44. 3 pl. 92 figs. [Gametophyte, *Tmesipteris.*]

    1921. *Ibid.* **53:** 386–422. 1 pl. 95 figs. [Gametophyte, *Tmesipteris.*]

JEFFREY, E. C. **1917.** The anatomy of woody plants. Chicago. 478 pp. 306 figs.

JURÁNYI, L. **1871.** *Bot. Zeitg.* **29:** 177–180. [Sporangium, *Psilotum.*]

KIDSTON, R., and W. H. LANG. **1917.** *Trans. Roy. Soc. Edinburgh* **51:** 761–784. 10 pl. [*Rhynia.*]

    1920. *Ibid.* **52:** 603–627. 10 pl. [*Rhynia.*]

    1920A. *Ibid.* **52:** 643–680. 17 pl. [*Asteroxylon.*]

    1921. *Ibid.* **52:** 831–854. 5 pl. [*Asteroxylon, Rhynia.*]

    1921A. *Ibid.* **52:** 855–902. 10 pl. 1 fig. [*Asteroxylon, Rhynia.*]

KRÄUSEL, R., and H. WEYLAND. **1923.** *Senckenbergiana* **5:** 154–184. 4 pl. [Psilophytales.]

    1926. *Abhandl. Senckenbergischen Naturf. ges. Frankfurt a/M.* **40:** 115–155. 15 pl. 46 figs. [*Asteroxylon.*]

    1929. *Ibid.* **41:** 319–359. 15 pl. 34 figs. [Psilophytales.]

    1933. *Palaeontographica* **78** Abt. *B:* 1–46. 7 pl. 39 figs. [*Pseudosporochnus.*]

LANG, W. H. **1931.** *Phil. Trans. Roy. Soc. London.* Ser. *B.* **219:** 421–442. 2 pl. [*Psilophyton.*]

LANG, W. H., and ISABEL C. COOKSON. **1930.** *Ibid.* **219:** 133–163. 3 pl. [Psilophytales.]

    1935. *Ibid.* **224:** 421–449. 4 pl. [Silurian Psilophytales.]

Lawson, A. A. **1917.** *Trans. Roy. Soc. Edinburgh* **51**: 785–794. 3 pl. [Gametophyte, *Tmesipteris.*]

1917A. *Ibid* **52**: 93–113. 5 pl. [Gametophyte; *Psilotum, Tmesipteris.*]

Scott, D. H. **1900.** Studies in fossil botany. 1st ed. London. 533 pp. 151 figs.

1920. *Ibid.* 3d ed. Vol. 1. London. 434 pp. 189 figs.

Seward, A. C. **1910.** Fossil plants. Vol. 2. Cambridge. 624 pp. 265 figs.

1933. Plant life through the ages. Cambridge. 603 pp. 140 figs.

Solms-Laubach, H. Grafen zu. **1884.** *Ann. Jard. Bot. Buitenzorg* **4**: 139–194. 6 pl. [Sporangium, *Psilotum.*]

Stiles, W. **1910.** *Ann. Bot.* **24**: 373–387. 1 pl. [Anatomy of *Psilotum.*]

Sykes, M. G. **1908.** *Ibid.* **22**: 63–89. 2 pl. 13 figs. [Anatomy of *Tmesipteris.*]

Thomas, A. P. W. **1902.** *Proc. Roy. Soc. London* **69**: 343–350. [Relationships, Psilophytales.]

Wettstein, R. von. **1933–1935.** Handbuch der systematischen Botanik. 4 Aufl. Leipzig. 1152 pp. 709 figs.

Zimmermann, W. **1930.** Die Phylogenie der Pflanzen. Jena. 452 pp. 250 figs.

CHAPTER VII

LYCOPODINAE

The Lycopodineae have a sporophyte differentiated into root, stem, and leaf. The leaves are microphyllous and generally spirally arranged. Steles of Lycopodineae may be protostelic, siphonostelic, or polystelic, but in no case are there leaf gaps above the leaves. The sporangia are borne singly upon the adaxial face of leaves and toward the leaf base.

The Lycopodinae, also known as the Lepidophyta, are represented in the present-day flora by the club mosses (*Lycopodium, Phylloglossum,* and *Selaginella*) and by the quillworts (*Isoetes*). There are also many extinct genera that are referable to this class. Most prominent among these are the tree-like giant lycopods which were such an important element in the Carboniferous forests of the Palaeozoic.

All members of the class are microphyllous. This does not necessarily mean that the leaves are small, since those of certain fossil species were half a meter or more in length. These plants are microphyllous in the sense that their leaves have but one vascular bundle that runs without branching through an unexpanded blade. In exceptional cases, as in certain fossil sigillarians, the leaf is traversed by two parallel bundles, but these forms with bifascicular leaves are immediately derived from forms with unifascicular leaves. Leaves of a majority of the genera have a distinct organ, the *ligule,* but this cannot be considered a characteristic of the entire class since it is lacking in genera referred to the Lycopodiales. Leaves of Lycopodinae are usually spirally arranged upon the stem, but in certain species of *Lycopodium* and *Selaginella* they are opposite or are in whorls.

The Lycopodinae are similar to the Equisetinae in that the fertile portion of the sporophyte is usually organized into a strobilus. They differ from the Equisetinae in that the sporangia are intimately associated with "sporophylls," each of which bears a single sporangium on the adaxial surface and near the leaf base. However, there is a certain amount of evidence for assuming that the Lycopodinae are sporangiophoric (page 223) and that the so-called sporophyll is really a bract fused with an axillary sporangiophore bearing a single terminal sporangium. Evidence tending to support this assumption includes (1) the origin of sporangia from tissues of the axis rather than from those of the subtending leaf;[1] (2) the sterile tissue, stalk and archesporial pad, subtending the

[1] Bower, 1894.

162

sporangium and the occasional occurrence of vascular-like elements in this sterile tissue;[1] and (3) abnormal sporophylls with more than one sporangium.[2] Whatever the nature of the sporophylls, the Lycopodinae are remarkable in that all of them, but the Lycopodiales, are markedly heterosporous.

The vascular organization of all genera referred to the class differs from that of other Pteridophyta in that there are no gaps above departing leaf traces when the central cylinder is a siphonostele. The discoverer[3] of this feature holds that the equisetaceous series has a similar organization, but, as noted elsewhere (page 222), this is open to question. Lack of leaf gaps does not mean that the Lycopodinae have undissected vascular cylinders since there is regularly a gap above each departing branch.

Most Lycopodinae have stems with a single stele, but those of *Selaginella* may be polystelic and contain two, three, four, or more parallel steles in the interval between two successive branches. From the standpoint of the stelar theory, the Lycopodinae are remarkable for their lack of evolutionary progress in the organization of the primary vascular tissues, and throughout the class the protoxylem is almost always exarch in position. However, there is frequently an advance from the condition where the protoxylem completely ensheaths the metaxylem to a polyarch condition where there are a number of protoxylem points. Many of the Lycopodinae have a protostelic vascular cylinder. This may be a simple haplostele, or it may be actinostelic and have few or many protoxylem points. Other Lycopodinae have the center of the xylem composed of parenchyma rather than tracheids. Such cylinders are to be considered true siphonosteles. In spite of the generally primitive vascular organization the stems of certain Lycopodinae have one advanced feature—the ability to form secondary vascular tissues by means of a cambium. It was this capacity to form secondary xylem, coupled with indefinite growth of the apical meristem that made possible the tree-like plant bodies of the extinct Lepidodendrons.

As previously indicated (page 135) the Lycopodinae represent one of the three general evolutionary lines leading away from the primitive Psilophyta. However, transitional forms between the most primitive Lycopodinae and the Psilophyta of the Early and Middle Devonian are not so well known as in the case of the other two phylogenetic series. Because of its general appearance and its internal organization, one is tempted to consider *Asteroxylon* as the beginning of the evolutionary line leading to the Lycopodinae. Even if this is true, it is a long jump from *Asteroxylon* to *Protolepidodendron*, the simplest of the known lycopods. It is very probable that the primitive Lycopodinae were small, herbaceous,

[1] Sykes, 1908.   [2] Bower, 1903; Dupler, 1922.
[3] Jeffrey, 1902, 1917.

microphyllous, and homosporous. The present-day herbaceous genera (*Selaginella* and *Lycopodium*) are usually considered reduced relics of the arboreal lycopods that flourished during the Carboniferous. On the other hand, geological evidence accumulated during the past two decades seems to show that these herbaceous genera are a very ancient stock and possibly direct successors of forms with the ancestral type of plant body.

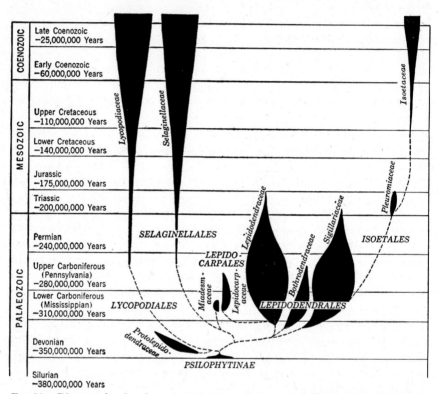

Fig. 91.—Diagram showing the geological range and the suggested interrelationships among the Lycopodinae.

Early in its history the lycopodian series appears to have begun evolving in two independent lines (Fig. 91), superficially distinguishable from each other by the presence or absence of a small laminate outgrowth (*ligule*) near the base of the leaves. The evolutionary line in which the leaves lack a ligule (*Lycopodinae eligulatae*) appears to have retained the simple herbaceous habit and the homospory of the hypothetical ancestral stock. Nowhere in this line was there an evolution of heterospory or the evolution of a large tree-like plant body. The other evolutionary line, the *Lycopodinae ligulatae*, became heterosporous early in its phylogeny, and this, in turn, lead to plants (the Lepidocarpales) whose mode of reproduction was quasispermatophytic. Certain members of the Ligulatae, the Selaginellales, seem to have retained the primitive herbaceous type of plant body. Other Ligulatae, the Lepidodendrons, became tree-like and woody. For some unknown reason all of these tree-like forms disappeared long ago. *Isoetes,* a present-day genus of debated systematic position, is generally considered a degenerate remnant of the arboreal stock.

The differences between the various groups among the Lycopodinae are generally considered sufficient to warrant the establishment of five orders.

ORDER 1. LYCOPODIALES

Sporophytes of Lycopodiales are herbaceous and without a secondary thickening of the stem. The leaves are microphyllous and without ligules. The sporangia are homosporous, and the sporophylls bearing them are usually organized in definite strobili. The gametophytes are wholly or partially subterranean. The antheridia are embedded in the gametophyte, and their antherozoids are biflagellate. Genera referred to the order range from the Lower Devonian to the present.

The Lycopodiales contain but two genera of living plants—*Lycopodium* a genus with many species, and *Phylloglossum* a genus with but one species. These herbaceous present-day genera are frequently considered degenerate relics of the woody arboreal Lycopodinae that were so abundant during the Carboniferous. The discovery in the Carboniferous of a few species of sterile and fertile *Lycopodium*-like plants, which are referred to the genus *Lycopodites*,[1] seems to show that *Lycopodium* and its immediate relatives are a very ancient stock that has persisted more or less unchanged for a very long time. This may be true, but it should be noted that the geological record between *Lycopodites* of the Carboniferous and the living Lycopodiales is almost a complete blank.

The Lycopodiales differ from other Lycopodinae in that they are the only order in which the sporophyte is homosporous. There is also a distinct, although inconspicuous, vegetative difference in that the leaves of Lycopodiales lack a ligule, whereas those of all other orders possess one. The herbaceous type of plant body without secondary thickening is not distinctive since it is also found in a majority of the Selaginellales.

The two living genera of Lycopodiales, together with the fossil *Lycopodites,* are usually considered the only members of the order. The recent discovery[2] of more adequate material shows that *Protolepidodendron,* one of the fossil Lycopodinae, has much more in common with the Lycopodiales than with the Lepidodendrales. Transfer of *Protolepidodendron* to the order results in its division into two families.

[1] Hirmer, 1927.　　[2] Kräusel and Weyland, 1932.

FAMILY 1. PROTOLEPIDODENDRACEAE

The Protolepidodendraceae had a herbaceous plant body in which the stem was clothed with numerous small leaves whose apices were forked. The leaves were without ligules and often left an oval depressed scar when they were shed from the stem. The sporophylls were of the same shape as the foliage leaves, and they were not borne in definite strobili.

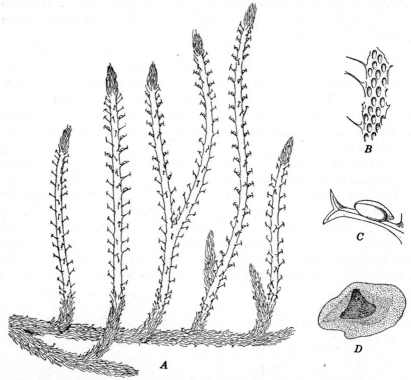

Fig. 92.—*Protolepidodendron Scharyanum* (Stur.) Krejci. *A*, reconstruction of the plant body. *B*, surface view of a fragment of a shoot. *C*, a fertile leaf. *D*, transverse section of a stem. (*A*, × ⅓; *B*, × ½; *C*, × 4; *D*, × 7½.) (*A, C–D, after Kräusel and Weyland, 1932; B, after Kräusel and Weyland, 1929.*)

The Protolepidodendraceae are known only in the fossil condition and from the Lower to the Middle Devonian.

Remains of *Protolepidodendron*, the single genus of the family, have been found in Middle and Early Devonian deposits in Scotland, Germany, and Bohemia.[1] For a considerable time the only known specimens of the plant were fragments of small branches, with or without remains of leaves. Because of the leaf scars it was thought that the plant was allied

[1] Kräusel and Weyland, 1929, 1932.

to *Lepidodendron* and that the known specimens were twigs of a large tree-like plant. The name *Protolepidodendron* has also been applied to fossil plants that were undoubtedly tree-like, but it has recently been shown[1] that the plants of the type species of the genus were relatively small and herbaceous.

Extensive and fairly well-preserved material of the type species [*P. Scharyanum* (Stur.) Krejci] shows that it had a leafy, branched, prostrate axis. The tips of certain branches of the axis bent upward and grew erect to a height of 20 to 30 cm. (Fig. 92*A*). These erect shoots sometimes had one or two dichotomies. The prostrate axis and the tips of the erect branches were densely clothed with small thorn-like leaves that were bifurcate at their apices. The leaves were without ligules. Certain of the erect branches bore sporophylls here and there along their entire length. The sporophylls had much the same shape and the same bifurcate apices as the sterile leaves. Each sporophyll had a single sporangium that was borne some distance out from the adaxial side of the leaf base (Fig. 92*C*).

The branches were protostelic in organization and had a simple parenchymatous cortex external to the stele (Fig. 92*D*). The xylem of the stele was triradiate and had smaller protoxylem elements a short distance in from the free face of each ray. Certain, if not all of the metaxylem tracheids were of the scalariform type. Leaf traces departed from the angles of the xylem mass, but it is not definitely known whether or not they were continuous with the midribs of leaves. The stem did not form secondary vascular elements, but there is a possibility that it formed a small amount of periderm by means of a phellogen.

FAMILY 2. LYCOPODIACEAE

Sporophytes of Lycopodiaceae are herbaceous and with the stem bearing many small leaves with simple apices. Sporophylls and foliage leaves may be similar or dissimilar, and the sporophylls may or may not be borne in definite strobili. Lycopodiaceae are known from the Upper Carboniferous to the present. The family contains two living genera: *Lycopodium*, which is world wide in distribution and with some 180 species, and *Phylloglossum*, a monotypic genus known only from Australia, Tasmania, and New Zealand.

A majority of the species of *Lycopodium* are tropical, but certain of them are widely distributed in temperate regions. All species of *Lycopodium* have relatively small, herbaceous or shrubby sporophytes (Fig. 93). Some species are epiphytic and have erect or pendant plant bodies; others are terrestrial and have an upright stem or one that grows hori-

---

[1] Kräusel and Weyland, 1932.

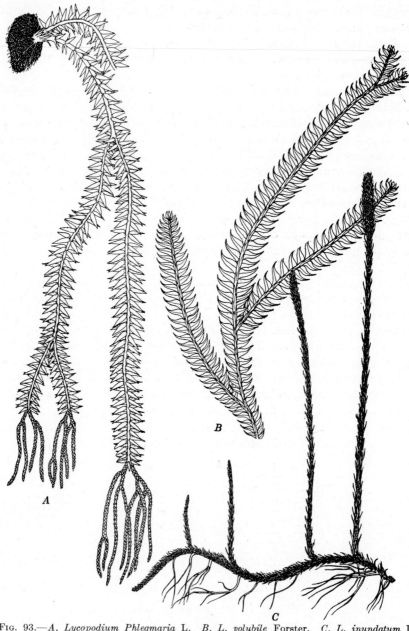

FIG. 93.—A, *Lycopodium Phlegmaria* L. B, *L. volubile* Forster. C, *L. inundatum* L.
(A, C, × ½; B, × 1½).

zontally above or below the surface of the soil. The stem and its branches are densely clothed with small leaves.

Lycopodium is divided into two subgenera that differ in general organization of the sporophyte. Species referred to the subgenus *Urostachya*[1] have branched or unbranched stems that are erect or pendant, but never creeping. If the stem is branched, the branching is always dichotomous and usually with successive dichotomies at right angles to one another. Species of this subgenus have no adventitious roots along the stem. Foliage leaves and sporophylls of most species in the subgenus are approximately the same size and both are green. There is, however, considerable variation in distribution of the two. In *L. Selago* L. and related species there are alternate sterile and fertile zones throughout the length of stem and branches. Certain other species of the subgenus have the sporophylls restricted to the distal part of stem and branches. Although such portions of the plant are properly called strobili, there is considerable variation in the distinctiveness of the strobili. These are most distinctive in the group of species related to *L. Phlegmaria* L. (Fig. 93*A*) where the strobili are dichotomously branched and where the sporophylls, although green and of the same shape, are much smaller than the foliage leaves.

Species of the subgenus *Rhopalostachya* typically have prostrate stems bearing upright branches. The branching in the first-formed portion of the sporophyte may be dichotomous; but in later-developed portions it is always monopodial. The species with a creeping stem generally have their adventitious roots borne along the entire length of the prostrate portion. All members of the subgenus have the sporophylls in well-defined strobili, which may be simple or branched. The sporophylls differ from foliage leaves in that they are smaller in size, are paler in color, and have a dentate margin. Most species of the subgenus have all foliage leaves alike but a few species are like *Selaginella* in that the leaves are of two sizes and in definite vertical rows along the stem.

Vegetative propagation of the sporophyte is of frequent occurrence in *Lycopodium* and may result in stands of considerable extent that have been derived from one original individual.[2] Species with creeping stems have the apical growth, branching, and the progressive death of the older portions found in other pteridophytes with prostrate stems. In addition to this there are several other methods by which the plant multiplies. It has been shown[3] that new plants may result from (1) vegetative propagation of the gametophyte, (2) vegetative propagation of the juvenile (protocorm) stage of the sporophyte, (3) gemmae produced from cortical cells of the root, (4) tubers developed at the apices of roots, and (5) bulbils. The bulbils, which are found only in species belonging to the

[1] Pritzel, 1900.   [2] Holloway, 1916.   [3] Holloway, 1917.

subgenus *Urostachya,* bear a general resemblance to the prótocormous stage of the young sporophyte.   They may be formed anywhere on the stem.   Bulbils have been variously interpreted as modified lateral branches in the axils of leaves, as modified sporangia, and as modified leaves.   The latter interpretation seems the most logical since a bulbil has the same position, dorsiventrality, and the same type of vascular supply as a leaf.[1]

In all cases where the structure of the growing stem apex has been studied, there is a mass of meristematic tissue instead of a well-defined

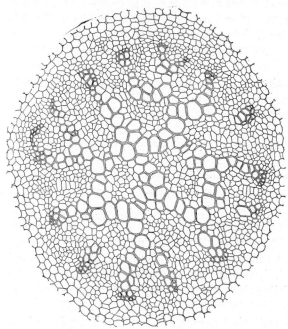

Fig. 94.—Transverse section of the vascular cylinder of *Lycopodium Phlegmaria* L. (× 110.)

apical cell as in stems of most other pteridophytes.[2]   Internodes only one or two removed from the apical meristem have a well-defined differentiation of the maturing tissues into epidermis, cortex, and stele.

The epidermis in mature portions of a stem is one cell in thickness and has stomata that appear to be similar in structure to those of the leaf. Stomata of leaves have been shown to be identical in structure with those of certain angiosperms.[3]   The cortex varies greatly in relative thickness

[1] Smith, R. W., 1920.

[2] Campbell, 1918; Holloway, 1910; Spessard, 1928; Turner, 1924; Wigglesworth, 1907.

[3] Copeland, 1902.

from species to species. In some species its radial thickness is several times that of the stele; in other species the two are approximately equal. There is also considerable variation in the structure of the cortex. Some species have a cortex that remains soft and parenchymatous throughout the life of the plant; other species have a sclerification of the outer or the inner portion of the cortex; still other species have a sclerification of the entire cortex in mature portions of the stem. At the inner face of the cortex there may be an endodermal layer which, at least in younger portions of the stem, has characteristically thickened radial walls. In view of the recent statements that the endodermal layer of *Selaginella*[1] and of *Pteris*[2] is of stelar origin, it may be possible that the endodermis of *Lycopodium* belongs to the stele rather than to the cortex.

Internal to the endodermis is a pericyclic layer which is usually three to six cells in thickness. As is well known, there is great variation in the organization of the vascular elements, even within the same species. The same species may vary greatly both from individual to individual and in different portions of the same individual. Study of young sporophytes and of the first-formed portions of mature sporophytes[3] shows that the vascular elements are organized into an exarch actinostele very similar in appearance to the actinosteles characteristic of roots of vascular plants. In some cases the actinostele has three or four protoxylem points; in other cases there may be as many as a dozen protoxylem points. Later-formed portions of a stem may retain the actinostelic organization characteristic of the juvenile plant (Fig. 94). Species with this type of organization in the mature stem are thought to be the most primitive of the genus as far as the vascular organization is concerned.[4] More frequently, however, later-formed portions of the stem tend to have a greater number of protoxylem masses and to lack a radial arrangement of the metaxylem and the phloem with respect to the protoxylem. Such stems may have the xylem and phloem in alternate transverse bands across the stele (Fig. 95*B*), or may have masses of xylem and phloem indiscriminately mixed with one another (Fig. 95*C*). Attempts have been made to correlate the actinostelic, plectostelic, and mixed haplostelic types of vascular organization with the growth habit of the plant. Thus, it has been held that the plectostelic organization is found chiefly in plagiotropic portions of the stem and the actinostelic in orthotropic portions,[5] but so many exceptions have been shown for the foregoing generalization[4] that its validity is to be questioned. According to another hypothesis[6] the size of the stele profoundly affects the organization of the vascular elements.

[1] Barclay, 1931.   [2] Chang, 1927.
[3] Chamberlain, 1917; Holloway, 1910; Jones, 1905; Spessard, 1928; Wardlaw, 1924; Wigglesworth, 1907.
[4] Hill, J. B., 1914.   [5] Holloway, 1910; Jones, 1905.   [6] Wardlaw, 1924.

The actinostelic mass of xylem in small first-formed portions of the stem has a relatively large surface in proportion to the volume. A large mass of xylem with the same type of organization would have a much smaller proportion of surface to volume. On the other hand, the change from an actinostelic to a mixed haplostelic or to plectostelic organization in later-formed portions of a stem results in a vascular system with approximately the same ration between surface and volume as that present in the young stem.

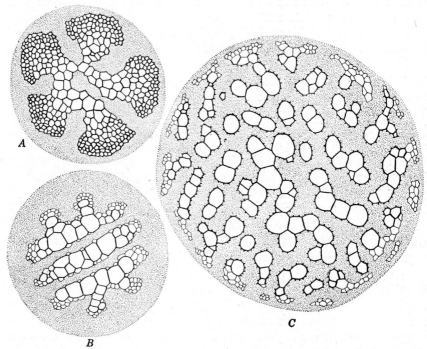

Fig. 95.—Transverse section of the vascular cylinders of *Lycopodium.* A, *L. serratum* Thbg. B, *L. volubile* Forster. C, *L. cernuum* L. (× 80.)

The root system of *Lycopodium* is largely adventitious. According to the subgenus, adventitious roots are restricted to the proximal portion of the stem or are formed along its entire length. Adventitious roots are formed chiefly from pericyclic tissue, but they may be formed both from it and from the endodermis.[1] A developing adventitious root does not grow directly out through the cortex but grows downward through it for a centimeter or more before emerging from the stem. As a result, transverse sections of stem frequently show several roots within the cortex.[2] Roots growing through the cortex are unbranched, but after

[1] Saxelby, 1908.   [2] Hill, J. B., 1919; Stokey, 1907.

emerging from the stem they may branch freely. The branching is always dichotomous and generally has successive dichotomies at right angles to one another.

Roots of *Lycopodium* (Fig. 96*B*) have the differentiation into epidermis, cortex, and stele typical of other vascular plants. The epidermis gives rise to numerous root hairs, but these are somewhat peculiar in that they lie in pairs. The occurrence of root hairs in twos results from the fact that the hair initials are formed in pairs by the oblique or anticlinal division of a young epidermal cell.[1] The cortex is several cells in

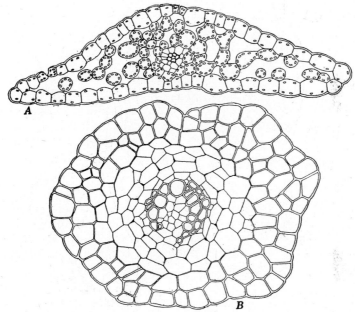

FIG. 96.—*A*, transverse section of leaf of *Lycopodium volubile* Forster.   *B*, transverse section of root of L. *serratum* Thbg.   (*A*, × 160; *B*, × 215.)

thickness and often becomes heavily sclerified in the outer half as the root grows older. In some cases the stele is *monarch* with the protoxylem in one mass; in other cases it is either *diarch* with two protoxylem masses, or *triarch* with three groups of protoxylem. Sometimes the same root is diarch in one portion and tetrarch in another.[2] Most roots are diarch and have a C- or U-shaped mass of xylem so oriented that the opening of the C or the U faces away from the stem. The protoxylem lies at the tips of the curved xylem mass, and the intervening portion consists of metaxylem. Diarch roots generally have but one mass of phloem, and this lies between the points of the C or the U.

[1] Stokey, 1907.   [2] Saxelby, 1908.

Most species have small leaves and in only a few species do they attain a length of 2 to 3 çm.   The leaves are generally lanceolate in outline, sessile, and have a broad base.   Their arrangement varies from species to species, and they may be spirally arranged or in whorls.   Some species with whorled leaves have them of two sizes and in the four-ranked arrangement so typical of *Selaginella*.   The first-formed leaves on a stem may be very simple in structure and without a vein.[1]   Later-formed leaves always have a single unbranched vein extending from the base part way to the leaf apex.   The vein connects with a leaf trace passing through

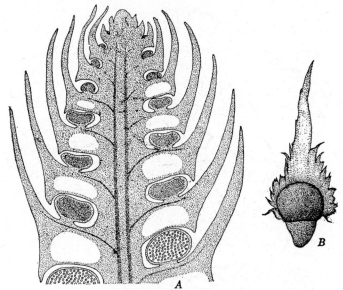

Fig. 97.—*Lycopodium cernuum* L.   *A*, vertical section of apical portion of a strobilus.   *B*, dorsal view of a sporophyll and sporangium.   (*A*, × 21; *B*, × 20.)

the cortex.   As is the case with other Lycopodinae there are no leaf gaps in the portion of the stele above the departing leaf trace.

Leaf primordia arise very close to the apical meristem, and it has been held[2] that the entire leaf is formed from a single embryonic epidermal cell.   Very young leaves consist of a homogeneous mass of embryonic cells.   Later on there is both a basipelatous and an acropetalous differentiation of an embryonic vein within the basal region.   All of the xylem elements in a mature leaf are spirally thickened, and the first ones to mature lie near the center of the vein (Fig. 96*A*).   This endarch mass of xylem may be ensheathed by an endodermis, or an endodermis may be lacking.   The intervening embryonic tissue between vein and epidermis matures into a parenchyma in which the cells may be angular in outline

---

[1] Wigglesworth, 1907.   [2] Turner, 1924.

and without intercellular spaces, or rounded and with intercellular spaces. Most species have stomata in the epidermal layer on both faces of the leaf, but species with two kinds of leaves frequently have the stomata restricted to one side of the leaf.

The sporangia are always borne singly upon sporophylls which, as previously noted, may be aggregated in definite strobili at apices of stem and branches (Fig. 97*A*) or may be in transverse series alternating with transverse series of foliage leaves. Sporangia of *Lycopodium* are always kidney-shaped and, according to the species, have a long and slender or

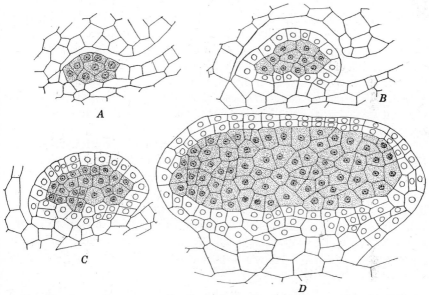

Fig. 98.—*Lycopodium cernuum* L. Stages in development of sporangia. (× 325.)

short and massive stalk. They always lie on the median axis of the leaf and close to its base (Fig. 97*B*).

Sporangia begin to develop at a time when the sporophyll is composed of embryonic cells. The first evidence of sporangial development is a periclinal division of a transverse row of three to seven or more epidermal cells on the upper side of the leaf and near its base.[1] Inner daughter cells formed by division of sporangial initials contribute to the stalk and basal portion of the sporangium, outer daughter cells give rise to the bulk of the sporangium (Fig. 98*A*). The first division of the outer daughter cells is also periclinal and into an outer row of *jacket initials* and an inner row of *archesporial cells*. The curved row of archesporial cells, by periclinal and anticlinal division, develops into a rather massive *sporogenous tissue*

[1] Bower, 1894.

(Fig. 98*B–D*). Practically all members of the last cell generation of the sporogenous tissue function as *spore mother cells* that become rounded, separate from one another, and float about in a viscous liquid as they divide into tetrads of spores in the well-known manner. The jacket initials external to the sporogenous tissue divide to form a jacket layer three or more cells in thickness (Fig. 98*D*). Shortly before the spore-mother-cell stage of development, there is a differentiation of a nutritive tissue (*tapetum*) about the sporogenous tissue. This is formed in part from the innermost layer of jacket cells and in part from sporangial cells just beneath the sporogenous tissue. *Lycopodium*, unlike most other pteridophytes, has no disintegration of the tapetum during the formation of spores. As the sporangium approaches maturity, there is the differentiation of a narrow transverse strip of cells (the *stomium*) across the apical portion of the outermost jacket layer. The cell walls in the stomial portion thicken differently from those of other cells in the sporangial jacket. When strains and stresses are set up by a drying out of cells in the mature sporangium, there is a transverse rupture of the sporangium apex along the line of the stomium.

Spores of *Lycopodium* may begin germination within a few days after they are shed,[1] but several species are known[2] in which germination does not begin until after the spores are three to eight years old. Development of the gametophyte to the point where there are mature sexual organs may, correspondingly, take from 8 months to 6 to 15 years. The rate of growth after the spores have begun to germinate is more or less correlated with the proportion of photosynthetic tissue and is slowest in those species that have a colorless and saprophytic gametophyte.

The first cell division of a germinating spore takes place before the outer spore wall layer is ruptured and results in two hemispherical daughter cells of approximately equal size.[2] One of these daughter cells, the *basal cell*, undergoes no further division than the cutting off of a small, lens-shaped, rudimentary *rhizoidal cell*. The other daughter cell, by two successive divisions, produces an *apical cell* with two cutting faces. All of the species with colorless gametophytes and most of those with chlorophyll may have an entrance of a symbiotic phycomycetous fungus into the basal cell at the time when the gametophyte is four- to five-celled (Fig. 99*A–B*). If there is no entrance of the fungus there is no further development of the gametophyte. Gametophytes developing beyond this early stage have the apical cell cutting off some half dozen segments and then becoming replaced by a group of meristematic cells. Segments cut off by the apical cell divide periclinally, and the outer cells thus formed become infected with the symbiotic fungus in the same manner as does the basal cell. The apical group of meristematic cells differentiated early

[1] Treub, 1888.   [2] Bruchmann, 1910.

in the ontogeny of the sexual generation produces the major portion of the adult gametophyte. There is great diversity in form and structure of the mature gametophyte. Attempts have been made to group them according to distinct types,[1] but intergrading types make any arbitrary classification impossible. Certain species are wholly subterranean and

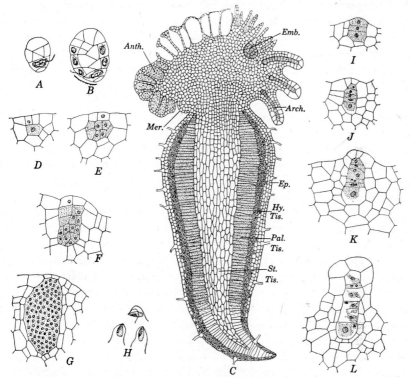

Fig. 99.—*A–B*, early stages in development of gametophyte of *Lycopodium annotinum* L. *C*, vertical section of a mature gametophyte of *L. complanatum* L. *D–L*, *Lycopodium clavatum* L. *D–G*, stages in development of antheridia. *H*, antherozoids. *I–L*, stages in development of archegonia. (*Anth.*, antheridium; *Arch.*, archegonium; *Emb.*, embryo; *Ep.*, epidermis; *Hy. Tis.*, hyphal tissue; (*Mer.*, meristem; *Pal. Tis.*, palisade tissue; *St. Tis.*, storage tissue.) (*A–B, after Bruchmann*, 1910; *C, H, after Bruchmann*, 1898; *D–G, I–L, after Lang*, 1899.) (*A–B*, × 235; *D–F*, × 265; *G, I–L*, × 185; *H*, × 275.)

have an erect, compact, conically shaped gametophyte or one that is freely branched. Other species are only partially subterranean, with the aerial portion branched and containing chloroplasts.

    L. lucidulum Michx. has a gametophyte that may be wholly subterranean or may have the apical portion above ground.[2] The bottle-shaped gametophyte of this species may be wholly vertical, may have the first-formed portion vertical and the later-formed horizontal, or may have

---

[1] Bruchmann, 1898.　　[2] Spessard, 1922.

the first-formed horizontal and the later-formed vertical.   Older portions of subterranean thalli are brownish, and the growing tips are whitish. Aerial portions of thalli are green on the upper side.   Both the erect, and the prostrate portions of this gametophyte are dorsiventrally differentiated.   The morphologically upper surface has a more or less distinct epidermis without rhizoids; the lower surface has an epidermis with rhizoids.   Rhizoids of *L. lucidulum* are described as arising by direct elongation of epidermal cells.   In certain species[1] the epidermal cells do not develop directly into rhizoids but divide diagonally into two daughter cells—one developing into a rhizoid, the other into a special cell concerned with the entrance of the symbiotic fungus into the prothallus.   Gametophytes of some species have a radially symmetrical subterranean portion. Such gametophytes frequently show considerable internal differentiations of tissues (Fig. 99*C*).

Sex organs of *Lycopodium* are formed from dorsal epidermal cells just back from the apical meristem.   The initial cell of an antheridium divides periclinally into an outer cell (the *jacket initial*) and an inner cell (the *primary androgonial cell*).[2]   Repeated anticlinal division of the jacket initial results in a jacket layer one cell in thickness which lies external to the androgonial tissue.   At the center of the jacket layer is a triangular cell, comparable to the *opercular cell* in antheridia of eusporangiate ferns (page 272) but differing in that it does not cut off so many daughter cells on each of the three sides.   The primary androgonial cell divides and redivides to form a large mass of *androgonial cells* that lie embedded within the thallus (Fig. 99*D–G*).   Metamorphosis of the last cell generation of androgonial cells, the *androcytes*, into antherozoids has not been followed in detail[3] but is thought to take place as in other pteridophytes. The antherozoids (Fig. 99*H*) are fusiform, broadly rounded at the posterior end, and with two flagella at the anterior end.[4]   Liberation of antherozoids is effected by a breaking down of the opercular cell.

The first division of an archegonial initial is periclinal and into an outer *primary cover cell* and an inner *central cell*.[5]   The central cell then divides periclinally into a *primary canal cell* and a *primary ventral cell* (Fig. 99*I*).   In some species the primary canal cell divides transversely to form four *canal cells*.   In other species six to eight, or even more, canal cells are formed (Fig. 99*J–L*).   The primary ventral cell eventually becomes slightly broader than the cells in the canal row.   There has been no critical investigation to show whether this cell functions directly as the egg or whether it divides to form a *ventral canal cell* and an *egg*. Meanwhile, by two successive anticlinal divisions at right angles to each

[1] Bruchmann, 1910; Haberlandt, 1918.		[2] Lang, 1899; Spessard, 1922.
[3] Lang, 1899.		[4] Bruchmann, 1898.
[5] Bruchmann, 1910; Lang, 1899; Spessard, 1922. .

other, the primary cover cell divides to form four *neck initials*. Transverse division of the neck initials results in a neck three to four cells in height and typically composed of four vertical rows of cells. The portion of the mature archegonium derived from the primary cover cell, together with the canal cells it ensheaths, projects vertically above the gametophyte. The remaining canal cells and the egg lie embedded within the prothallus. The cells lateral to the egg and lower portion of the canal row are not portions of the archegonium since they are formed by division and redivision of prothallial cells immediately adjacent to the archegonial initial. As is the case with archegonia of Bryophyta, all members of the axial row except the egg disintegrate shortly before the archegonium is

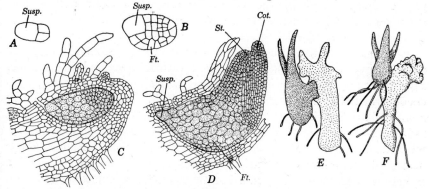

Fig. 100.—*A–D*, stages in development of embryos of *Lycopodium Phlegmaria* L. *E–F*, vertical sections of gametophytes and young sporophytes of *L. cernuum* L. (*Cot.*, cotyledon; *Ft.*, foot; *St.*, stem; *Susp.*, suspensor) (*A–D, after Bruchmann*, 1910; *E, after Holloway*, 1920; *F, after Holloway*, 1916.) (*A–B*, × 120; *C–D*, × 48; *E*, × 15; *F*, × 7½.)

mature. Opening of the apex of the archegonial neck seems to take place by a spreading apart and partial disintegration of the uppermost neck cells.

The first division of a zygote is always transverse.[1] The daughter cell next to the neck of the archegonium becomes a *suspensor* which pushes the other daughter cell, sometimes called the *embryonic cell*, more deeply into the gametophyte. The suspensor may remain one-celled, or it may become three-celled. The embryonic cell eventually develops into the mature sporophyte. Its first division is vertical, and this is followed by a vertical division of the two daughter cells thus formed (Fig. 100*A*). Transverse division of each of these cells results in an eight-celled embryo in which the cells are in two superimposed tiers of four cells each. The tier of cells adjoining the suspensor eventually develops into the *foot* of the young sporophyte; the distal tier develops into the remaining portions of the sporophyte. In some species it is possible to trace the parts of the

[1] Bruchmann, 1910.

young sporophyte back to particular cells in the distal tier of four. It has been held[1] that the two cells facing the apical meristem of the gametophyte develop into the *stem* and the two facing away from the meristem develop into the *cotyledon* and the primary *root*. However, the young sporophyte is a many-celled structure before the cotyledon and the embryonic stem become evident (Fig. 100*B–D*). Differentiation of the primary root takes place even later and at one side of the region where cotyledon and foot adjoin each other. Until this time the embryo remains embedded within the gametophyte, growing downward and forward toward the meristem of the gametophyte. Eventually the growing stem and cotyledon burst through the apical region of the gametophyte. Following this, the cotyledon and stem show a markedly negative geotropic response and start to grow upward into the air.

Sometimes the distal four cells of the eight-celled stage develop into a massive globose structure (the *protocorm*) which grows through the gametophyte, becomes green, and develops rhizoids on its lower surface. From the upper surface of the protocorm arise a few to many erect, conical outgrowths (*protophylls*) which are leaf-like in function and which have stomata in their epidermal layer (Fig. 100*E–F*). After having formed an indefinite number of protophylls, the protocorm then differentiates a meristematic region which develops into the stem of the adult plant. The protocorm has been variously interpreted. Some[2] consider it a structure of great antiquity and the phylogenetic percursor of the stem. Others[3] hold that it is a late phylogenetic specialization and represents a "gouty interlude" in the early ontogeny of the sporophyte.

ORDER 2. SELAGINELLALES

Sporophytes of Selaginellales are herbaceous and usually without any indication of a secondary thickening of the stem. The leaves are microphyllous and ligulate. The roots are borne upon leafless branches (rhizophores). The sporophytes are heterosporous and with the sporophylls producing the sporangia borne in strobili. The macro- and microgametophytes are markedly different in size, and the antherozoids produced by the male gametophyte are biflagellate. Genera referred to the order range from the Upper Carboniferous to the present.

The Selaginellales have but one genus of living plants—*Selaginella*. The fossil genus *Selaginellites* whose few species are known chiefly from the Carboniferous[4] is also referred to the order. Thus, similar to the Lycopodiales, there is a certain amount of evidence for believing that the Selaginellales are a series of ancient origin.

[1] Bruchmann, 1910.   [2] Treub, 1890.
[3] Bower, 1908; Holloway, 1910.   [4] Hirmer, 1927.

The Selaginellales have the same type of herbaceous plant body as the Lycopodiales, but each of their leaves has a single ligule. Except for one anomalous species,[1] there is no secondary thickening of the stem. Another distinctive vegetative feature of the living genus is the widespread restriction of adventitious roots to the apices of leafless downward-growing branches, the *rhizophores*. Both genera of the order are heterosporous, and with the sporophylls in definite strobili. *Selaginella,* similar to *Lycopodium,* has biflagellate antherozoids. The embryo differs from that of other living Lycopodinae in having two cotyledons.

There is but one family, the Selaginellaceae.

Selaginella, with 600 or more species, is world wide in distribution, but most of the species grow in the damp forests of tropical countries. Of the species growing in temperate regions, some 37 are found in the United States. Certain of these grow in damp, shady habitats; others are xerophytic and grow on dry rocky cliffs or on dry sandy soil. These xerophytic species are able to withstand desiccation for months, the rosette-like system of branches coiling tightly together as the plant dries out and reexpanding when it is moistened.

There are two general types of plant body in the genus. In the 50 or so species referred to the subgenus *Homoeophyllum,*[1] the stem is generally erect and has all the leaves of the same size and spirally arranged. The remaining species, belonging to the subgenus *Heterophyllum,* generally have prostrate stems with erect branches in which the foliage leaves are of two sizes and arranged in two vertical rows. The size of the plant body varies greatly from species to species. At one extreme are those species in which it is not much larger than an ordinary moss; at the other are those in which it is a slender vine attaining a length of 20 meters.

S. oregana D. C. Eaton, a species found in the costal region of Oregon and Washington, is representative of the subgenus *Homoeophyllum.* It is an epiphyte on the trunks and branches of moss-covered forest trees. The plant body is pendant and lax, with numerous slender, recurved, loosely interwoven branches. The branches are densely clothed with small lanceolate leaves which lie in a spiral, many-ranked arrangement. The strobili are numerous, straight or curved, and not sharply differentiated from sterile portions of the plant.

S. Kraussiana A. Br. (Fig. 101), an African species frequently cultivated in greenhouses, is fairly typical of species belonging to the subgenus *Heterophyllum.* It has a creeping stem which grows along the surface of the soil and bears lateral branches at more or less regular intervals. Early-formed portions of a plant have the main axis and branches developing with equal vigor; later-formed portions have the axis developing more vigorously than the branches. Slightly posterior to each forking

[1] Hieronymus, 1900.

of the stem is an elongate, downward-growing, colorless, leafless, cylindrical appendage—the *rhizophore*—which typically develops a small tuft of adventitious roots at its apex. The arrangement of the leaves is seen to best advantage on the main axis. In this markedly dorsiventral portion of the shoot, they are in pairs and conspicuously different in size. The smaller leaf of each pair is inserted on the dorsal side of the stem, the larger leaf on the ventral side. Successive pairs of leaves are so oriented that large leaf alternates with large leaf, and small leaf with small leaf. The strobili are always borne on short erect branches. The sporophylls are in four vertical rows, but unlike the foliage leaves all are of the same size.

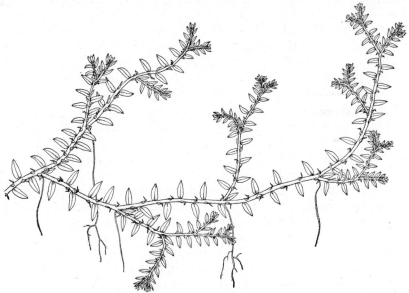

Fig. 101.—Sporophyte of *Selaginella Kraussiana* A. Br. (× 1½.)

The growing apex of a stem may consist of a mass of meristematic tissue (*S. oregana*), but more frequently there is a single well-defined apical cell (*S. Kraussiana*). In the only species where the apical cell has been studied in detail (*S. Wildenovii* Bak.),[1] it has been shown that the first division of segments cut off by the apical cell is periclinal. The outer cell thus formed contributes to the epidermis and the cortex; the inner cell contributes to the stele, the outermost layer of which is the endodermis.

Except for the rhizomes of certain species, the stems differ from those of other pteridophytes in that the vascular tissue is set off from the cortex by an intervening region of radially elongate cells (the *trabeculae*) with conspicuous intercellular spaces (Fig. 102*B*). The cortex generally

[1] Barclay, 1931.

consists of angular cells without intercellular spaces, but in a few cases[1] the cells are rounded and have small intercellular spaces. All cells of the cortex may be thin-walled, or those toward the exterior may be heavily sclerified. The epidermis is one cell in thickness and without stomata.

The organization of the stele ranges all the way from that of a simple protostele to that of a polycyclic siphonostele, perforated here and there

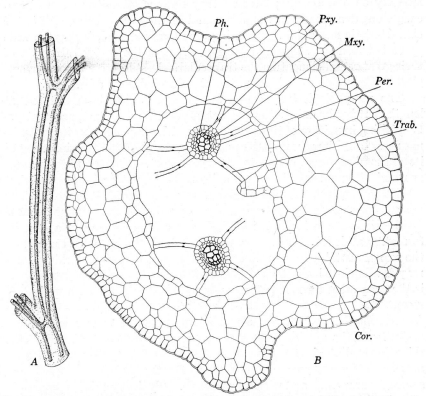

Fig. 102.—*Selaginella Kraussiana* A. Br.   *A*, portion of a stem cleared to show the vascular tissues.   *B*, transverse section of a stem.   (*Cor.*, cortex; *Mxy.*, metaxylem; *Per.*, pericycle; *Ph.*, phloem; *Pxy.*, protoxylem; *Trab.*, trabecula.)   (*A*, × 15; *B*, × 160.)

by branch gaps.   The stem may also be polystelic and have 2, 3, 4, or as many as 16 separate steles running through the intervening region between two successive branchings of the stem.[2]   *S. Kraussiana*, one of the polystelic species, is distelic in the intervals between successive branchings (Fig. 102*A*).   Both of the steles in this stem are protostelic in organization, and each has a single exarch mass of protoxylem.   The protoxylem masses of the two are so oriented with respect to one another that they face in opposite directions.   The metaxylem of each bundle lies

[1] Harvey-Gibson, 1894.   [2] Wardlaw, 1925.

centripetal to the protoxylem. The xylem is ensheathed by a layer of parenchyma one to two cells in thickness. External to this is a single layer of sieve tubes except in the region radial to the protoxylem.[1] Parenchyma and sieve tubes are in turn surrounded by a pericylic layer one cell in thickness. The outermost layer in each stele is an endodermis, also one cell in thickness. When first formed, the endodermal cells abut laterally on one another; later on they become laterally separated and each elongates greatly in the axis radial to the stele. The result is the characteristic mass of long radiating cells (trabeculae) bridging the wide space between the steles and the inner face of the cortex. In spite of their great radial elongation the trabecular cells still retain the transverse girdles (Casparian strips) characteristic of endodermal cells.

The morphological nature of the rhizophore has been debated at length. It has been held to be a root, a branch of the stem, and a structure falling in neither of these categories. The argument for its root-like nature is based largely upon its positive geotropism and the similarity of its anatomical organization to that of a root.[2] One of the strongest anatomical arguments in favor of its root-like nature is the fact that species with polystelic stems always have a monostelic rhizophore. The reasons for considering the rhizophore a portion of the stem seem more conclusive. These include: its exogenous origin, its lack of a cap, its formation at definite places with respect to dichotomies of the stem,[3] and the experimental demonstration[4] that apices of decapitated rhizophores may develop into leafy shoots. Against the two foregoing interpretations is the suggestion that it is an organ *sui generis*[5] and neither a root nor a stem.

All roots borne by the adult plant are adventitious in origin. In a majority of the species these are formed only at the distal end of the rhizophores, but in a few species, as *S. Wallichii* Spr., adventitious roots may develop anywhere along the stem.[6] Roots of *Selaginella* are delicate, sparingly branched, and with a small stele. Typically this is monarch in organization and has one phloem and one xylem mass.

Foliage leaves are small, simple, and symmetrical or asymmetrical in outline. According to the species, all foliage leaves are alike in size, or they are of two different sizes. In either case, there is always a small membranous outgrowth, the *ligule*, on the adaxial side of the leaf and near its base (Fig. 104*A*).

Leaf primordia are formed very close to the stem apex. In some cases the young primordium seems to be derived from a single epidermal cell near the growing point of the stem. During the course of devel-

---

[1] Harvey-Gibson, 1894.   [2] Harvey-Gibson, 1902; Uphof, 1920.
[3] Bruchmann, 1905.   [4] Wordsell, 1910.
[5] Bower, 1908, 1935; Goebel, 1905.   [6] Harvey-Gibson, 1902.

opment of the primordium, there is the differentiation of a single embryonic vascular bundle which extends without branching to the apex of the leaf. At the leaf base this connects with a single embryonic leaf trace which runs diagonally down through the cortex to the stele.

The vascular bundle of a mature leaf is very simple. In *S. Kraussiana*, for example, the xylem near the base of the leaf consists of four to five tracheids, one of which is annular and the others spiral (Fig. 103*A*). All cells of the mesophyll between vein and epidermis contain chloroplasts. According to the species, each mesophyll cell contains a single large cup-shaped chloroplast or several chloroplasts. In either case there are several spindle-shaped, pyrenoid-like bodies at the center of the chloro-

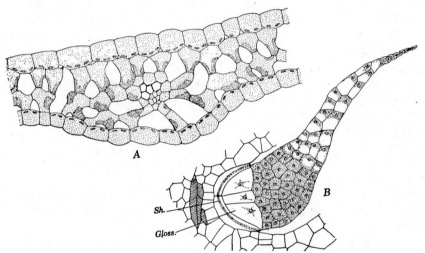

Fig. 103.—*Selaginella Kraussiana* A. Br. *A*, transverse section of a leaf. *B*, vertical section of a ligule passing through the sheath (*Sh.*) and glossopodium (*Gloss.*). (× 325.)

plast.[1] Each of the pyrenoid-like bodies may be transformed into a rudimentary starch grain. The only other archegoniates with a similar chloroplast structure are *Isoetes* and the Anthocerotae. The mesophyll has conspicuous intercellular spaces. The entire tissue may be organized into a spongy parenchyma, or there may be the differentiation of a distinct palisade layer toward the morphologically upper side of the leaf. The epidermis, which is one cell in thickness, may have stomata on the adaxial, on the abaxial, or on both surfaces. Stomata are largely restricted to portions of the epidermis external to the midrib.[2]

The ligule is a structure differentiated early in the ontogeny of a leaf and is one that matures early. It is formed from a transverse strip of the embryonic epidermis two to three cells tall and six to eight cells broad.[3]

[1] Ma, 1931.   [2] Harvey-Gibson, 1897.   [3] Harvey-Gibson, 1896.

Periclinal division of each of these cells results in an inner layer, which ultimately becomes the sheath of the ligule, and an outer layer, which develops into the remainder of the ligule. A mature ligule is tongue- to fan-shaped and more than one cell in thickness, except at the apex (Fig. 103B). Its base consists of a cup-shaped *sheath* whose cells are tubular in shape and without protoplasts when mature. In *S. Kraussiana* the sheath cells have a Casparian strip similar to that of endodermal cells. Immediately adjoining the sheath is the *glossopodium*, a hemispherical mass of thin-walled cells with greatly vacuolate protoplasts. The remaining cells of the ligule are more or less cubical and densely filled

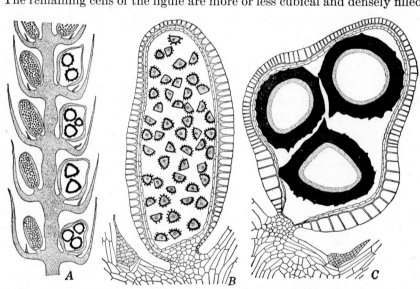

Fig. 104.—*Selaginella oregana* D. C. Eaton. *A*, vertical section of a portion of a strobilus. *B*, vertical section of a microsporangium. *C*, vertical section of a macrosporangium. (*A*, × 14; *B*, × 105; *C*, × 80.)

with protoplasm. The significance of the ligule is not apparent. It has been held that its precocious maturation results in a protective structure that prevents undue drying out of the stem apex and the young leaves, but this does not seem to hold in all cases since there are species whose ligules never overarch the growing apex.

The sporophylls of *Selaginella* are similar in structure to foliage leaves and each has a ligule at its base. A sporophyll bears a single stalked sporangium that lies on the adaxial face and between the ligule and base of the sporophyll. As is well known, the sporangia are of two distinct kinds, *macrosporangia* and *microsporangia*, so called because they contain, respectively, *macrospores* and *microspores*. According to the nature of their sporangia, the sporophylls are called *macrosporophylls* and *microsporophylls*. These are always in definite strobili. Strobili are always developed at the apices of branches, but the apex may continue vegetative growth after the sporophylls have been formed and thus produce a shoot with sporophylls and foliage leaves in alternate zones along the stem.[1] The sporophylls are always spirally arranged upon the strobilar axis, but the spiral is generally so condensed that the leaves appear to lie opposite each other in pairs and in four distinct vertical rows. Most species have macrosporophylls and microsporophylls borne in the same strobilus, but there are certain species in which a strobilus has only macrosporophylls or only microsporophylls.[2] When the strobilus has both kinds of sporophylls, all of those in the lower portion may be macrosporophylls and all in the upper portion microsporophylls, or there may be two vertical rows of each kind (Fig. 104A).

Development of macro- and microsporangia is identical up to the spore-mother-cell stage. There is considerable diversity of opinion as to whether the sporangium comes from a single initial cell or a transverse row of initials.[3] Some species have embryonic epidermal cells of the stem functioning as the sporangial initials, other species have cells at the leaf base developing into the sporangia. However, in both cases the end result is the same since the mature sporangium is a distinctly axillary structure at the base of the sporophyll. Irrespective of whether there is one or a group of initials, the first division is periclinal and into an outer *jacket initial* (or initials) and an inner *archesporial cell* (or cells) (Fig. 105A). Vertical and transverse division of the archesporial cell (or cells) results in a mass of sporogenous tissue (Fig. 105B). Development of the sporogenous tissue is accompanied by a development of the jacket initial (or initials) into a *jacket layer* two cells in thickness. Cells in the outer layer of the jacket eventually become thick-walled, those in the inner layer remain thin-walled. Even before the jacket has become two cells in thickness there is the differentiation of a conspicuous tapetum (Fig. 105C–D). Except for the portion immediately above the stalk all of this is derived from the outermost layer of sporogenous cells.

In microsporangia all sporogenous cells of the last cell generation in the sporogenous tissue are potential spore mother cells, but 10 to 20 per cent of them may disintegrate. The functional spore mother cells round up and become separated from one another during the reduction divisions. Each of the four microspores formed by division of a mother cell is broadly pyramidal with a rounded base (Fig. 104B). Its wall may be composed of two or of three layers.[4] These differences in wall structure are correlated with differences in the development of the microgametophyte. Unlike most other pteridophytes, the microspore begins to develop into a microgametophyte before it is shed from the sporangium. Liberation of

---

[1] Mitchell, 1910; Steel, 1923; Sykes and Stiles, 1910.   [2] Mitchell, 1910.
[3] Bower, 1894; Campbell, 1918; Lyon, 1901.   [4] Belajeff, 1885.

these immature microgametophytes from the sporangium is due to a vertical apical dehiscence of the sporangial jacket into two valves caused by differential hygroscopic changes in the apical and lateral parts of the jacket.   The sporangial jacket opens with a sudden jerk that ejects only a portion of the contained microgametophytes.   Those not immediately liberated may be ejected by subsequent closings and openings of the

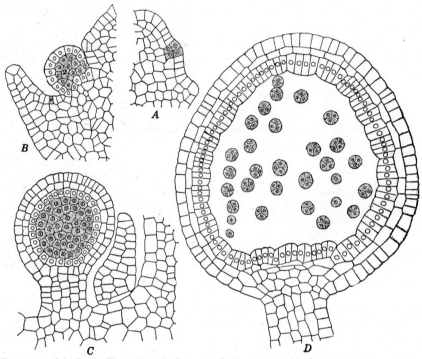

Fig. 105.—*Selaginella Kraussiana* A. Br.   *A*, thallus apex with initials of a microsporangium.   *B–D*, stages in development of microsporangia.   (× 325.)

jacket, or they may be dislodged from the opened sporangium by air currents.[1]

Developing macrosporangia produce a considerable number of macro-spore mother cells.   Generally all but one of these eventually disinte-grate, but the finding of 8, 12, and 24 macrospores in macrosporangia of exceptional individuals[2] shows that more than one spore mother cell of a macrosporangium may be functional.   Most macrosporangia with a single functional spore mother cell have it dividing to form four small macro-spores which increase equally in size as sporangial development continues. In certain species one or more of the four may regularly fail to enlarge, so

---

[1] Duthie, 1923, 1924; Mitchell, 1910.   [2] Duerden, 1929.

that the mature sporangium typically contains one, two, or three functional macrospores.[1]

Adult macrosporangia are generally four-lobed, as seen in top view, and have a single macrospore in each of the four lobes. During maturation of the sporangial jacket most of the cells in the outer layer have a thickening of the radial and inner tangential walls (Fig. 104*C*). However, there is no thickening of walls in a vertical apical strip of cells. Drying out of the sporangial jacket initiates a hygroscopic movement of the thick-walled cells that splits the sporangium along the strip of thin-walled jacket cells. In some species breaking of the jacket into two valves may be so abrupt that all macrospores, or the macrogametophytes

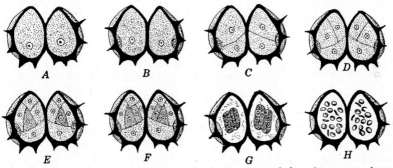

Fig. 106.—Stereodiagrams of stages in the development of the microgametophyte of *Selaginella Kraussiana* A. Br. The spores and microgametophytes are drawn as if they were split longitudinally and the two halves spread apart. (*Diagrams based upon Slagg, 1932.*)

into which they have developed, are catapulted from the sporangium;[2] in other species there is no ejection of them when the sporangium opens.[3]

Development of microspores into microgametophytes begins before the microsporangium dehisces. In *S. Kraussiana*, as in all other species, the first cell division is markedly asymmetrical and into a small lens-shaped *prothallial cell* and a large *antheridial cell*. The antheridial cell then divides in a plane perpendicular to the prothallial cell and both of its daughter cells divide in a plane at right angles to the first plane of division (Fig. 106*C*). One daughter cell of each pair thus formed divides no further and becomes the first cell of the jacket layer of the antheridium. The other daughter cell of each pair divides by means of a curving cell plate parallel to the prothallial cell (Fig. 106*D*). Of the two daughter cells thus formed, that nearest the prothallial cell divides periclinally into a *primary androgonial cell* and a *jacket cell* (Fig. 106*E*). Anticlinal division of its sister cell and periclinal division of one of the

---

[1] Duerden, 1929; Mitchell, 1910.
[2] Duthie, 1923; Mitchell, 1910.   [3] Lyon, 1901.

daughter cells thus formed results in two jacket cells and a primary androgonial cell (Fig. 106E–F). Development of the gametophyte halts for a time at this 13-celled stage when it consists of one prothallial cell, four primary androgonial cells, and eight jacket cells. It is at this stage of development that the gametophyte is shed from the microsporangium of *S. Kraussiana*. Development is resumed after shedding of the microgametophyte, and each of the four primary androgonial cells may undergo six successive divisions. The 256 androcytes thus formed become metamorphosed into biflagellate antherozoids. There is a disintegration of the jacket layer and of the prothallial cell during the later stages in development of the androgonial tissue (Fig. 106G). Thus, a mature microgametophyte consists only of a mass of antherozoids swimming about within the old microspore wall (Fig. 106H). For some species it is definitely known that these later stages in development take place upon the soil.[1] For other species it is definitely known[2] that the dust-like, immature microgametophytes sift into the partially opened macrosporangia and there complete their development. The advantage of the incipient type of pollination found in these latter species is obvious.

The microgametophyte of *Selaginella* is so reduced in size and so compressed because of its development within the microspore wall that its homologies with gametophytes of homosporous pteridophytes are obscure. It is generally agreed that the prothallial cell is vegetative and homologous with the entire vegetative tissue of homosporous forms. There is considerable difference of opinion concerning the nature of the antheridial cell. Some[3] hold that it is the initial of a single antheridium. Others[4] think that the antheridial cell is one that divides to form, depending upon the species, two or four antheridial initials.

Macrogametophytes also begin to develop while the macrospore is still within the sporangium, but the stage of development at which the macrogametophyte is shed is extremely variable. The macrogametophyte may be ejected from the sporangium before any trace of cellular organization is evident;[1] it may be shed shortly after the first archegonia are formed;[5] or it may be retained within the sporangium until after fertilization and a considerable development of the embryo.[6]

The structure and development of the macrogametophyte varies from species to species. Development of that of *S. Kraussiana*[7] begins with a conspicuous enlargement of the germinating macrospore and a secretion of a two-layered spore wall. Early in the enlargement there is a division of the macrospore nucleus, but this is not followed by cell division (Fig. 107A). Continued nuclear division results in a multinucleate protoplast

[1] Duthie, 1923.   [2] Lyon, 1901.   [3] Campbell, 1918; Slagg, 1932.
[4] Bruchmann, 1912.   [5] Campbell, 1918.   [6] Geiger, 1934; Lyon, 1901.
[7] Bruchmann, 1912; Campbell, 1902, 1918.

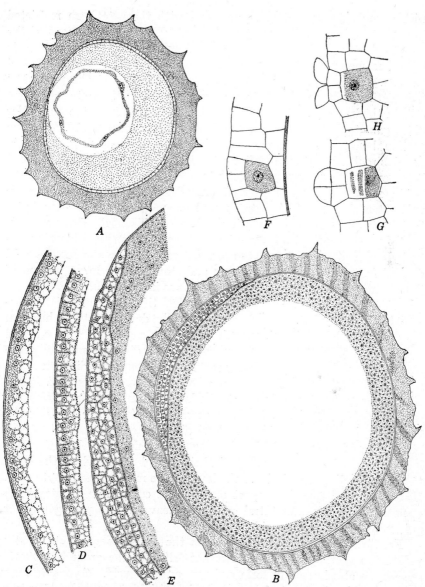

Fig. 107.—*Selaginella Kraussiana* A. Br. *A*, a very young macrogametophyte. *B*, macrogametophyte just before the formation of archegonia. *C–E*, stages in the development of cellular tissue of macrogametophytes. *F–H*, stages in the development of archegonia. (*A–B*, × 160; *C–E*, × 325; *F–H*, × 485.)

with a conspicuous central vacuole and with the cytoplasm restricted to a thin layer next the spore wall (Fig. 107C). Enlargement of the multinucleate gametophyte slows down after a time, and the cytoplasmic layer becomes thicker and thicker, eventually obliterating the central vacuole. Long before this time, free cell formation at the pyramidal end of the macrogametophyte produces a cellular tissue two to three cells in thickness (Fig. 107D–E), which is separated from the remainder of the gametophyte by a fairly conspicuous diaphragm (Fig. 107B). The portion below the diaphragm, which is densely packed with starch, remains multinucleate until after the embryo has begun to develop, but it too eventually becomes multicellular. Shortly after the apical tissue is formed, it becomes exposed by a cracking of the portion of the spore wall external to it. This tissue may become green, and gametophytes that have fallen upon soil may even develop rhizoids.[1] However, this photosynthetic tissue is of minor importance as far as nutrition of gametophyte and developing embryo are concerned, since the reserve food derived from the parent sporophyte and stored in the lower portion of the gametophyte is of far greater importance in their nutrition.

Most of the superficial cells of the apical tissue are potential archegonial initials, and several of these generally develop into archegonia. An archegonial initial divides periclinally into a *primary cover cell* and a *central cell* (Fig. 107F). The central cell next divides periclinally into a *primary canal cell* and a *primary ventral cell*. Periclinal division of the primary ventral cell produces a *ventral canal cell* and an *egg* (Fig. 107G). The primary canal cell does not divide but functions directly as the single *canal cell* of the mature archegonium. Meanwhile the primary cover cell, by two successive anticlinal divisions at right angles to each other, forms four *neck initials*. Transverse division of each of the neck initials results in a neck two cells in height, and one in which the outer tier of four cells projects above the level of the macrogametophyte (Fig. 107G–H). The spreading apart of the neck cells, after disintegration of neck canal cell and ventral canal cell, leaves a free passageway for swimming of the antherozoid to the egg.

Fertilization may take place while the macrogametophyte is still within the sporangium[2] or after it has fallen to the ground. Several species are also known to form embryos apogamously. Apogamy may be due to a development of an archegonial initial into an embryo[3] or to a parthenogenetic development of eggs lying within unopened archegonia.[4] There are also several species that are presumptively apogamous since they produce macrospores only or viable macrospores and abortive microspores.[5]

[1] Bruchmann, 1912.   [2] Lyon, 1901.   [3] Lyon, 1904.
[4] Bruchmann, 1912, 1919; Geiger, 1934.   [5] Goebel, 1915.

The developing embryo of *Selaginella* always pushes deeply into the macrogametophyte by means of a *suspensor*. In some cases this is composed of a few cells;[1] in other cases it appears to be a one-celled structure.[2] The first division of the zygote is generally (if not always) transverse. The two daughter cells that lie next to the neck of the archegonium may develop either into the suspensor; into the suspensor, foot, and rhizophore; or into all of these structures and the hypocotyledonary portion of the stem as well.

S. Martensii Spring. is representative of those species in which all parts of the embryo but the suspensor come from the lower daughter cell

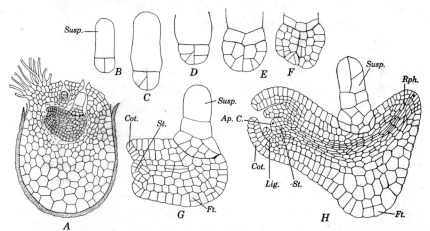

Fig. 108.—*Selaginella Martensii* Spring. *A*, macrogametophyte and embryo. *B–H*, stages in the development of embryos. (*Ap.C.*, apical cell; *Cot.*, cotyledon; *Ft.*, foot, *Lig.*, ligule; *Rph.*, rhizophore; *St.*, stem; *Susp.*, suspensor.) (*After Bruchmann*, 1909) (*A*, × 75; *B–G*, × 175; *H*, × 110.)

formed by division of the zygote. The first division of this cell is vertical, and the two daughter cells thus formed also divide vertically (Fig. 108*B*). One of these four cells, by a diagonal vertical division, forms the apical cell of the future stem (Fig. 108*C*). The remaining three cells, together with the sister cell of the apical cell, then divide transversely. All of the cells, in both the upper and lower tier of four, then undergo repeated vertical and transverse division (Fig. 108*D–F*). Cell division is somewhat more active in one of the lower quadrants, and this eventually leads to a differentiation of the *foot* of the embryo. As is the case with embryos of other Pteridophyta, the foot is a haustorial organ absorbing food from the gametophyte. About the time the foot begins to be apparent, a superficial cell in each of two diagonally opposed quadrants in the upper tier begins to function as the apical cell of a *cotyledon*. The two cotyledons developing from these two apical cells are identical in

[1] Bruchmann, 1912.　　[2] Bruchmann, 1913.

appearance.   They are similar to foliage leaves in that they have a ligule, but their internal structure is simpler.   Cotyledonary development is accompanied by an active division of the apical cell of the stem. The portion of the embryo immediately posterior to the cotyledons develops into the hypocotyledonary part of the stem.   Soon after cotyledons and stem apex have begun to develop, there is a differentiation of an apical cell from a superficial cell on one flank of the foot. Segments cut off from this apical cell develop into a structure that is root-like in appearance but one that is considered a rhizophore rather than a primary root.[1]

The developing sporophyte eventually grows through the macrogametophyte—the stem and its appendages growing upward and the rhizophore growing down into the soil.   The juvenile sporophyte is quite different from that of other Pteridophyta in that the cotyledons are borne directly upon the stem and in that there is a conspicuous hypocotyledonary stem below the level of the cotyledons.

ORDER 3.   LEPIDODENDRALES

Sporophytes of the Lepidodendrales were tree-like and had a secondary thickening of stem and roots.   The leaves were microphyllous and ligulate.   The roots were borne upon large rhizophores.   The sporophytes were heterosporous, and the sporophylls producing the sporangia were borne in strobili.   Members of the order are known only in the fossil condition from the Upper Devonian to the Triassic.

The Lepidodendrales, which include most of the giant lycopods, appeared during the Devonian, attained their peak during the Carboniferous, and disappeared at the end of the Triassic.[2]   Most of the genera in this order had a tree-like plant body in which the trunk frequently increased in thickness by cambial activity.   In spite of their tree-like size and secondary thickening, the stems of these plants were of a primitive type in that their primary vascular cylinders were protostelic to siphonostelic and had the protoxylem exarch in position.   As is the case with other members of the class, there were no gaps in the vascular cylinder above the points of departure of the leaf traces.

The leaves of Lepidodendrales were relatively large, were spirally arranged in most cases and generally, if not always, had ligules at their base.

The subterranean portions of the plant body are so much alike in genera referred to the order that it is impossible to distinguish between genera.   Remains of subterranean portions of Lepidodendrales, which were first placed in a separate genus (*Stigmaria*), are of widespread occurrence as casts but are also known as petrefactions.   A stigmarian

---

[1] Bruchmann, 1909, 1912.   [2] Berry, 1920.

"root system" consisted of four horizontal branches radiating from the base of the erect trunk of the plant. These horizontal branches, which were often dichotomously forked, approximated in size the aerial portions of the plant. They increased in diameter through secondary thickening of the vascular cylinder and through the formation of a periderm. The surface in older parts of each branch was rather closely beset with circular scars, each marking the former position of a rootlet. Fossil remains of portions of branches near the ultimate dichotomes have been found with the rootlets still attached instead of with scars. The rootlets, which were usually but a few millimeters in diameter and rarely more than 25 cm. in length, grew in all directions in the soil. Often they penetrated decaying vegetable matter lying on the ground, as is evidenced by the frequent occurence of stigmarian rootlets within various tissues of contemporary vegetation. Fossil remains of stigmarian rootlets almost always have a space between the cortex and the excentrically located stele. This space is generally interpreted as an artefact resulting from imperfect preservation of the inner cortical tissues. The occurrence of a similar space and a similar excentric location of the stele in roots of *Isoetes* (see Fig. 119) seems to show that the space in stigmarian rootlets is not an artefact.

From the physiological standpoint the stigmarian portion of lepidodendroid plants is comparable to a root system. From the anatomical standpoint, the primary branches are stem-like since the primary vascular tissue is an endarch siphonostele. However, the short lateral appendages (rootlets) borne by the dichotomously forking horizontal branches are more root-like than stem-like in structure. The most probable interpretation of the stigmarian "root system" is that it consists of four rhizophores similar in nature to those of *Selaginella*.[1] That is, it consists of horizontally growing leafless branches which bear numerous true roots.

The Lepidodendrales are divided into three families.

FAMILY 1. LEPIDODENDRACEAE

The Lepidodendraceae include a number of tree-like genera, all of which are readily distinguishable from other Lepidodendrales by the conspicuous spirally arranged leaf scars on their trunks. These scars are so distinctive that it is possible to assign plants to the family even when they are known only as casts.

Over a hundred species have been described for *Lepidodendron*, the best-known member of the family. This genus appeared in the Late Devonian, flourished abundantly throughout the Carboniferous, and

[1] Scott, 1920; Wordsell, 1920.

disappeared during the Permian or shortly thereafter.   A majority of the
Lepidodendrons were tall trees, in some cases attaining an estimated
height of 40 meters, with straight shafts that did not branch for some

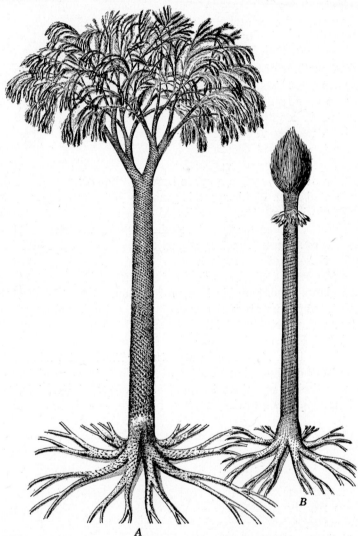

Fig. 109.—*A*, reconstruction of *Lepidodendron obovatum* Sternb.   *B*, reconstruction of a
species of *Sigillaria*.   (*After Hirmer, 1927.*)

distance above the ground (Fig. 109*A*).   The crown of the tree was
freely and dichotomously branched, with the smaller branches clothed
with spirally arranged leaves.   The leaves, which were ultimately shed
from the tree, were simple, acicular to linear, and up to 18 mm. in length.

Certain species are known in which a typical trunk of *Lepidodendron* is attached to a typical stigmarian "root system."

Most species of the genus had a secondary thickening of the stem, but certain species seem to have lacked a cambium. The central cylinder of the stem was protostelic or siphonostelic, but in either case the protoxylem was exarch in position and polyarch (Fig. 110*A*). The steles were small in proportion to the size of the cortex, and the latter was frequently complicated in structure. In *L. vasculare* Binney (*L.*

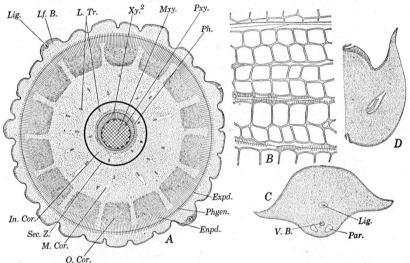

Fig. 110.—*A–B, Lepidendron vasculare* Binney. *A*, transverse section of a stem. *B*, transverse section of secondary xylem. *C–D*, radial and tangential vertical sections of leaf base of *Lepidodendron aculeata* Sternb. (*Enpd.*, endophelloderm; *Expd.*, exophelloderm; *In. Cor.*, inner cortex; *L. Tr.*, leaf trace; *Lf. B.*, leaf base; *Lig.*, ligule; *M. Cor.*, middle cortex; *Mxy.*, metaxylem; *O. Cor.*, outer cortex; *Par.*, parichnos; *Phgen.* phellogen; *Ph.*, phloem; *Pxy.*, protoxylem; *Sec. Z.*, secretory zone; *V.B.*, vascular bundle; *Xy.²*, secondary xylem.) (*B*, × 40; *C–D*, × 2.)

selaginoides Sternberg) the cortex consisted of the following parts:[1] (1) a parenchymatous *inner cortex*, homogeneous except for the leaf traces; (2) a *secretory zone* composed of intermingled large and small cells, many of which were filled with a dark-colored substance; (3) a *middle cortex*, similar in appearance to the inner cortex; (4) an *outer cortex* consisting of alternate radial masses of thick- and thin-walled elements. Early in the ontogeny of this stem and even before secondary thickening of the vascular cylinder, there was the differentiation of a *periderm* in the outer cortex. This was formed by a *phellogen* that cut off many more *endophelloderm* elements toward its inner face than *exophelloderm* elements toward its outer face.

[1] Seward, 1910.

Secondary thickening of the stele of *L. vasculare* was due to a *cambium* that formed secondary xylem toward the interior and secondary phloem toward the exterior.   The appearance of the secondary tissues in *Lepido-dendron* differs from that of corresponding tissues in modern Spermato-phyta in that the cells in the cambium do not exactly correspond with the radial elements in the secondary xylem.   In many cases the cambial activity of *L. vasculare* was restricted to one side of the vascular cylin-der; later it encircled the entire cylinder.   Stems of these plants, there-fore, had an excentric cylinder of secondary wood.   The secondary xylem of *Lepidodendron* consisted of radial rows of tracheids in which groups of tracheids were laterally separated from one another by *wood rays* (Fig. 110*B*).   Some rays were uniseriate and one to many cells in height; other rays were multiseriate.   Cells in the xylem portion of the rays were radially elongate and had spirally thickened walls.   Relatively little secondary phloem was formed external to the cambium.   In the few cases where this has been found well preserved, it seems to be com-posed of elongate thin-walled elements.

The only portions of leaves in most petrifactions of *Lepidodendron* are the leaf bases which persist after the leaves have fallen away.   When cut close to their attachment to the stem, the leaf bases are triangular in cross section; when cut farther out, they are rhomboidal (Fig. 110*C*). In the median vertical axis and close to the lower epidermis, the leaf base has a single small vascular bundle.   This is flanked on either side by a *parichnos*.   These are bundle-like strands of parenchymatous tissue that parallel the vascular bundle for some distance but eventually become indistinguishable from the mesophyll cells of the leaf.   Because of its association with aerenchyma tissue in the leaf and because of its inward extension into the cortex, it is thought[1] that the parichnos had the function of taking in air through the leaf, or the leaf base, and con-ducting it inward to the stem and downward to the subterranean portion of the plant.   Leaf bases of *Lepidodendron* usually have a small *ligule* on the upper surface.   In many leaves, as in those of *L. aculeatum* Sternberg, the ligule was so deeply embedded in a flask-shaped cavity that it appears to be a central structure when the leaf base is seen in transverse section.   The distal portions of the leaf were essentially like those of *Selaginella* or *Lycopodium*.[2]

Numerous fossil lepidodendraceous strobili are known.   These are generally referred to the genus *Lepidostrobus*, but in certain cases the strobili have been found attached to a branch identical in structure with that of *Lepidodendron*.   According to the species, the strobili were 2.5 to 30 cm. long and 1 to 7.5 cm. broad.   They bore numerous densely crowded sporophylls (Fig. 111*A*).   In most cases these were spirally

[1] Weiss, 1907.   [2] Scott, 1920.

arranged, but in a few instances they were verticillate. Each sporophyll bore a single sessile elongate sporangium on its adaxial face. Just beyond the sporangium the sporophyll had a small ligule. Sporangia of certain species have been shown to be incompletely septate in a manner somewhat similar to those of *Isoetes*. It has been suggested[1] that these septa or trabeculae were concerned with the nutrition of the spore mass rather than with mechanical support of the sporangial jacket.

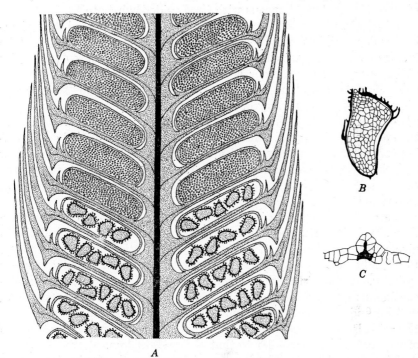

A

Fig. 111.—*A*, Diagram showing a portion of a strobilus of *Lepidostrobus* in vertical section. *B–C*, gametophyte and archegonium of *Lepidostrobus Veltheimianus* Sternb. (*B–C, after Scott, 1920.*)   (*B*, × 25, *C*, × 135.)

In spite of the fact that a few strobili of *Lepidostrobus* have been found only with small-sized spores, there is considerable evidence for presuming that all species were heterosporous.[2]   In the cases where the cones are known to be heterosporous, the upper sporophylls bear microsporangia and the lower ones macrosporangia. The macrosporangia regularly contained more than four macrospores, but the number was small and probably never more than 16. The macrospores began to develop into macrogametophytes while still within the sporangium. The discovery of cellular macrogametophytes with archegonia[3] (Fig.

[1] Bower, 1894.   [2] Scott, 1920.   [3] Gordon, 1910.

111*B–C*) shows that the macrogametophytes were quite like those of *Selaginella*.

FAMILY 2.   SIGILLARIACEAE

The Sigillariaceae are distinguishable from other Lepidodendrales by their massive, sparingly branched trunks on which the leaf scars are in vertical series and often borne on vertical ribs.   The family was more or less contemporaneous with the Lepidodendraceae.

Sigillaria, with a hundred or more species, is widespread in Carboniferous deposits, but most of these species are known only as casts.   The trunk of *Sigillaria*, which was unbranched or with a few dichotomies at its apex, was a columnar shaft that tapered slightly from base to apex (Fig. 109*B*).   The discovery of trunks more than 2 meters in diameter and the discovery of trunks in which the known portions are more than 22 meters long shows that the genus included some of the largest tree-like lycopods.   The apex of the trunk terminated in a sheathing tuft of grass-like leaves, and in certain species these were a meter or so in length.[1]   Leaves of *Sigillaria* were similar in structure to those of *Lepidodendron*.   The basal portion of the sigillarian tree was a typical stigmarian system.

Petrified remains of *Sigillaria* are of much less frequent occurrence than are those of *Lepidodendron*, but enough material has accumulated to give a general knowledge of the internal organization of the sporophyte.   Practically all of the stems thus far found have a siphonostelic vascular cylinder.   Some of the more recent members of the genus have a discontinuous siphonostele.   In either case the protoxylem is exarch in position and polyarch.   The secondary xylem consists of radially arranged tracheids laterally separated from one another by rays.   The structure of the cortex is quite similar to that of *Lepidodendron*.

The Sigillariaceae differ more markedly from the Lepidodendraceae in their fructifications than they do in vegetative structure.   The strobili were borne in transverse whorls below the leaves and appear to have been shed after spore production was completed.   Strobili associated with *Sigillaria* are of two types: those referred to the genus *Sigillariostrobus* and those referred to the genus *Mazocarpon*.   Strobili of the former had long peduncles closely beset with acicular leaves.   The leaves at the distal end (the *bracts*) were sterile; the lower leaves were sporophylls and had a single sporangium on the adaxial surface.[2]   Both the bracts and the sporophylls were shed from the axis of the strobilus before the latter dropped from the plant.   There is a strong presumption that *Sigillariostrobus* was heterosporous, and this has been definitely established for *Mazocarpon*.[3]

[1] Scott, 1920.   [2] Kidston, 1897.   [3] Benson, 1918.

FAMILY 3. BOTHRODENDRACEAE

The Bothrodendraceae, of which *Bothrodendron* is the best known, are the oldest family of the Lepidodendrales and have a chronological range from the Devonian to early in the Upper Carboniferous.

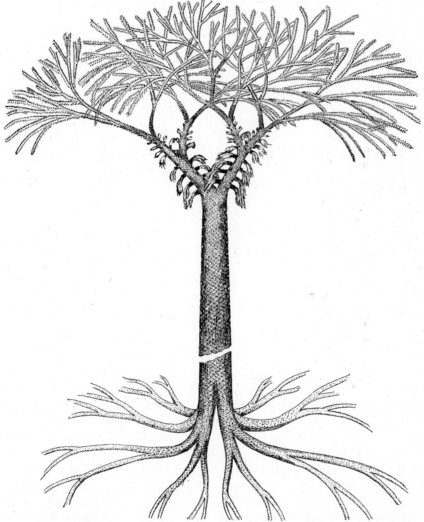

Fig. 112.—Restoration of *Bothrodendron minutifolium* Boulay. (*After Hirmer,* 1927.)

The sporophyte of *Bothrodendron* was a tree of much the same proportions as *Lepidodendron*. The lower part of this tree was massive and unbranched; the upper part was repeatedly branched in progressively

smaller dichotomies (Fig. 112). The leaves, which were restricted to
the branchlets, were small, lanceolate, and similar in size and arrangement to those of *Lycopodium*.[1] The "root system" was the stigmarian
type typical of Lepidodendrales.

The surface of the trunk was relatively smooth and had small leaf
scars in low spirals. Fossil trunks of certain species have two opposite
vertical rows of conspicuous circular scars. These scars are due to the
abscission of branches,[2] and it is thought that these were foliage branches
rather than fertile ones.

B. mundum (Will.) Lomax, which is here selected to show internal
organization of the stem, had either a protostelic or a siphonostelic

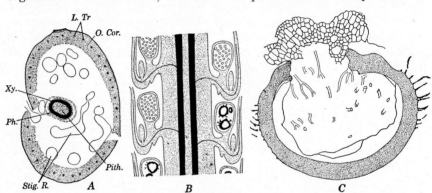

Fig. 113.—*A*, transverse section of a stem of *Bothrodendron mundun* (Will.) Lomax. *B*,
portion of a strobilus of *B. mundum*. *C*, gametophyte of a species of *Bothrodendron*.
(*L. Tr.*, leaf trace; *O. Cor.*, outer cortex; *Ph.*, phloem; *Stig. R.*, stigmarian rootlets; *Xy.*,
xylem.)   (*B, after Watson*, 1908; *C, after McLean*, 1912.)   (*A*, × 2; *B*, × 6.)

vascular cylinder (Fig. 113*A*).   In either case the protoxylem was exarch.
Most specimens of this species that have been found show no secondary
thickening of the vascular cylinder, but one stem with a conspicuous
development of secondary xylem has been recorded.[3] The cortex of *B.
mundum* was several times broader than the stele. The exterior portion
of it, which contained numerous leaf traces, was composed of radially
arranged, thick-walled cells. The inner portion of the cortex, except
for that immediately external to the stele, is always lacking in specimens of this plant. This shows that the inner cortex was a delicate
thin-walled tissue.

Bothrodendron was heterosporous and had the sporophylls similar in
shape to those of *Lycopodium*. It is uncertain whether they were borne
at the apices of vegetative branches or on special lateral branches on
older parts of the trunk. *B. mundum* has been shown to have had both
types of sporophyll in the same strobilus with the microsporophylls

[1] Scott, 1920.   [2] Lindsey, 1915.   [3] Williamson, 1889.

above the macrosporophylls (Fig. 113*B*).   The sporophylls were ligulate and with a single axillary sporangium at their bases.[1]

A single fossil macrogametophyte, found external to a macrosporangium, has been referred to *Bothrodendron*.[2]   This gametophyte has a pad of prothallial tissue external to the apex of the old macrospore wall (Fig. 113*C*).   Within the prothallial tissue are several deeply embedded, archegonia-like cavities.   On the ventral side of the tissue and growing into the cavity of the old macrospore are several rhizoid-like outgrowths.   It is thought that these are fungi rather than rhizoids.

ORDER 4.   LEPIDOCARPALES

Sporophytes of Lepidocarpales were either like those of Lepidodendrales or like those of Selaginellales.   The sporangia were heterosporous, but, unlike all other Lycopodineae, there was a permanent retention of the macrogametophytes within the macrosporangia.   Lepidocarpales are known only in the fossil condition and from the Carboniferous.

The Lepidocarpales include two fossil genera whose incipient seed-like mode of reproduction is so different from that of other Lycopodinae that they are placed in a separate order.   This order is not a natural one, since the two families into which it is divided (*Lepidocarpaceae* and *Miadesmaceae*) differ markedly in structure.

FAMILY 1.   LEPIDOCARPACEAE

The single genus of this family (*Lepidocarpon*) has three species, all known only from the Carboniferous of Great Britian.   The vegetative structure of *Lepidocarpon*, so far as known, was similar to that of *Lepidodendron*.   The sporophylls were heterosporous and united in strobili similar to those of *Lepidostrobus*.   Young macrosporangia, which were radially elongate to the axis of the strobilus, were freely exposed on the upper surface of the macrosporophyll.[3]   Older sporophylls had the tissue beneath the lateral flanks of the sporangium growing up, or becoming upturned, to form an integument that completely surrounded the macrosporangium (Fig. 114).   This integument was open at its apex, but the opening differs from the micropyle of gymnosperms in that it is a slit along the entire apex of the integument.   Very young sporangia contained four macrospores.   Later on one of these developed into a gametophyte which completely filled the sporangium.   The other three spores disintegrated.   The seed-like structure thus developed (gametophyte, sporangium, and integument), together with the remainder of the sporophyll, became detached from the strobilus and fell to the ground. It is not known whether fertilization took place before or after this abscission, but the failure to find remains of microspores within the

[1] Watson, 1908.   [2] McLean, 1912.   [3] Scott, 1901.

integument or to find embryos within the macrogametophytes[1] indicates that this may have taken place after abscission.

FAMILY 2. MIADESMIACEAE

The other Carboniferous seed-like lycopod (*Miadesmia*) seems to have been evolved independently. The sporophyte of *Miadesmia* resembles that of *Selaginella* in external appearance, and its internal organization is also similar, even to the trabecular cell between stele and inner cortex. The sporophylls were in lax strobili, but it is uncertain whether micro- and macrosporophylls were borne in the same strobilus. The difficulty

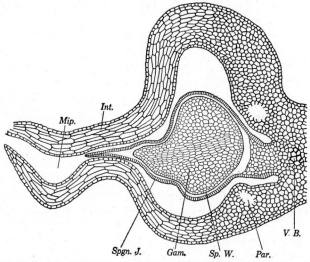

FIG. 114.—Diagrammatic longitudinal section of "seed" of *Lepidocarpon Lomaxi* Scott. (*Gam.*, macrogametophyte; *Int.*, integument; *Mip.*, micropyle; *Par.*, parichnos; *Sp.W.*, wall of macrospore; *Spng. J.*, jacket of macrosporangium; *V.B.*, vascular bundle. (× 55.)

in determining this question is due to the fact that both types of sporo- phyll were shed after they became mature. The macrosporangia con- tained but one functional macrospore, and this grew into a gametophyte which completely filled the sporangium.[2] As the macrogametophyte became mature, there was a breaking of the sporangial apex and a slight protrusion of the gametophyte. The sporangium and its contained gametophyte became completely ensheathed, except for a small micro- pyle-like opening at the distal end, by an enfolding of the macrosporophyll (Fig. 115). This ensheathing structure of the sporangium looks like the integument and micropyle of a gymnosperm but is a structure of an entirely different morphological nature.

[1] Scott, 1901.   [2] Benson, 1908.

It is universally agreed that seed-bearing plants have been evolved from heterosporous pteridophytes. Development of the seed habit involves certain features not found in heterosporous pteridophytes. These include: (1) permanent retention of the macrogametophyte within the sporangium; (2) lack of dehiscence of the sporangium; (3) surrounding of the sporangium by an outgrowth from the sporophyll, the integument; (4) a receptive structure, pollen chamber or stigmatic surface, where microgametophytes may mature in the vicinity of macrogametophytes; and (5) abscission of the seed from the sporophyll.

Application of these criteria to the Lepidocarpales shows that they are quasispermatophytic rather than true seed plants. They are seed-

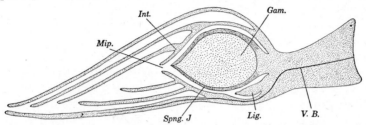

Fig. 115.—Diagram of a longitudinal section of a "seed" of *Miadesmia membranacea* Bern. (*Gam.*, macrogametophyte; *Int.*, integument; *Lig.*, ligule; *Mip.*, micropyle; *Spng. J.*, jacket of macrosporangium. *V.B.*, vascular bundle.) (*Based upon Benson*, 1908.)

like in their permanent retention of the macrogametophyte within the macrosporangium. One genus (*Miadesmia*) is not seed-like in its dehiscent sporangium, the other may have had the same opening of the sporangium. The enclosing layer surrounding the macrosporangium is not a typical integument in *Lepidocarpon* and is merely an enfolded sporophyll in *Miadesmia*. The reproductive structures of Lepidocarpales also differ from those of true seed plants in that they do not become detached from the macrosporophyll but are shed with and remain attached to it.

ORDER 5. ISOETALES

Sporophytes of Isoetales are herbaceous and have a secondary thickening of the stem. The leaves are microphyllous and ligulate. The roots are borne upon massive rhizophores. The sporophytes are heterosporous, with or without the sporophylls grouped in definite strobili. The antherozoids of the single living genus are multiflagellate. Members of the order are known from the Middle Triassic to the present.

Isoetes differs so markedly from other living Pteridophyta that its proper systematic position has long been a matter of dispute. During recent years, a majority of botanists, with or without reservations, have adhered to the view that its affinities are with the lycopodiaceous Pteridophyta. The arguments favoring this include: the lycopsidan vascular organization, the ligulate leaves, and the single sporangium on the adaxial face of the sporophylls. There are a number of additional features which, when taken collectively, seem to show that *Isoetes* has more in conmon with the Lepidodendrales than with other Lycopodinae. These include: the presence of a stigmaria-like rhizophore, roots with the same distinctive structure as stigmarian "rootlets," a vestigial parichnos in the leaves, a lepidodendroid trabeculation of the sporangia, and the regular formation of more than four macrospores in the macrosporangia. Some botanists think that *Isoetes* differs too much from the lycopods to be placed with them. One of the chief arguments of those adhering to this view is the multiple flagellation of the antherozoid. Those who do not place *Isoetes* with the lycopods either think that it is more nearly related to the Filicineae[1] or think that it is so different from other Pteridophyta that it should be placed in a class by itself.[2]

Many botanists include only *Isoetes* and its fossil relative *Isoetites* among the Isoetales. The phylogenetic connection between *Isoetes* and *Pleuromeia* has been recognized by many, but Seward[3] is one of the few who have formally assigned *Isoetes* and *Pleuromeia* to the same group. He places them in the same family (the Isoetaceae), but the families that he recognizes among the lycopods are the equivalent of the orders in most other systems of classification. As will be shown on a later page, *Isoetes* and *Pleuromeia* have a similar stem structure. The two are also alike in their ligulate leaves, their root structure, and their trabeculate sporangia. The abaxial position of sporangia on the sporophylls of *Pleuromeia* cannot be entirely disregarded, but except for this there is a remarkable resemblance between *Pleuromeia* and *Isoetes*. On the other hand, except for its peculiar rhizophore, *Pleuromeia* has much in common with *Sigillaria*. Thus it is a connecting link between *Isoetes* and *Sigillaria*, but one whose affinities are more with the former than with the latter. On this account *Pleuromeia* and the imperfectly known genera related to it should be referred to the Isoetales and the order tentatively divided into two families.

FAMILY 1. PLEUROMEIACEAE

Sporophytes of the Pleuromeiaceae had an upright unbranched stem with leaves at the upper end and a massive rhizophore at the basal end. The sporophylls, which bore their sporangia on the abaxial face, were in definitely organized strobili.

Pleuromeia, the best-known member of the family, is a fossil with a chronological range limited to the Middle Triassic. The plant body, which attained a height of about two meters, consisted of an erect

---

[1] Campbell, 1918; Farmer, 1890.
[2] Engler and Gilg, 1924; West and Takeda, 1915.   [3] Seward, 1910.

unbranched axis subtended by a massive quadriradiate rhizophore (Fig. 116). The upper part of the axis was densely clothed with spirally arranged long narrow leaves, each of which had a ligule at its base.[1] The lower part of the axis had numerous spirally arranged leaf scars. The axis terminated in a distinct strobilus with closely over-lapping shield-shaped sporophylls. *Pleuromeia* was heterosporous, but with macro- and microsporophylls borne on separate plants. One con-spicuous difference between sporo-phylls of this genus and those of the Lycopodinae previously discussed is that the single sporangium produced by each sporophyll is borne on the underside of the leaf. The sporangia were relatively large and had the same internal trabeculation as in those of *Lepidostrobus* and of *Isoetes*.

The stelar portion of the axis was an actinostele with the protoxylem exarch in position. The only sec-ondary thickening of the axis was that resulting from the activity of a phellogen arising toward the ex-terior of the cortex. This produced a thick periderm quite similar to that found in Lepidodendrales. The rhizophoric portion of the plant body differed from the stigmarian type of rhizophore in that each of the four rhizophores was unbranched and grew but very little in length.

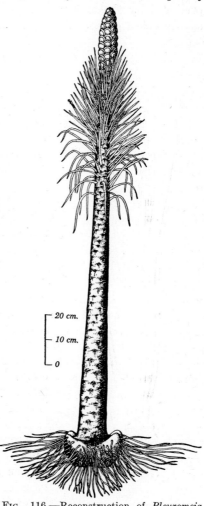

Fig. 116.—Reconstruction of *Pleuromeia Sternbergii* Corda. (*After Hirmer*, 1933.)

However, each of the four massive rhizophores bore numerous roots on the lower surface, and the roots thus borne were identical in structure with stigmarian "rootlets."

FAMILY 2. ISOETACEAE

Sporophytes of the Isoetaceae have a corm-like stem that is not externally differentiated into axis and rhizophore. The sporophylls,

---

[1] Hirmer, 1933; Mägdefrau, 1931.

which bear their sporangia on the adaxial face, are not arranged in definite strobili. The sporophytes are heterosporous and antherozoids produced by the male gametophytes are multiflagellate. This family contains two genera: *Isoetes*, a genus of living plants, and *Isoetites*, a fossil genus with a record extending back to the Lower Cretaceous.

Isoetes has 64 species,[1] 19 of which occur in the United States. A large majority of the species are hydrophytes that grow immersed in water or that grow on swampy land. A few species, including certain ones found in southern California, grow in habitats that are completely dry for a portion of the year.

The plant body of *Isoetes* is 5 to 50 cm. tall. It consists of a very short, two- or three-lobed, corm-like "stock" which bears a densely crowded rosette of stiff awl-shaped leaves on its upper surface (Fig. 117). The lowest (outermost) leaves on the stock are sterile; successively within them are macrosporophylls, microsporophylls, and leaves with immature sporangia.[2] The lower surface of the stock bears many dichotomously branched roots. These appear to cover the entire lower surface; in reality, they are in two or three groups accordingly as the stock is two-or three-lobed.

The term stock has been proposed[3] for the tuberous axis bearing the roots and leaves, since it has been interpreted both as a stem[4] and as a stem combined with a stigmarian type of rhizophore.[5] When stripped of its leaves and roots, the stock has, according to the species, two or three deep vertical furrows that make it, respectively, deeply two- or three-lobed. Even in this denuded condition, the external form gives no indication of its true morphological nature. The answer to this question rests upon the analysis of the vascular system. Vertical sections of two-lobed stocks, cut both parallel to and at right angles to the

Fig. 117.—*Isoetes Bolanderi* Engelm. (Natural size.)

[1] Pfeiffer, N. E., 1922.   [2] Osborn, 1922; Smith, R. W., 1900.
[3] Lang, 1915.   [4] Scott and Hill, 1900; Stokey, 1909.
[5] Lang 1915; West and Takeda, 1915.

furrows, taken in conjunction with serial transverse sections, show that the portion of the vascular system connected with the leaf traces is a vertical cylinder (Fig. 118*A–C*). The lower portion of the vascular system, connected with steles of the roots, is a spade-shaped structure flattened in the plane of the surface furrows on the stock. Three-lobed stocks differ from the foregoing in that the lower part of the vascular

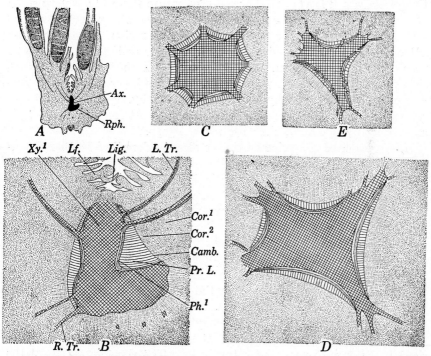

Fig. 118.—*Isoetes Nuttallii* A.Br. *A*, vertical section of "corm" and bases of leaves borne by it. *B*, diagram of the vascular portion of Fig. *A*. *C*, diagram of a transverse section through the axis portion of Fig. *A*. *D–E*, diagrams of transverse sections through the upper and the lower regions of the rhizophore portion of Fig. *A*. (*Ax.*, axis; *Camb.*, cambium; *Cor.*[1], primary cortex; *Cor.*[2], secondary cortex; *Lf.*, leaf; *Lig.*, ligule; *L. Tr.*, leaf trace; *Ph.*[1], primary phloem; *Pr. L.*, prismatic layer; *Rph.*, rhizophore; *R. Tr.*, root trace; *Xy.*[1], primary xylem.) (*A*, × 5; *B–E*, × 60.)

system consists of four radiating arms. One pair of arms diverge widely from each other. The other pair are more or less fused with each other (Fig. 118*D–E*). Thus, the lower portion of the vascular system appears to be triradiate. When taken by itself, the vascular system of *Isoetes* shows a remarkable resemblance to the plant body of *Pleuromeia*. In *Pleuromeia* the plant body is externally differentiated into an unbranched erect axis subtended by a massive recurved rhizophore. In *Isoetes* the plant body is so telescoped and the cortex is so thick that differentiation into axis and rhizophore is not externally evident. However, the differentiation into axis and rhizophore does become apparent when the vascular system is taken by itself and viewed as a three-dimensional object.

The growing point of the axis lies in a shallow depression at the distal end of the stock. Growth seems to be initiated by a group of meristematic cells rather than by a single apical cell. Vertical elongation of the stock is very slight, and the mature tissues lie a very short distance back from the embryonic region. The stelar portion of the mature region differs sharply from the cortical region, but the two are not delimited by an endodermis. The vascular cylinder of the axis is protostelic in organization. In very young portions of the stem, it consists of a central core of xylem ensheathed by a layer of phloem. The xylem consists of parenchyma intermingled with very short spiral and reticulate tracheids. Numerous leaf traces depart from the stele, and, as in other Lycopodinae, these are without gaps.

Maturation of the primary tissues already described is followed by the differentiation of a cambium just external to the phloem. There is great diversity of opinion as to functioning of this cambium and as to the nature of the tissues formed by it. It has been held[1] that the cambium forms derivatives toward its inner face only, but there is good evidence to show that it cuts off a secondary cortex externally and a secondary tissue internally. The secondary tissue cut off internally has been interpreted as secondary xylem,[2] as secondary phloem,[3] and as a secondary tissue containing both tracheids and sieve tubes.[4] Probably the best solution of the difficulty is to follow the practice of the older anatomists and to refer to this tissue as the *prismatic layer*. The first few derivatives cut off inward from a cambial cell may mature into reticulate tracheids (secondary tracheids), but all of the later-formed derivatives mature into sieve tubes or into parenchymatous cells. The sieve tubes are of the same size as the parenchymatous cells but may be distinguished from the latter by the sieve plates on their walls and by the lack of starch within their protoplasts.

Except for the leaf traces, the primary cortex in the stem portion of the stock consists of a homogeneous, starch-filled, parenchymatous tissue with conspicuous intercellular spaces. The radial diameter of the mature cortex is several times that of the vascular cylinder (Fig. 118A). This, in conjunction with the lack of vertical elongation, frequently results in a stock broader than it is tall. The stem portion of the stock produces a new set of leaves each year. As the new leaves develop, the old leaves are sloughed off by the formation of an abscission layer in the outer portion of the cortex. In certain cases the abscission layer is a layer of

[1] Lang, 1915A. [2] Stokey, 1909.
[3] West and Takeda, 1915. [4] Scott and Hill, 1900.

mucilage-filled cells. The cortex in older portions of the stem is externally bounded by a scar tissue formed by this abscission of the outer portion of the cortex, and the outermost cells of the scar tissue may be sclerified.

There is also a cortical region external to the rhizophore portion of the stock. Development of cortical tissue is greater on the lateral than on the lower face of the rhizophore. The production of a smaller amount of cortical tissue external to the lower face of the rhizophore is the reason for the vertical grooves evident on the surface of the stock. The growing

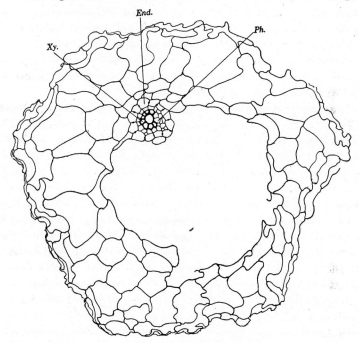

Fig. 119.—Transverse section of root of *Isoetes Nuttallii* A.Br. (*End.*, endodermis; *Ph.*, phloem; *Xy.*, xylem.) (× 215.)

apex of the rhizophore portion of the stock also produces a new set of roots every year, and they lie in a row on either side of the median axis of each lobe. Accordingly as the stock is two or three lobed, there is a formation of either two or three double rows of roots each year. Roots formed in previous growing seasons come to lie farther and farther back from the growing apices of the rhizophore as new sets of roots are formed each year. These old roots may persist for more than one year, or they may function for one year only and then be sloughed off by the formation of an abscission layer at the surface of the cortex of the rhizophore.[1]

[1] Osborn, 1922.

The embryonic apex of an *Isoetes* root has an apical meristem instead of a single apical cell. Now and then the apical meristem becomes divided into two portions which grow at equal rates and so produce the characteristic dichotomy of the roots. Posterior to the apical meristem the root becomes differentiated into stele and cortex (Fig. 119). The vascular cylinder matures into a monarch protostele. The xylem and phloem of this stele are collateral and so oriented that the xylem is on the side of the root next to, and the phloem on the side away from, the rhizophore. At the periphery of the stele is an endodermal layer, readily recognizable because of the Casparian strips in the radial walls. Portions of the roots extending outward from the stock contain a large C-shaped intercellular space in their cortices. This space results from a breaking down of cortical cells external to the phloem side of the stele. The occurrence of a similar cavity in stigmarian "rootlets" furnishes another reason for linking *Isoetes* with the Lepidodendrales.

The leaves, both fertile and sterile, taper abruptly from a broad base to an elongate acicular portion. Each leaf bears a single ligule on the adaxial surface and at the juncture of the acicular and basal portions. The ligule is similar in structure to that of *Selaginella*. Within the leaf is a single vascular bundle, continuous with a leaf trace departing from the central cylinder. The bundle is collateral throughout its entire length, but sometimes it tends to become concentric toward the tip of the leaf. Sporophylls of certain species have the lower portion of the bundle flanked on either side by a mucilage canal. These canals are thought to be homologous with the parichnos strands found in leaves of Lepidodendrales.[1] The awl-shaped portion of the leaf is traversed longitudinally by four cylindrical air chambers that may be transversely septate. The mesophyll lateral to the air chambers may be wholly parenchymatous, or it may contain four longitudinal strands of sclerenchyma, so located that they alternate with the air chambers. The superficial layer of a leaf is a well-defined epidermis in which there are stomata if the plant does not grow submerged in water.

Each sporophyll bears a single flattened sporangium between the ligule and leaf base, and on the adaxial face. The sporangium lies within a depression in the leaf base which is completely or incompletely roofed over by a membranous outgrowth (the *velum*) arising just below the ligule (Fig. 120A).

Early stages in the ontogeny of macro- and microsporangia are alike. The first evidence of sporangial development[2] is the periclinal division of a group of embryonic epidermal cells somewhat below the ligule. Cells in the outer layer formed by this division are jacket initials, those of the inner layer are archesporial cells (Fig. 120C). The velum is developed

[1] Hill, T. G., 1906.　　[2] Bower, 1894.

from epidermal cells between the sporangial initials and the ligule. Development of the velum proceeds rapidly, and it is a clearly evident structure before the sporangial initials divide periclinally (Fig. 120*B*). The margin of the velum toward the sporangium develops much more extensively than does the margin toward the ligule. Downward development of the velum margin may continue until the sporangium is completely overarched, or it may cease before overarching is completed. The archesporial cells divide and redivide to form a massive sporogenous

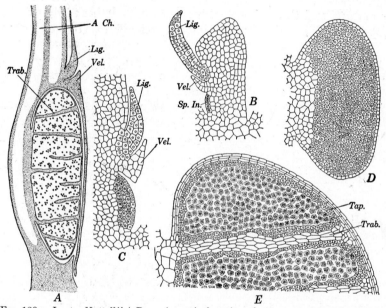

Fig. 120.—*Isoetes Nuttallii* A.Br. *A*, vertical section of a mature microsporangium and leaf base. *B*, a young leaf with primordium of a sporangium. *C–E*, stages in development of sporangia. (*A. Ch.*, air chambers; *Lig.*, ligule; *Sp. In.*, sporangial initials; *Tap.*, tapetum; *Trab.*, trabecula; *Vel.*, velum.) (*A*, × 14; *B–E*, × 140.)

tissue (Fig. 120*D*). Late in development of the sporogenous tissue, it becomes differentiated into blocks of fertile cells laterally separated from one another by plates and columns of sterile cells. The sterile cells eventually mature into the *trabeculae* that incompletely divide the cavity within the mature sporangium. The sporogenous cells adjacent to the trabeculae, as well as those adjacent to the sides of the sporangium, become a tapetum that is generally two cells in thickness (Fig. 120*E*). The remaining sporogenous cells are all potential spore mother cells. The jacket layer of the sporangium remains one cell in thickness for a considerable time, but, as tapetal differentiation takes place, it may become a layer three or four cells in thickness.

All fertile cells in microsporangia are potential spore mother cells, and most of them form tetrads in the usual manner.   Only a limited number of fertile cells of macrosporangia are potential macrospore mother cells. These cells begin to enlarge early in development of the sporogenous tissue[1] and become densely filled with cytoplasm.   Eventually 40 to 80 of the enlarged sporogenous cells divide to form four macrospores each. The remaining fertile cells of the macrosporangium, both large and small, disintegrate while the reduction divisions are taking place.

Sporangia of most species of *Isoetes* remain indehiscent after they are fully mature, and the spores are liberated by a death and decay of the sporophylls.   The spores thus freed usually remain close to the plant that

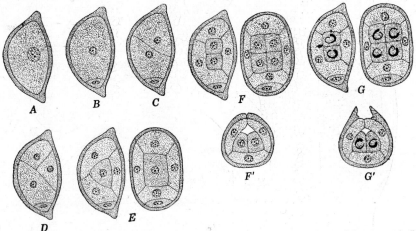

Fig. 121.—Diagrams showing development of the microgametophyte of *Isoetes*.   A–D, in vertical section perpendicular to flat surface of spore wall.   E–G, in vertical section perpendicular and parallel to flat surface of spore wall.   F[1]–G[1], in transverse section. (*Diagrams based upon Liebig, 1931.*)

produced them, but they may be scattered by the wind or through the agency of worms.[2]   In at least one species there is a dehiscence of the sporangia after abscission of the sporophylls from the stock.

Development of microspores into microgametophytes begins immediately after they are liberated from the sporangium and is completed within a few days.   Germination begins with a migration of the nucleus to one end of the microspore.[3]   After this, the microspore divides asymmetrically into a small cell (the prothallial cell), which does not divide again, and a large cell (the antheridial initial) which undergoes several divisions (Fig. 121B).   The first division of the antheridial initial is transversely diagonal to the long axis of the old microspore (Fig. 121C).

[1] Smith, R. W., 1900.   [2] Duthie, 1929.
[3] Belajeff, 1885; Campbell, 1918; Liebig, 1931.

The daughter cell nearest the prothallial cell is the first cell of the jacket layer of the antheridium. This cell does not divide, but its sister cell divides in a plane perpendicular to the previous plane of division (Fig. 121*D*). Of the two daughter cells thus formed, the one farthest from the prothallial cell becomes the second cell of the jacket layer. Its sister cell divides in a plane approximately parallel to the preceeding plane of division. One daughter cell thus formed becomes the third cell of the jacket layer; the other divides periclinally into the fourth jacket cell and the primary androgonial cell (Fig. 121*E*). The primary androgonial cell, by two successive divisions, forms four androcytes, each of which becomes metamorphosed into an antherozoid bearing a tuft of some 15 flagella near one pole (Fig. 121*F–G*). Metamorphosis of androcytes into antherozoids

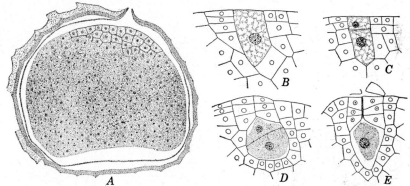

Fig. 122.—*Isoetes Braunii* Dur. *A*, vertical section of a young macrogametophyte. *B–E*, stages in development of archegonia. (*A*, × 110; *B–E*, × 215.)

is accompanied by a disintegration of the prothallial cell and the four jacket cells. Shortly after this, the antherozoids are liberated by a dehiscence of the old microspore wall along its straight face.

The nucleus of a germinating macrospore may lie in the apical or in the basal portion of the spore.[1] In either case, germination begins with a series of nuclear divisions. Multinucleate macrogametophytes of *Isoetes* differ from those of *Selaginella* in that their protoplasts never have a conspicuous central vacuole at any stage of development. During the later multinucleate stages the nuclei become more numerous in the apical portion of the gametophyte. It is here that the first cells are formed as a result of free cell formation[2] by means of cell plates produced between the nuclei (Fig. 122*A*). The lower portion of the gametophyte eventually becomes cellular, but this may be delayed until the embryo is fairly well advanced (Fig. 123*C*). The first-formed prothallial tissue, which becomes

---

[1] Campbell, 1891; La Motte, 1933.   [2] Campbell, 1891.

exposed by a cracking of the old spore wall,[1] lacks chlorophyll but it may develop numerous rhizoids.[2]

Two or three of the superficial cells in the prothallial tissue generally function as archegonial initials. If fertilization does not take place within archegonia developed from these initials, other superficial cells function as archegonial initials. Formation of additional archegonia continues until fertilization does take place or until the reserve food supply of the gametophyte is exhausted. The first division of an initial is periclinal and

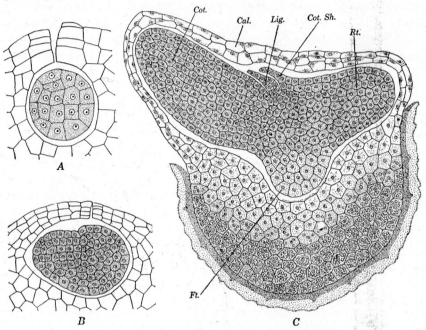

Fig. 123.—*Isoetes Braunii* Dur. *A–B*, early stages in development of embryos. *C*, macrogametophyte containing an embryo at an advanced stage of development. All figures diagrammatic. (*Cal.*, calyptra; *Cot.*, cotyledon; *Cot. Sh.* cotyledonary sheath; *Ft.*, foot; *Lig.*, ligule; *Rt.*, root.) (*A*, × 325; *B–C*, × 160.)

into a primary cover cell and a central cell (Fig. 122*B–C*). Two successive divisions of the primary cover cell form four neck initials and from these is developed a neck three or four cells in height (Fig. 122*D*). Meanwhile, the central cell divides into a primary canal cell and a primary ventral cell. The primary canal cell may become binucleate, but this is rarely followed by a division to form two canal cells. The primary ventral cell divides transversely into a ventral canal cell and an egg. The last steps in archegonial development consist of a disintegration of the ventral and canal cells and a spreading apart of the neck cells (Fig. 122*E*).

[1] Campbell, 1891; Liebig, 1931.　　[2] La Motte, 1933.

Embryos of *Isoetes* differ from those of other living Lycopodinae in that they do not have a suspensor. The first division of a zygote is approximately transverse. Division and redivision of the lower daughter cell (that farthest from the neck) results in a massive foot that ultimately burrows deep into the macrogametophyte (Fig. 123*A*). The upper daughter cell of the zygote divides vertically. The scanty evidence at hand[1] seems to indicate that one daughter cell thus formed develops into the cotyledon and the other into the remainder of the sporophyte. Early in its development, the cotyledon begins to elongate perpendicular to the vertical axis of the archegonium (Fig. 123*B*). For a time the elongating cotyledon is ensheathed by a calyptra-like mass of gametophytic tissue, but it eventually breaks through this sheath, bends, and grows vertically in the air. A cotyledon resembles a leaf in that it has a ligule, a single vascular bundle, and four longitudinal air chambers. The sister cell of the cotyledonary initial divides to form a mass of cells, and then several cells toward the exterior of this "root quadrant" develop into a root that grows transversely through the gametophyte and in a direction opposite to that of the cotyledon. The root develops root hairs and grows downward into the soil after it has pushed through the gametophyte. The stem is developed from superficial cells of the "root quadrant" in the region next to the cotyledon. It is not formed until the embryo is well advanced. The first evidence of stem formation is the development of a ligule-like structure (the "cotyledonary sheath") from superficial cells of the "root quadrant." The stem is differentiated in the axil of this sheath. It never becomes a well-defined organ, and it can only be recognized as the stem of an embryo because it is the region producing all leaves but the cotyledon.

Bibliography

BARCLAY, B. D. **1931.** *Bot. Gaz.* **91**: 452–461. 19 figs. [Anatomy, *Selaginella*.]

BELAJEFF, W. **1885.** *Bot. Zeitg.* **43**: 793–802, 809–819. 1 pl. [Microgametophyte, *Isoetes*.]

BENSON, MARGARET. **1908.** *Phil. Trans. Roy. Soc. London*, Ser. B. **199**: 409–425. 5 pl. [*Miadesmia*.]

    1918. *Ann. Bot.* **32**: 569–589. 2 pl. 4 figs. [Strobili, Sigillariaceae.]

BERRY, E. W. **1920.** *Ann. Rept. Smithsonian Inst.* **1918**: 289–407. 6 pl. 42 figs. [Fossil Pteridophyta.]

BOWER, F. O. **1894.** *Phil. Trans. Roy. Soc. London.* Ser. B, **185**: 473–572. 11 pl. [Sporangia, Lycopodinae.]

    1903. *Ann. Bot.* **17**: 278–280. 1 fig. [Sporophylls, *Lycopodium*.]

    1908. The origin of a land flora. London. 727 pp. 359 figs.

    1935. Primitive land plants. London. 658 pp. 449 figs.

BRUCHMANN, H. **1898.** Über die Prothallien und die Keimpflanzen mehrerer europäischer Lycopodien. Gotha. 111 pp. 7 pl.

[1] Campbell, 1918; La Motte, 1933; Liebig, 1931.

1905.   *Flora* **95:** 150–166. 2 pl.   [Rhizophore, *Selaginella.*]

1909.   *Ibid.* **99:** 12–51. 44 figs.   [Macrogametophyte, *Selaginella.*]

1910.   *Ibid.* **101:** 220–267. 35 figs.   [Development of gametophyte, *Lycopodium.*]

1912.   *Ibid.* **104:** 180–224. 67 figs.   [Gametophytes, *Selaginella.*]

1913.   *Ibid.* **105:** 337–346. 16 figs.   [Suspensor, *Selaginella.*]

1919.   *Ibid.* **113:** 168–177. 10 figs.   [Apogamy, *Selaginella.*]

CAMPBELL, D. H.   **1891.**   *Ann. Bot.* **5:** 231–256. 3 pl.   [Gametophytes, *Isoetes.*]

1902.   *Ibid.* **16:** 419–428. 1 pl.   [Gametophytes, *Selaginella.*]

1918.   The structure and development of mosses and ferns. 3d ed.   New York. 708 pp. 322 figs.

CHAMBERLAIN, C. J.   **1917.**   *Bot. Gaz.* **63:** 51–65. 2 pl.   [Gametophyte, *Lycopodium.*]

CHANG, C. Y.   **1927.**   *Ibid.* **83:** 288–306. 18 figs.   [Rhizome, *Pteridium.*]

COPELAND, E. B.   **1902.**   *Ann. Bot.* **16:** 327–364. 1 pl.   [Stomata, *Lycopodium.*]

DUERDEN, H.   **1929.**   *Ibid.* **43:** 451–457. 4 figs.   [Macrosporangia, *Selaginella.*]

DUPLER, A. W.   **1922.**   *Bot. Gaz.* **74:** 331–332. 1 figs.   [Sporophyll, *Lycopodium.*]

DUTHIE, A. V.   **1923.**   *Trans. Roy. Soc. S. Africa* **11:** 131–144. 20 figs.   [Strobili, gametophytes, *Selaginella.*]

1924.   *Ibid.* **11:** 275–295. 26 figs.   [Strobili, *Selaginella.*]

1929.   *Ann. Bot.* **43:** 411–412.   [Spore dispersal, *Isoetes.*]

ENGLER, A., and E. GILG.   **1924.**   Syllabus der Pflanzenfamilien. 10th ed.   Berlin. 420 pp.

FARMER, J. B.   **1890.**   *Ann. Bot.* **5:** 37–62. 2 pl. 1 fig.   [Anatomy, *Isoetes.*]

GEIGER, H.   **1934.**   *Flora* **129:** 140–157. 10 figs.   [Macrogametophyte, *Selaginella.*]

GOEBEL, K.   **1905.**   Organography of plants. Part II.   English ed.   Translated by I. B. Balfour.   Oxford. 707 pp. 417 figs.

1915.   *Flora* **108:** 324–326.   [Apogamy, *Selaginella.*]

GORDON, W. T.   **1910.**   *Ann. Bot.* **24:** 821–822. 2 figs.   [Macrogametophyte, *Lepidodendron.*]

HABERLANDT, G.   **1918.**   *Beitr. Allgem. Bot.* **1:** 293–300. 1 pl.   [Gametophyte, *Lycopodium.*]

HARVEY-GIBSON, R. J.   **1894.**   *Ann. Bot.* **8:** 133–206. 4 pl.   [Anatomy, *Selaginella.*]

1896.   *Ibid.* **10:** 77–88. 1 pl.   [Ligule, *Selaginella.*]

1897.   *Ibid.* **11:** 123–155. 1 pl.   [Leaf, *Selaginella.*]

1902.   *Ibid.* **16:** 449–466. 2 pl.   [Root, *Selaginella.*]

HIERONYMUS, G.   **1900.**   Selaginellaceae.   In A. Engler and K. Prantl, Die natürlichen Pflanzenfamilien.   Teil. 1. Abt. 4. Pp. 621–715. 21 figs.

HILL, J. B.   **1914.**   *Bot. Gaz.* **58:** 61–85. 28 figs.   [Anatomy, *Lycopodium.*]

1919.   *Ibid.* **68:** 226–231. 5 figs.   [Anatomy, *Lycopodium.*]

HILL, T. G.   **1906.**   *Ann. Bot.* **20:** 267–273. 2 pl.   [Parichnos, *Isoetes.*]

HIRMER, M.   **1927.**   Handbuch der Paläobotanik.   Bd. 1.   Berlin. 708 pp. 817 figs.

1933.   *Palaeontographica* **78:** Abt. *B*: 47–56. 15 figs.   [*Pleuromeia.*]

HOLLOWAY, J. E.   **1910.**   *Trans. New Zealand Inst.* **42:** 356–370. 4 pl. 8 figs.   [Anatomy, *Lycopodium.*]

1916.   *Ibid.* **48:** 253–303. 2 pl. 102 figs.   [Vegetative multiplication, *Lycopodium.*]

1917.   *Ibid.* **49:** 80–93. 2 pl. 24 figs.   [Vegetative multiplication, *Lycopodium.*]

JEFFREY, E. C.   **1902.**   *Phil. Trans. Roy. Soc. London.* Ser. *B.*, **195:** 119–146. 6 pl.   [Anatomy, Pteridophyta.]

1917.   The anatomy of woody plants.   Chicago. 478 pp. 306 figs.

JONES, C. E.   **1905.**   *Trans. Linn. Soc. London.* 2 ser. **7:** 15–35. 3 pl.   [Anatomy, *Lycopodium.*]

KIDSTON, R.   **1897.**   *Trans. Roy. Soc. Edinburgh* **39:** 33–62. 3 pl. 2 figs.   [Strobili, Sigillariaceae.]

Kräusel, R., and H. Weyland. **1929.** *Abhandl. Senckenbergischen Naturf. Ges. Frankfurt a/M.* **41**: 317–359. 15 pl. 34 figs. [*Protolepidodendron.*]

1932. *Senckenbergiana* **14**: 391–403. 18 figs. [*Protolepidodendron.*]

La Motte, C. **1933.** *Amer. Jour. Bot.* **20**: 217–233. 17 figs. [Macrogametophyte, *Isoetes.*]

Lang, W. H. **1899.** *Ann. Bot.* **13**: 279–317. 2 pl. [Gametophyte, *Lycopodium.*]

1915. *Mem. Proc. Manchester Lit. Phil. Soc.* **59**: No. 3: 1–28. 6 figs. [Anatomy, *Isoetes.*]

1915A. *Ibid.* **59**, No. 8: 29–56. 4 pl. 1 fig. [Anatomy, *Isoetes.*]

Liebig, Johanna. **1931.** *Flora* **125**: 321–358. 3 pl. 18 figs. [Microgametophyte, *Isoetes.*]

Lindsey, Marjorie. **1915.** *Ann. Bot.* **29**: 223–230. 1 pl. 3 figs. [*Bothrodendron.*]

Lyon, Florence M. **1901.** *Bot. Gaz.* **32**: 124–141, 170–194. 5 pl. [Gametophytes, *Selaginella.*]

1904. *Ibid.* **37**: 280–293. 16 figs. [Sex organs, Pteridophyta.]

Ma, Roberta M. **1931.** *Bull. Torrey Bot. Club* **57**: 277–284. 1 pl. [Chloroplasts, *Selaginella.*]

McLean, R. C. **1912.** *New Phytol.* **11**: 305–318. 2 pl. 2 figs. [Macrogametophyte, *Bothrodendron.*]

Mägdefrau, K. **1931.** *Beih. Bot. Centralbl.* **48**: 119–140. 5 pl. 9 figs. [*Pleuromeia.*]

Mitchell, Gertrude. **1910.** *Ann. Bot.* **24**: 19–33. 2 pl. [Strobilus, *Selaginella.*]

Osborn, T. G. B. **1922.** *Ibid.* **36**: 41–54. 15 figs. [Roots, *Isoetes.*]

Pfeiffer, Norma E. **1922.** *Ann. Missouri Bot. Gard.* **9**: 79–232. 8 pl. [Isoetaceae.]

Pritzel, E. **1900.** Lycopodiales. In A. Engler and K. Prantl, Die natürlichen Pflanzenfamilien. Teil. 1. Abt. 4. Pp. 563–606. 27 figs.

Saxelby, E. Mary. **1908.** *Ann. Bot.* **22**: 21–33. 1 pl. [Roots, *Lycopodium.*]

Scott, D. H. **1901.** *Phil. Trans. Roy. Soc. London,* Ser. B. **194**: 291–333. 6 pl. [*Lepidocarpon.*]

1920. Studies in fossil botany. 3d ed. Vol. 1. London. 434 pp. 190 figs.

Scott, D. H., and T. G. Hill. **1900.** *Ann. Bot.* **14**: 413–454. 2 pl. 2 figs. [Anatomy, *Isoetes.*]

Seward, A. C. **1910.** Fossil plants. Vol. 2. Cambridge. 624 pp. 265 figs.

Slagg, R. A. **1932.** *Amer. Jour. Bot.* **19**: 106–127. 4 pl. 15 figs. [Microgametophyte, *Selaginella.*]

Smith, R. W. **1900.** *Bot. Gaz.* **29**: 225–258, 323–346. 8 pl. [Sporangia, *Isoetes.*]

1920. *Ibid.* **69**: 426–437. 21 figs. [Bulbis, *Lycopodium.*]

Spessard, E. A. **1922.** *Ibid.* **74**: 392–413. 3 pl. [Gametophyte, *Lycopodium.*]

1928. *Ibid.* **85**: 323–333. 2 pl. 9 figs. [Young sporophyte, *Lycopodium.*]

Steel, Jessie K. **1923.** *Proc. Linn. Soc. New South Wales* **48**: 287–300. 19 figs. Anatomy, *Selaginella.*]

Stokey, Alma G. **1907.** *Bot. Gaz.* **44**: 57–63. 2 pl. 1 fig. [Roots, *Lycopodium.*]

1909. *Ibid.* **47**: 311–335. 3 pl. [Anatomy, *Isoetes.*]

Sykes, M. G. **1908.** *New Phytol.* **7**: 41–60. 2 pl. 8 figs. [Sporangia, *Lycopodium.*]

Sykes, M. G., and W. Stiles. **1910.** *Ann. Bot.* **24**: 523–536. 1 pl. [Strobilus, *Selaginella,*]

Treub, M. **1888.** *Ann. Jard. Bot. Buitenzorg* **7**: 141–150. 4 pl. [Gametophyte, *Lycopodium.*]

1890. *Ibid.* **8**: 1–37. 12 pl. [Embryo, *Lycopodium.*]

Turner, J. J. **1924.** *Bot. Gaz.* **78**: 215–225. 7 figs. [Anatomy, *Lycopodium.*]

Uphof, J. C. T. **1920.** *Ann. Bot.* **34**: 493–517. 13 figs. [Rhizophore, *Selaginella.*]

Wardlaw, C. W. **1924.** *Trans. Roy. Soc. Edinburgh* **53**: 503–532. 18 figs. [Size and internal morphology.]

1925.   *Ibid.* **54**: 281–308. 17 figs.   [Anatomy, *Selaginella.*]

WATSON, D. M. S.   **1908.**   *Mem. Proc. Manchester Lit. Phil. Soc.* **52**: No. 3: 5–16. 1 pl. 2 figs.   [Strobilus, *Bothrodendron.*]

WEISS, F. E.   **1907.**   *Ibid.* **51**, No. 8: 1–22. 1 pl. 8 figs.   [Parichnos.]

WEST, C., and H. TAKEDA.   **1915.**   *Trans. Linn. Soc. Bot. London.* 2 ser. **8**: 333–376. 8 pl. 20 figs.   [Anatomy, *Isoetes.*]

WIGGLESWORTH, GRACE.   **1907.**   *Ann. Bot.* **21**: 211–234. 1 pl. 4 figs.   [Young sporophyte, *Lycopodium.*]

WILLIAMSON, W. C.   **1889.**   *Phil. Trans. Roy. Soc. London,* Ser. *B.* **180**: 195–214. 4 pl.   [Lepidodendrales.]

WORDSELL, W. C.   **1910.**   *New Phytol.* **9**: 242–253. 2 figs.   [Rhizophore, *Selaginella.*]

CHAPTER VIII

EQUISETINAE

Sporophytes of the Equisetinae are differentiated into root, stem, and leaf. The sterile leaves, whether microphyllous or macrophyllous, are usually borne in transverse whorls. The stem usually has a siphonostelic vascular cylinder and is without leaf gaps. The sporangia are borne upon a distinctive type of appendage, the sporangiophore.

The Equisetinae, sometimes called the Articulatae, are familiarly known as the horsetails. Genera definitely ascribable to this subdivision of the Pteridophyta appeared as early as the Middle Devonian. Evolution within the class was quite rapid once it appeared, and in the Carboniferous the Equisetinae are represented by a variety of species, including some which were tree-like and grew to a height of 25 or more meters. At this time the horsetails were a conspicuous element in the vegetation of the earth. Following the Palaeozoic, the Equisetinae are no longer conspicuous in the fossil flora, and after the Jurassic there are no other known members of the class other than *Equisetum* and some of its close relatives. There is no apparent reason why the majority of fossil Equisetinae failed to hold their own in competition with contemporary plants since, when conditions are favorable, members of the single surviving genus (*Equisetum*) maintain themselves with singular persistency.

The Equisetinae differ from other Pteridophyta in a number of respects. Irrespective of whether the leaves are scale-like or expanded, they are never in alternate arrangement. Usually there is a whorl of leaves at each node. Correlated with this is a longitudinal ribbing of the stem surface and one in which there are parallel ribs extending the length of each internode. In most cases the ribs of an internode are alternate with those of abutting internodes. Ribbing of the stem is so characteristic a feature that one is justified in referring to the Equisetinae fossil plants which are known only from casts or impressions of their stems.

The arrangement of appendages borne by the stem is also distinctive. In the filicinean and lycopodian series, branches always arise axillary to the leaves; in the Equisetinae, leaves and branches alternate with each other at the nodes.

The primary vascular skeleton may be a protostele, but more frequently it is a siphonostele. Siphonostelic stems have the internodal portion of the vascular cylinder dissected by parallel lacunae extending vertically through the entire internode. Dissection of the vascular cylinder in lycopodian siphonosteles is due to branch gaps only. It has been held[1] that the perforations of the equisetaceous siphonostele are also branch gaps. The correctness of the interpretation of equisetaceous perforations as appendicular gaps is open to question. Typical appendicular gaps, whether of a branch or of a leaf, always abut directly on the traces which underlie them. In the Equisetinae there is always nodal wood intervening between the departing trace (either leaf or branch) and the lacuna above. Thus, the perforations in woody cylinders of Equisetinae are not strictly comparable to the perforations in cylinders of other Pteridophyta. Furthermore, branch traces of the Equisetinae do not have a constant orientation with respect to the perforations above them.

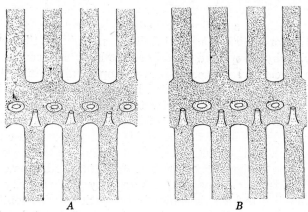

A   *B*

Fig. 124.—Diagrams of the vascular anatomy of the nodes of Equisetinae. *A, Equisetum.* *B, Archaeocalamites.* (*Diagrams based upon Jeffrey, 1917.*)

In some cases, as *Equisetum* (Fig. 124*A*), the perforations lie above the leaf traces, and the internode is solid above the branch traces. In other cases, as *Archaeocalamites* (Fig. 124*B*), the opposite condition obtains, and the internode is solid above the leaf traces. In view of the foregoing, it is better to consider the perforations in vascular cylinders of Equisetinae as something other than appendicular gaps. Such an interpretation casts considerable doubt upon the supposed affinities between lycopods and horsetails, since the suggestion that the two belong to the same general phylogenetic series[2] is based largely upon the assumption that perforations in the equisetaceous stele are branch gaps.

The fertile portion of the equisetaceous sporophyte also differs from that of other Pteridophyta. The appendages bearing the sporangia are usually called *sporangiophores*, and this term is especially suitable since there is considerable evidence showing that these structures are not

[1] Jeffrey, 1899.   [2] Jeffrey, 1917.

sporophylls. The sporangiophores are always localized at the ends of certain branches. This portion of the branch is usually called the strobilus, but the application of this term to fructifications of Equisetinae is incorrect if the sporangiophores are something other than sporophylls. Several types of sporangiophore have been found among the horsetails. In primitive forms, the Hyeniales, the sporangiphore is cylindrical. The terminal portion is once or twice-forked and has each dichotomy recurved and terminating in a single sporangium (Fig. 126C). Such a structure is, perhaps, but little different from a sporophyll. Among the Sphenophyllales the sporangia-bearing appendages consist of two portions: a simple or forked, leaf-like, sterile portion, and a branched fertile portion resembling the sporangiophore of the Hyeniales. The fertile portion always lies next the dorsal face of the sterile portion and is more or less united with it (Fig. 130). For this reason the whole appendage might be considered a sporophyll with ventral sporangia. However, the vascular supply to the fertile portion is more or less distinct from that to the sterile portion. On this account the fertile portion is usually referred to as the sporangiophore and the sterile portion as the bract. Among the Equisetales the sporangiophore has a slender stalk terminating in a peltate expansion bearing sporangia on the side toward the central axis of the strobilus. Strobili of Equisetales generally have bracts, but these are independent of the sporangiophores. In some cases, as *Palaeostachya* (Fig. 133A), the sporangiophores seem to be axillary to the bracts, but the vascular supply to bract and sporangiophore are independent of each other. More often bracts and sporangiophores are in separate whorls The whorls of sporangiophores and bracts may alternate with one another, as in *Calamostachys* (Fig. 133B); or there may be two or more whorls of sporangiophores between two successive whorls of bracts. Some genera have many whorls of sporangiophores before there is a whorl of bracts. *Equisetum*, with a single whorl of rudimentary bracts (the annulus) below the sporangiophores, is an extreme example of this type.

The morphological criteria distinguishing advanced from primitive forms are in such accord with the geological record that there is not much diversity of opinion concerning evolution within the class. All are agreed that the Hyeniales, represented by two genera in the Middle Devonian, are the most primitive known members of the class. From this group of plants evolution proceeded in two directions (Fig. 125). The Sphenophyllales, typified by *Sphenophyllum*, constitute one evolutionary line. This series includes a few genera besides *Sphenophyllum*, and one of them (*Pseudobornia* Nathorst) is sometimes placed in an order by itself.[1] *Equisetum* typifies the other evolutionary line, the Equisetales. Accordingly as the stems have or lack secondary thickening, the numerous genera

[1] Berry, 1920; Hirmer, 1927.

of Equisetales fall into two families.   The Calamitaceae, the family in which the stems are secondarily thickened, appeared in the Upper Devonian and became extinct in the Triassic.   The Equisetaceae, in which the stems are without secondary thickening, are known mostly from after the time the Calamitaceae were becoming extinct.   Possibly these are degenerate forms of Calamitaceae.   Although there is no geological evidence, it is equally possible that the Equisetaceae diverged from the Calamitaceae very early in the evolution of the order.

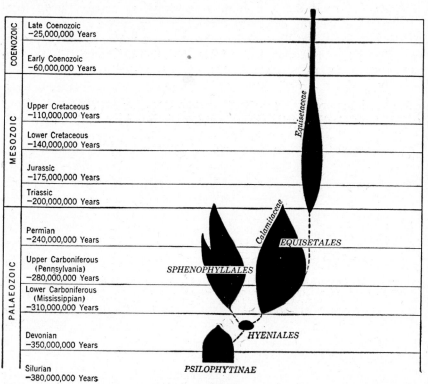

Fig. 125.—Diagram showing the geological range and the suggested interrelationships among the Equisetinae.

Differences in external appearance, internal structure, and structure of the fructification among the three series are of sufficient magnitude to justify the establishment of three orders.

ORDER 1.   HYENIALES

Sporophytes of the Hyeniales had a jointed stem, but one in which the leaves were not borne in a pronounced verticillate arrangement.   The leaves were elongate, narrow, and once or twice forked at the apex.   The sporangiophores were cylindrical, were once or twice branched, and had the apex of each branch recurved and terminating in a single sporangium. The sporangiophores were borne in lax strobili without sterile appendages. Hyeniales are known only in the fossil condition and from the Middle Devonian.

The Hyeniales, also called the Proto-articulatae [1] include two genera, *Hyenia* and *Calamophyton,* both known only from the Middle Devonian. These two genera are of particular interest in that they have certain features more like those of Psilophyta than those of Equisetinae.

The known fossil remains of these plants are chiefly aerial shoots, but one species of *Hyenia* has been found with a stout rhizome.[2] The height which aerial shoots of *Calamophyton* attained is unknown, but branch systems 20 cm. long have been found. The branching of *Calamophyton* is atypical for Equisetinae in that it is dichotomous (Fig. 126A). Small branches of this genus have the articulation characteristic of Equisetinae; large branches have a somewhat obscure articulation. Specimens of *Calamophyton* are sufficiently well preserved to show that the stem was siphonostelic and had a triangular mass of primary xylem surrounding a triangular pith. The xylem consisted largely of scalariform tracheids. It is thought that there was secondary thickening in older parts of the stem, but this is not definitely established.

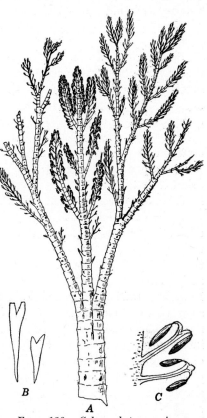

Fig. 126.—*Calamophyton primaevum* Kräusel and Weyland. *A*, reconstruction of aerial shoot. *B*, sterile leaves. *C*, sporangiophores. (*After Kräusel and Weyland*, 1926.)

The leaves of *Calamophyton* were restricted to the branchlets and were borne in whorls as is typical of Equisetinae. The leaves were 8 to 10 mm. long, narrowly cuneate, and once- or twice-forked at the expanded distal end (Fig. 126B). Lower down on the shoot the leaves were replaced by spiny outgrowths which are interpreted as persistent leaf bases.

Fertile branches of *Calamophyton* were about the same length as those bearing leaves but were much stouter. Fertile branches were lax

[1] Kräusel and Weyland, 1926.   [2] Kräusel and Weyland, 1932.

strobili which bore sporangiophores only, never sterile appendages of a bract-like nature. As is the case with leaves, the sporangiophores were borne in whorls. Each sporangiophore was about 10 mm. long and consisted of a cylindrical stipe that was bifurcate at the distal end.[1] The bifurcations were reflexed toward the central axis, and each terminated in a narrowly ovoid sporangium some 2 to 3 mm. long (Fig. 126C).

ORDER 2. SPHENOPHYLLALES

Sporophytes of the Sphenophyllales had stems with longitudinally ridged internodes and whorls of leaves at the nodes. The leaves were sessile and had an entire wedge-shaped blade or a dichotomously divided blade. The primary xylem was a triarch or hexarch actinostele and had the protoxylem exarch. The stems contained considerable secondary xylem. The fertile portion of the sporophyte was a strobilus with densely crowded verticillate appendages, each differentiated into a sporangiophoric and a bract-like portion. The sporangia were homosporous or primitively heterosporous. Members of the order are known only in the fossil condition and from the Upper Devonian to the Triassic.

Sphenophyllum is the only member of the order of which there is adequate knowledge of both the vegetative and reproductive portions of the sporophyte. The genus appeared in the Upper Devonian, flourished throughout the Carboniferous, and became extinct in the Triassic. The aerial shoots had a slender, irregularly branched, central axis less than 1 cm. in diameter. The small diameter in proportion to the great length suggests that the plants were partially supported by adjoining plants, if not actually vine-like in habit. The stem had the longitudinally ribbed internodes typical of Equisetinae, but, unlike most of the Equisetales, ribs of successive internodes are not alternate with one another. The number of leaves at each node was some multiple of three. Six is the most frequent number on nodes of fossil specimens, but there may be as many as 18 leaves at a node. Leaves at one node are directly above and not alternate with those of the node below (Fig. 127). Leaves of certain species were entire; those of other species were dichotomously divided into several lobes. Some species had both types of leaf on the same shoot. Certain of these heterophyllous species had entire leaves in the upper part of the shoot and dissected leaves in the lower part. At one time this was thought to be similar to the heterophylly in aquatic species of *Ranunculus*, and the inference was drawn that *Sphenophyllum* was an aquatic plant in which only the lower part of the shoot was submerged. The finding of shoots with the dissected leaves above the entire leaves shows the incorrectness of this inference. Taken as a whole, the leaf surface, as found on fossil specimens, is considerably greater than the stem surface. This

[1] Kräusel and Weyland, 1926.

indicates that the leaves were the chief photosynthetic organs of the plant.

The internal organization of the plant was unique, and students seeing a cross section of a stem for the first time often think that it is a cross

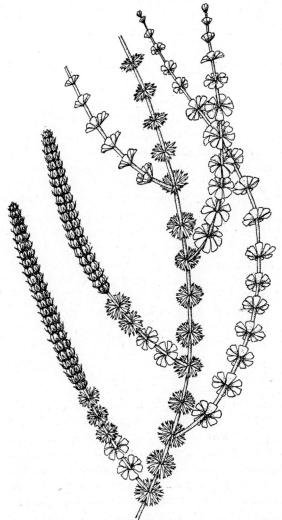

Fig. 127.—Reconstruction of shoot of *Sphenophyllum cuneifolium* Sternb. (× ⅓.)

section of a root. At the center of the stem was a triangular mass of primary xylem (Fig. 128). This was an actinostele and had the exarch protoxylem restricted to the angles of the actinostele. Most species had but one protoxylem mass at each angle, but some had two protoxylem

masses.   Stems of the latter type were hexarch even though the actinostele was triangular in outline.   Little is known concerning the organization of the primary phloem.   The cortex external to the stele was
relatively narrow and consisted of thick-walled elements at the exterior
and thin-walled elements toward the interior.[1]

Stems of all species of *Sphenophyllum* were thickened secondarily by
means of a cambium.   The cambium arose just outside the primary xylem
and completely encircled it.   The secondary xylem was dimorphic in the
sense that elements radial to the protoxylem were smaller in diameter

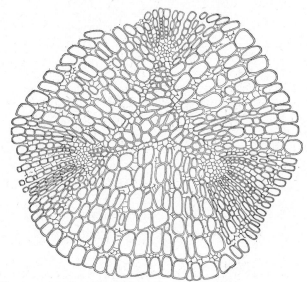

Fig. 128.—Transverse section of xylem cylinder of the stem of *Sphenophyllum plurifoliatum*
Williamson.   (× 40.)

than those radial to the metaxylem.   There were two elements in the
secondary wood; pitted tracheids and parenchyma.   The tracheids were
laid down in radial rows and had their pits largely restricted to the radial
walls.   The xylem parenchyma was composed of elongate cells whose
long axes were parallel to the long axes of the tracheids.   The parenchyma
is usually evident only in the angles between the tracheids.   The parenchymatous portion of the secondary xylem is interpreted as a series of
wood rays[2] and not as a wood parenchyma.   The cambium also formed
secondary phloem at its outer face.   This was composed of radially
arranged, thin-walled elements.   Sooner or later after cambial activity
began, there was a development of a periderm in the inner portion of the
cortex.   The regular radial arrangement of cells in the periderm suggests

[1] Williamson and Scott, 1894.   [2] Jeffrey, 1917.

that it was formed by a cambial layer similar to the cork cambium of seed plants. Ultimately there was a sloughing off of all cortical tissues external to the periderm. As is the case with many seed plants, the cork cambium became inactive after a time, and a new cork cambium was developed from tissues internal to the original cork cambium. Because of this the bark at the outside of a stem sometimes consisted of two or more concentric layers of periderm.

The root of *Sphenophyllum* was similar to the stem in that it increased in diameter by cambial activity. The primary xylem was usually diarch, but sometimes it was triarch (Fig. 129). Unlike the stem, secondary

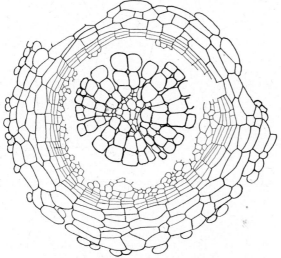

Fig. 129.—Transverse section of the root of *Sphenophyllum* sp. (× 60.)

elements radial to the protoxylem were not smaller than the others. The root also had a well-developed periderm formed by a cork cambium which seems to have arisen in the pericycle. The root was unusual in that the relatively narrow cortex persisted after the periderm was well developed.

There is considerable diversity in structure of strobili associated with plant bodies of the *Sphenophyllum* type. In the case of *S. Dawsoni* Williamson the strobilus was over 1 cm. in diameter and several centimeters in length. Its central axis was 2 to 3 mm. in diameter and bore numerous whorls of bracts at equidistant intervals. The 14 to 20 bracts of each whorl were free from one another at their apices and laterally united at their bases (Fig. 130). These cup-like whorls of bracts were so nested one above the other that the apical portion of one whorl ensheathed the basal portions of the next two or three whorls above (Fig. 130*A*). Although not definitely known, it is thought that bracts of successive whorls were superimposed, not alternate. Axillary to each bract was a single three-pronged sporangiophore that was partially united with the bract.

The sporangiophores were of two sorts: those with two long distal prongs and a short median one, and those with one long distal prong and two short median ones (Fig. 130*B*). These alternated with one another in each whorl. Each prong of the sporangiophore, whether long or short, was reflexed and terminated in a single sporangium. The general appearance of the prong and its sporangium is similar to that of an anatropous ovule. *Sphenophyllum* was usually homosporous, but strobili have been

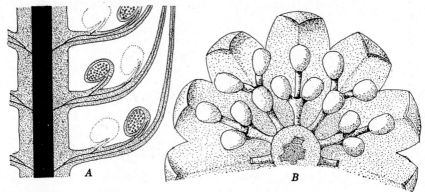

Fig. 130.—*Sphenophyllum Dawsoni* Williamson. Diagrams of the strobilus in vertical and transverse section. (*Based upon Hirmer*, 1927.)

found in which there is a 20 per cent difference in size of spores in adjacent sporangia. This is considered an incipient type of heterospory.[1]

ORDER 3. EQUISETALES

Sporophytes of the Equisetales have a branching stem in which the branches are generally in verticils. The internodes of branches are longitudinally ridged; each node bears a whorl of leaves that are usually small and scale-like. The vascular cylinder is an endarch siphonostele, entire at the nodes and perforated through the internodes. Some genera have a secondary thickening of the vascular cylinder; other genera lack it entirely. Fertile portions of a sporophyte are strobili with transverse whorls of peltate sporangiophores. Strobili of most genera have whorls of bracts distinct from the sporangiophores. The sporangia may be homosporous or heterosporous. Fossil genera are known from the Upper Devonian onward. One genus has living species.

The Equisetales appeared in the Upper Devonian and reached their greatest diversity in the Upper Carboniferous. Most of them disappeared shortly after this epoch but one genus, *Equisetum*, has persisted until

[1] Scott, 1920.

today. The plant body may be a herbaceous shrub, a clambering vine-like plant, or a tree in which there is considerable development of secondary wood. All three types of plant body generally have a verticillate branching in which the branches have verticils of small bract-like leaves at the nodes. The surface of the stem is longitudinally ridged, and the ridges have a definite orientation with respect to the leaves and to the parallel internodal vascular bundles. The strobili differ from those of other Equisetinae in that they have peltate sporangiophores. The strobili may have or may lack bracts. There are three families in the order, the two most important of which are discussed below:

FAMILY 1. CALAMITACEAE

The Calamitaceae had a tree-like sporophyte in which there was considerable secondary thickening of the stem and root. The strobili had alternate whorls of peltate sporangiophores and sterile bracts.

The Calamitaceae are the true giant horsetails. These plants appeared in the Upper Devonian, were most abundant during the Carboniferous, and disappeared shortly after the Triassic. The Calamitaceae are known from impressions, casts, and from petrifactions. As is the case with other groups of fossil plants, certain species are known only from their stems, others only from their twigs, and still others only from their roots, rhizomes, or strobili. In a few cases all parts of a single species are known. Thus,[1] the leafy twigs known as *Annularia radiata* Brongniart and the fructifications known as *Calamostachys ramosa* Weiss have been shown to belong to the stem known as *Calamites ramosus* Artis.

Casts of the central cavity of the trunk of Calamitaceae have been found which are 3 to 8 meters in length and up to 30 cm. in breadth. From this it has been estimated that the plant was a tree 20 to 30 meters tall. *Calamites* is one of the members of the family which was tree-like. In spite of its tree-like proportions, it had a horizontal underground rhizome with aerial branches just as does the present-day *Equisetum* (Fig. 131). Fossil specimens of rhizomes are differentiated into nodes and internodes and have a whorl of adventitious roots at each node. Their considerable size shows that they formed secondary wood. Specimens have been found with erect branches arising from the upper side of the rhizome. The fact that several of the lowermost nodes in the erect branches have whorls of adventitious roots shows that the rhizome grew at some distance below the surface of the soil. The erect branches are generally constricted where they depart from the rhizome, a condition probably due to lessened cambial activity in this region. The tree-like above-ground portion of the erect branch had a conspicuous central axis bearing whorls of lateral branches. In some species the lateral branches

[1] Scott, 1920.

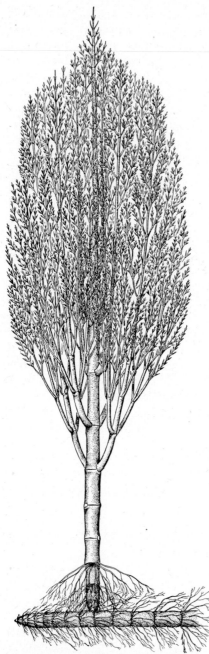

Fig. 131.—Reconstruction of an undetermined species of *Calamites*. (*After Hirmer*, 1927.)

persisted for a long time and became nearly as thick as the central axis. Such plants looked like an *Equisetum* of tree-like proportions. Other species shed their lateral branches after a time. Such plants, which had a naked central axis bearing a tuft of branches at the apex, looked somewhat like palms. The surface of a *Calamites* stem had the same longitudinally ribbed internodes as that of the present-day *Equisetum*, but the ribs of successive internodes were sometimes above, instead of alternate with, one another.

The stem of *Calamites* was internally differentiated into epidermis, cortex, and stele. The structure of the cortex is seen to best advantage in the fossil forms of young twigs. Here it has been shown that fossil twigs have a cortex with an inner region of thin-walled parenchyma and an outer region of thick-walled cells. Sometimes the latter are in longitudinal strands as in *Equisetum*.[1] The cortex differs from that of *Equisetum* in that there are no vertical cavities (vallecular canals) in the internodes.

The stele of *Calamites* was siphonostelic. The pith internal to the vascular cylinder was solid at the nodes and hollow at the internodes. Young twigs had parallel strands of vascular tissue extending the whole length of the internodes. The protoxylem was toward the inner face of the bundle, and it matured in centrifugal

[1] Scott, 1920.

succession. The metaxylem external to the protoxylem was composed of scalariform tracheids. The protoxylem elements (both annular and spiral tracheids) disintegrated immediately after they matured, leaving, precisely as in *Equisetum*, a vertical cavity (*carinal canal*) at the inner face of each metaxylem mass. The stelar organization thus far described is almost identical with that of *Equisetum*. Fossil stems of *Calamites* differ markedly from those of *Equisetum* in that they have a cambium. Secondary xylem formed toward the inner face of the cambium was composed of radial rows of tracheids (Fig. 132*A*). The first-formed secondary tracheids were scalariform, later-formed ones were generally pitted and had the pits restricted to the radial walls. The cylinder of secondary wood attained a thickness of 6 cm. or more, but did not have a differentiation of annual

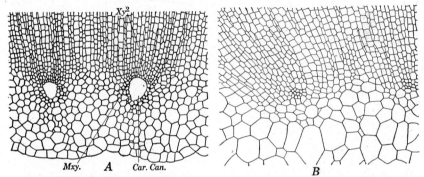

Fig. 132.—*Calamites*. *A*, transverse section of a portion of a stem. *B*, transverse section of a portion of a root. (*Car. Can.*, carinel canal; *Mxy.*, metaxylem; *Xy.*², secondary xylem.) (*A*, × 40; *B*, × 30.)

rings. This shows that the plant retained its foliage throughout the year and that climatic conditions were approximately uniform throughout the year. Secondary thickening was accompanied by the formation of a periderm in the outer portion of the cortex. The periderm often became a bark several centimeters in thickness.

The roots of *Calamites*, to which the generic name *Astromeylon* was originally applied, differed in structure according to their size. Small rootlets had di-, tri-, or tetrarch actinosteles[1] with the protoxylem exarch and with the typical alternation of masses of phloem with the protoxylem points. Such roots had a cambium, but it formed only a limited amount of secondary xylem. As in *Equisetum*, the endodermis seems to have been a double layer. External to the endodermis was a thin-walled parenchyma with conspicuous intercellular spaces, and at the outside of the cortex was a zone of thick-walled cells similar in appearance to the exo-

[1] Williamson and Scott, 1894.

dermis in roots of many angiosperms. Larger roots had a polyarch actinostele, in which the center was either solidly filled with parenchyma or was hollow. The primary xylem superficially resembled that of a stem but differed in that it was exarch and did not have a disintegration of the protoxylem to form carinal canals. Roots of this type produced a considerable amount of radially arranged secondary xylem (Fig. 132*B*). Polyarch roots had a periderm, and the cork cambium producing it probably arose in the outer portion of the cortex.

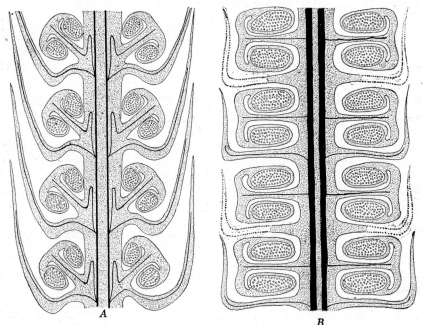

A

B

Fig. 133.—Diagrams of vertical sections of strobili of Calamitaceae. *A, Palaeostachya. B, Calamostachys. (Based upon Scott, 1920.)*

Each node of a *Calamites* stem had a single whorl of leaves. In some species the leaves of a whorl were free from one another; in other species the leaves were laterally united along their lower margins. Although the leaves were generally of small size, their structure shows that they were photosynthetic organs. In one type of fossil leaf found in association with a *Calamites*-like stem, the internal structure resembles that of a pine leaf. This leaf has a single axial vascular bundle surrounded by a sheath. External to this is a radiate palisade tissue with conspicuous intercellular spaces. The palisade layer is surrounded by an epidermis, one cell in thickness, in which there are numerous stomata.

Several types of strobili have been found on the fossil calamitean type of plant body. Although decidedly different in organization, they are all alike in that they have transverse whorls of peltate sporangiophores and transverse whorls of bracts. In the case of the fructification known as *Calamostachys*, the whorls of bracts and sporangiophores are alternate and lie equidistant from one another on the central axis (Fig. 133*B*). Other types of strobili have several equidistant whorls of sporangiophores between two successive whorls of bracts. In still other cases, as *Palaeostachya* (Fig. 133*A*), the sporangiophores are axillary to the bracts. However, the sporangiophores are not true appendages of the bracts because the two have entirely independent vascular supplies.

Some fossil calamitean fructifications are homosporous; others are heterosporous and have the macrospores three times the diameter of the microspores.[1] Generic distinctions are not based solely on this character and in certain cases, as in *Calamostachys*, the same genus may have both homosporous and heterosporous species. There is also variation in the manner in which the two types of sporangia occur. In some fossil sporangiophores, as *Calamostachys Binneyana* Carruthers, three of the sporangia are macrosporangia and one a microsporangium. In other cases, as *C. Casheana* Williamson, all the sporangiophores in a whorl bear macrosporangia, all bear microsporangia, or both types may be present in the same whorl. Macro- and microsporangia of *Calamostachys* were identical in size. The smaller number of spores in macrosporangia resulted from abortion of certain of the young spores shortly after or during the tetrad stage in spore formation.[1]

FAMILY 2. EQUISETACEAE

The Equisetaceae differ from the Calamitaceae in that the stem usually lacks secondary tissues and in the lack of distinct whorls of bracts in the strobili. Most fossil species are not known from earlier than the Triassic. Since this coincides with the disappearance of the Calamitaceae, it suggests that the Equisetaceae are degenerate forms of the latter. However, a few species have been found as far back as the middle of the Upper Carboniferous. This seems to show that the origin of the Equisetaceae is to be sought in the more primitive of the Calamitaceae or in the ancestral stock leading to them.

Equisetum is the only genus of the family in which there are living representatives. There are about 25 species. The genus is world wide in distribution, except for Australia, and the various species grow in a variety of habitats. Certain species grow in ponds and marshes, others grow in damp shaded places; and still others grow in exposed, relatively dry habitats. Most of the species have sporophytes that are not more than a meter in height, but the aerial branches of *E. giganteum* L., found in tropical South America, may grow to a height of 12 meters. However,

[1] Williamson and Scott, 1894.

this species is vine-like in habit, and its stem, which is but 0.5 to 2.0 cm. in diameter, clambers over adjacent trees.

The sporophyte of *Equisetum* has a horizontal, much branched, perennial, subterranean rhizome which often penetrates to more than a meter below the surface of the soil. The rhizome is conspicuously differentiated into nodes and internodes. At each node is a whorl of small, slender, scale-like leaves, more or less laterally united with one another to form a brown sheath around the node. Alternating with each leaf at a node is a branch primordium. Branch primordia of the rhizome may immediately develop into branches, either aerial or subterranean, or they may remain dormant for an indefinite period. Sometimes the primordia develop into short rounded branches one internode long. These tubers are capable of developing into new plants when separated from the parent rhizome and thus afford a means of propagating the sporophyte generation vegetatively. Nodes of the rhizome also bear whorls of slender much-branched adventitious roots. These usually function for one growing season only.

Aerial branches from rhizomes of most species are of two sorts, sterile and fertile (Fig. 134*A*). Sterile branches are green and have a whorl of lateral branches at each node. Frequently the lateral branches bear whorls of similar, but smaller, branches. Fertile branches of most species are colorless, are unbranched, and have a single strobilus at the branch apex. Fertile branches of this type usually appear above ground, attain their full development, and shed their spores before the vegetative branches appear. Other species, as *E. palustre* L. (Fig. 134*B*), have green, branched, fertile shoots with a strobilus at the apex of each lateral branch. Fertile shoots of this type persist after the spores are shed and function as vegetative organs.

The general organization of the stem is the same in aerial and in subterranean portions but is best exemplified by aerial branches. Each internode of an aerial branch is longitudinally ribbed and has the ribs alternate with the leaves of the subtending node. Since the leaves of successive internodes are alternate, ribs of successive internodes are alternate.

Internodes of *Equisetum* have definitely arranged vertical cavities extending the length of the internode. Primary branches of aerial shoots have a conspicuous space (the *central canal*) occupying most of the pith. Internodes of small branches and of the rhizome lack a central canal. At the inner face of each internodal vascular bundle is another space, the *carinal canal*. The carinal canals lie in a ring and each one is internally radial to a rib of the stem surface. External to the carinal canals and alternate with them is a ring of larger intercellular spaces (*vallecular canals*) that lie in the cortex. These various intercellular spaces are not

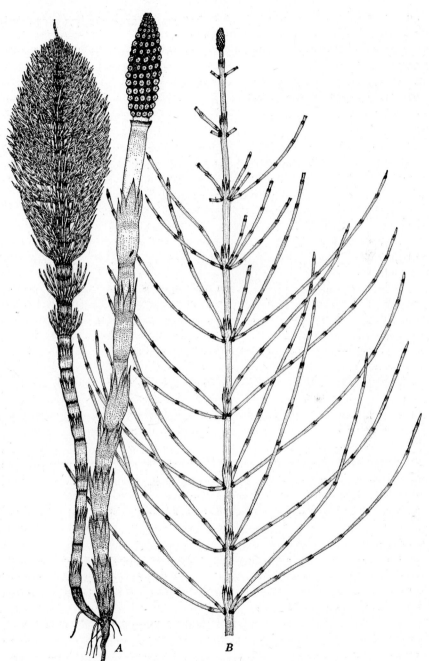

FIG. 134.—*A, Equisetum telmateia* Ehrh. *B, E. palustre* L. ($\times \frac{1}{2}$.)

alike in function: the central and carinal canals are usually water-filled, the vallecular canals always contain air.

The stem of *Equisetum* is organized into epidermis, cortex, and stele. The limits between cortex and stele are clearly marked in certain species, as *E. arvense* L., because of the endodermis surrounding the entire stele. The demarcation between the two is not clearly evident in other species, as *E. giganteum* L., where each vascular bundle is encircled by an endodermal layer.

As is well known, the epidermal layer of *Equisetum* has highly silicified cell walls in which the silica may be uniformly deposited or may be

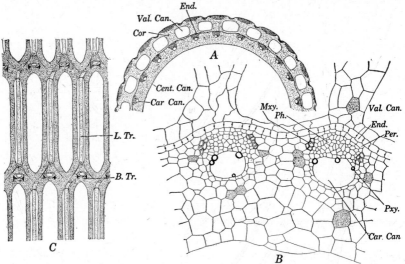

Fig. 135.—*A–B*, transverse sections through the internode of a shoot of *Equisetum telmateia* Ehrh. *C*, diagram of the vascular skeleton of *Equisetum*. (*B.Tr.*, branch trace; *Car. Can.*, carinal canal; *Cent. Can.*, central canal; *Cor.*, cortex; *End.*, endodermis; *L.Tr.*, leaf trace; *Mxy.*, metaxylem; *Per.*, pericycle; *Ph.*, phloem; *Pxy.*, protoxylem; *Val. Can.*, vallecular canal.) (*A*, × 7; *B*, × 110.)

deposited in granules. Stomata are largely restricted to aerial branches and to portions of the epidermis between longitudinal ridges of the internodes. The development of a stoma is unusual in that there are two successive longitudinal divisions of the initial, the two innermost cells maturing into a pair of guard cells and the two outermost into a pair of accessory cells. Silica deposited in walls of guard cells is in transverse bands radial to the stoma.

The cortex of an aerial branch is highly differentiated. Beneath each of the externally evident ribs of the internode is a vertical rod-like mass of sclerenchyma. The sclerenchyma may be restricted to the peripheral portion of the cortex or, as in *E. giganteum*, may extend inward to the central cylinder. In addition there are frequently smaller vertical masses of sclerenchyma in the periphery of the cortex and at the bases of the grooves between the ribs. The columns of sclerenchyma, especially those internal to the ridges, are the chief mechanical elements of a branch. The peripheral portion of the cortex lateral to the sclerenchyma is a chlorenchyma with intercellular spaces that are especially conspicuous just beneath the stomata. Since the leaves are small and have but few chloroplasts, the chlorenchyma of the cortex is of major importance in the photosynthetic work of the aerial branch.

Cross sections of internodes show a well-defined ring of vascular strands toward the periphery of the stele. In very young bundles the protoxylem, consisting of a few annular and spiral tracheids, lies toward the inner face of the bundle. The maturation of the protoxylem is in centrifugal succession,[1] but this is exceedingly difficult to determine in older stems because the protoxylem elements separate from one another as growth continues, and they are in a more or less disorganized condition within the carinal canals thus formed. External to the carinal canal is a phloem mass composed of phloem parenchyma and of sieve tubes with sieve plates in the diagonal walls. On both lateral flanks of the phloem is a small metaxylem mass consisting of scalariform tracheids. The vascular strands of the internode are laterally separated from one another by parenchymatous cells similar in size and appearance to those of the pith. The peripheral portion of the stele, the pericycle, is one cell in thickness (Fig. 135*A–B*).

The vascular skeleton of the *Equisetum* stem is siphonostelic. Nodal portions of this hollow cylinder (the *nodal wood*) are uninterrupted; internodal portions are longitudinally perforate and have each perforation running the length of an internode. As already noted (page 222) these perforations do not seem to be branch gaps, as some maintain,[2] but structures different in nature from true gaps. The internodal strands of vascular tissue (the so-called vascular bundles) between the perforations contain both metaxylem and protoxylem. The vascular supply to a leaf trace consists wholly of protoxylem. This arises at a node, extends vertically through the node above, and departs at the succeeding node[3] (Fig. 135*C*). The metaxylem of the internode joins directly with the nodal wood above and below. Branch traces, which lie alternate with the leaf traces, join immediately with the nodal metaxylem beneath them.

Terminal growth of rhizome and branches is initiated by a pyramidal apical cell with three cutting faces (Fig. 136). Each segment cut off by the apical cell ultimately develops into a sector of the stem. The first division of the segment is anticlinal, the upper and lower cells thus formed developing, respectively, into a nodal and an internodal sector of the stem. Each of the two cells then divides periclinally. The small inner

[1] Eames, 1909. [2] Jeffrey, 1917. [3] Browne, 1922.

cell thus formed contributes to the pith; the elongate outer cell contributes to all other parts of the sector.   Lateral branch initials arise several nodes back from the apical cell.   When the stem is seen in longitudinal section, they appear to be axillary in origin, but this is not actually the case because the superficial stem cell functioning as the branch initial lies midway between two adjoining leaves.

All of the roots borne at nodes of the rhizome and aerial branches are adventitious in origin.   Primordia of adventitious roots arise from the lower side of branch primordia at the node, not directly from the node itself.   In the case of rhizomes the branch primordia usually remain dormant, and the root primordia develop vigorously.   In aerial branches the opposite condition obtains, the branch primordia developing vigorously and the root primordia remaining dormant.

A young root primordium differentiates a group of initials, which form the root cap, and a pyramidal apical cell, which forms the root proper.   The stele of a root is tri- or tetrarch, and with three or four protoxylem points surrounding a single axial metaxylem element (Fig. 137).   The angles between the protoxylem are completely

Fig. 136.—Vertical section of the apex of a shoot of *Equisetum telmateia* Ehrh.   Portions derived from successive segments from the apical cell are outlined with a heavy line.   (× 110.)

filled with phloem.   *Equisetum* is unusual in that it lacks a pericycle. Instead, there is an endodermal layer two cells in thickness, and one in which the inner layer functions as a pericycle if there is a production of secondary branches.   The cortical tissue external to the endodermis is three or four cells in thickness.   A short distance posterior to the root cap, its cell walls are of uniform thickness; farther back from this, the outer portion of the cortex is thick-walled and constitutes an exodermis.

Strobili of *Equisetum* have several whorls of densely crowded peltate appendages which bear the sporangia (Fig. 138*A*).   In spite of the fact that occasional tetratological appendages are leaf-like, it is better, for reasons already given (page 222), to call the appendages sporangiophores, not sporophylls.   Immediately below the sporangiophores, the central axis bears a small ring-like outgrowth, the *annulus*.   This structure is often interpreted as a vestigial remainder of the bracts characteristic of strobili of Calamitaceae.   However, the fact that annuli of certain species regularly bear small sporangia shows that the annulus may be sporangiophoric in nature.

Each sporangiophore has a slender stalk. The free end is expanded
into a flattened disk which lies at right angles to the stalk. The disk is
generally hexagonal in outline because of crowding by disks of adjoining
sporangiophores. The sporangia, of which there are 5 to 10, are borne in
a ring and on the side of the disk facing the central axis of the strobilus
(Fig. 138*B–C*). Each sporangium is an elongate cylinder with a rounded
apex. When fully mature, the sporangia open along a single longitudinal
line of dehiscence.

The sporangia of *Equisetum* are of the eusporangiate type (page 252)
in the sense that they are not entirely derived from a single initial cell.

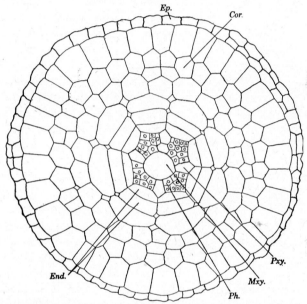

Fig. 137.—Transverse section of a young root of *Equisetum telmateia* Ehrh. (*Cor.*,
cortex; *End.*, endodermis; *Ep.*, epidermis; *Mxy.*, metaxylem; *Ph.*, phloem; *Pxy.*, protoxylem.) (× 215.)

However, all of the sporogenous tissue in a sporangium can be traced
back to a single superficial cell of the young sporangiophore.[1] The first
division of this initial is periclinal. The inner daughter cell contributes
only to the sporogenous tissue; the outer daughter cell contributes both
to the sporogenous tissue and to the portion of the sporangial jacket radial
to the sporogenous tissue (Fig. 138*F*). The remainder of the jacket layer
is derived from cells lateral to the original initial. The jacket ultimately
becomes a tissue several cells in thickness, in which the innermost cell
layer functions as a tapetum (Fig. 138*G–H*). During the course of spore
development, there is a disintegration of the tapetal layer and all but

[1] Bower, 1894.

the two outermost layers of jacket cells. Thus, when fully mature, the sporangium has a jacket two cells in thickness, in which cells of the outermost layer have spirally thickened walls (Fig. 138*I*).

There is a disintegration of about a third of the spore mother cells shortly before the reduction divisions begin. The remaining spore mother cells separate from one another, assume a spherical shape, and float about in the plasmodial liquid resulting from disintegration of tapetum and spore mother cells. This liquid persists until the spores are

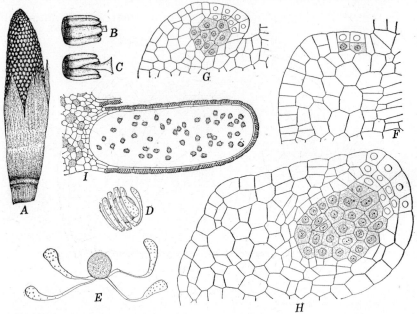

Fig. 138.—*Equisetum temateia* Ehrh. *A*, strobilus. *B–C*, sporangiophores. *D–E*, spores with coiled and uncoiled elaters. *F–I*, stages in development of sporangia. (*A*, × ⅔; *B–C*, × 5; *D–H*, × 210; *I*, × 40.)

well along toward maturity. The spore secretes a wall composed of four concentric layers.[1] The outermost layer (*exosporium*) is laid down in four spiral strips. Later the four strips split away from the remainder of the wall except for one common point of attachment. These strips remain tightly coiled about the spore until the sporangium dehisces. The strips are strongly hygroscopic and they uncoil or coil accordingly as the air is dry or moist (Fig. 138*D–E*). The strips are called *elaters*, but it should be noted that they are different in nature from the elaters of Bryophyta. The function of the elaters is uncertain. Possibly their expansion may assist in dehiscence of the sporangium; possibly their expansion and contraction may assist in spore dispersal. Mature spores

[1] Beer, 1909.

are relatively large and contain numerous chloroplasts. Similar to other pteridophytes whose spores contain chloroplasts, they only remain viable for a few days after they are shed.

When developing under natural conditions, the gametophytes of *Equisetum* are generally found growing upon clayey soil and in the mud belt along the banks of streams. The first cell division in the development of a gametophyte takes place 10 to 12 hours after the spore is sown. One of the two daughter cells is small and develops into the first rhizoid, the other is large and develops into the remainder of the thallus.[1] Divi-

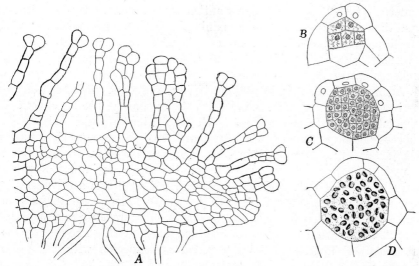

Fig. 139.—*A*, vertical section of a gametophyte of *Equisetum debile* Roxb. *B–D*, stages in development of antheridia of *E. telmateia* Ehrh. (*A*, × 55; *B–D*, × 210.)

sion and redivision of the larger cell is in irregular sequence and produces a small cushion-like tissue, several cells in thickness, which bears numerous rhizoids on its lower surface. Cells in the upper portion of the cushion contain chloroplasts, those in the lower portion are colorless. The entire margin of the cushion is meristematic in nature. If growth is uniform throughout the meristematic region, the result is a circular gametophyte, if growth is more active at one side the result is a gametophyte of irregular shape. Rather early in development of the gametophyte the upper surface sends forth irregularly shaped upright plates (Figs. 139*A*, 141*A*). These densely crowded green lobes completely cover the disk below. Gametophytes of *Equisetum* are long-lived and certain of them grown in culture have persisted for more than two years.[2]

[1] Campbell, 1918; Kashyap, 1914; Walker, 1931.   [2] Walker, 1931.

Those of most species rarely become a centimeter in diameter, but in *E.* *debile* Roxb. they may become 3 cm. in diameter.[1]

If conditions of growth are favorable, the first sex organs are formed when the gametophytes are 30 to 40 days old. The initials developing into sex organs are in the meristematic region of the cushion. The mature sex organs lie between plates somewhat in from the margin of a thallus, because the marginal meristem continues marginal growth and a formation of vertical plates. There has been considerable debate as to whether *Equisetum* is homothallic or heterothallic. In the case of *E.* *arvense* L. it has been shown[2] that about half of the spores develop into gametophytes which produce only antheridia no matter how the cultural conditions are changed. The remaining half of the spores develop into gametophytes which produce archegonia when cultural conditions are favorable. If fertilization does not take place, the prothallia with archegonia may then develop antheridia.

An initial developing into an antheridium is a superficial cell of the meristematic region. This initial divides periclinally into an outer cell (the jacket initial) and an inner cell (the primary androgonial cell). Subsequent development[3] is identical with that of eusporangiate ferns. The jacket initial develops into a jacket layer one cell in thickness, and one with a triangular opercular cell as in the Eusporangiatae. Division and redivision of the primary androgonial cell results in a considerable number of androgonial cells (Fig. 139B–C). Two blepharoplasts become evident at the androcyte mother cell stage of development,[4] and one goes to each of the two androcytes formed by a mother cell. The androcytes are metamorphosed into spirally coiled antherozoids with numerous flagella (Fig. 139D).

Archegonial initials are also superficial cells of the marginal meristem. The first division of the initial is periclinal (Fig. 140A). The outer daughter cell is the primary cover cell. The inner daughter cell is the mother cell of the central cell. The primary cover cell divides quadrately to form four primary neck cells. Transverse division of these cells results in an archegonial neck three or four cells in height and one that projects vertically above the thallus (Fig. 140C–D). The central cell divides transversely into a primary canal cell and a primary ventral cell (Fig. 140B). Some species rarely have a division of the primary canal cell, other species regularly have it dividing vertically into two boot-shaped neck canal cells. In all cases there is an asymmetrical transverse division of the ventral cell to form a ventral canal cell and an egg (Fig. 140C). The last step in archegonial development is the usual disintegration of all axial cells but the egg.[5]

[1] Kashyap, 1914.   [2] Schratz, 1928.   [3] Campbell, 1918.   [4] Sharp, 1912.
[5] Campbell, 1918; Jeffrey, 1899; Kashyap, 1914; Sethi, 1928; Walker, 1921.

Fertilization is effected by the antherozoid swimming down the canal of the archegonium. Frequently many antherozoids enter the venter, but only one of them penetrates the egg.[1] Unlike most other Pterido-phyta, several sporophytes may develop on the same prothallus (Fig. 141*A*). In *E. debile* it is not unusual to find 8 to 10 young sporophytes on a single gametophyte and as many as 15 have been observed.[2]

The first division of the zygote is usually transverse.[3] The cell walls of the next division are usually at right angles to the first (Fig. 140*E*).

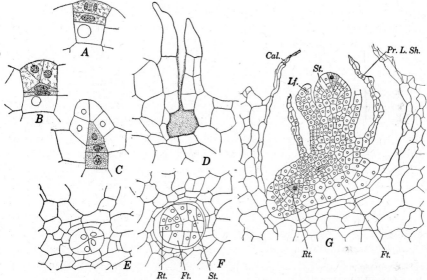

Fig. 140.—*A–C*, stages in development of archegonia of *Equisetum telmateia* Ehrh. *D–G, E. debile* Roxb. *D*, open archegonium. *E–F*, young embryos. *G*, embryo at an advanced stage of development. (*Cal.*, calyptra; *Ft.*, foot; *Lf.*, leaf; *Pr. L.Sh.*, primary leaf sheath; *Rt.*, root, *St.*, stem.) (*A–B*, × 325; *C–D*, × 210; *E–G*, × 110.)

Although the embryo thus has the early differentiation into quadrants typical of leptosporangiate ferns, the four quadrants do not give rise, respectively, to stem, root, cotyledon, and foot. In some cases, as *E. debile*,[4] the whole of the lower (hypobasal) half of the embryo develops into a foot (Fig. 140*F*); in other cases, as *E. arvense*,[5] both foot and root come from the hypobasal half. Rather early in the development of the upper (epibasal) half of the embryo, there is a differentiation of the apical cell of the stem. The cells lateral to this develop into the first leaf sheath of the young stem. Typically there are three leaves in this first sheath, but there may be two or four leaves. These leaves, unlike the first leaves

[1] Sethi, 1928.   [2] Kashyap, 1914.
[3] Campbell, 1918, 1928; Jeffrey, 1899; Walker, 1921.
[4] Campbell, 1928.   [5] Sadebeck, 1878.

developed by embryos of other Pteridophyta, are small, scale-like, and of little importance as photosynthetic organs when the sporophyte begins to manufacture its own food. If the entire hypobasal half of the embryo has developed into a foot, the apical cell of the root is differentiated from a superficial cell of the epibasal half that lies near the hypobasal half.

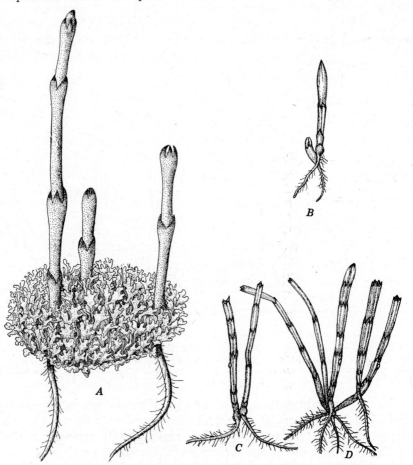

Fig. 141.—A, gametophyte and young sporophytes of *Equisetum* sp. B–D, young sporophytes of *E. hiemale* L. (B–D, after Jeffrey, 1899.)

Growth and elongation of the stem and root portions of the embryo are rapid. The root grows directly downward through the underlying gametophytic tissues and into the soil. The stem portion of the embryo bursts through the neck of the archegonium (the calyptra) and grows upright. The stem is differentiated into nodes and internodes and has a whorl of leaves (generally three) at each node. Apical development of this branch is limited, and all growth ceases after it has become 10 to

15 internodes long. A secondary branch then grows out from the base of the primary branch (Fig. 141*B*). This branch differs in that it generally has four to five leaves at the nodes. Growth of the second branch, like that of the first, is limited (Fig. 141*C*). It has been definitely shown for *E. debile*,[1] and the same is probably true of other species, that the secondary branch is endogenous in origin and arises from tissues of the primary root. The second branch has a root of its own and one which is developed adventitiously near its base. The young sporophyte may successively produce several secondary erect branches of limited growth (Fig. 141*D*). Presumably these branches also arise endogenously. Eventually there is the formation of a secondary branch that bends downward, grows into the soil, and develops into a rhizome capable of unlimited growth.

Bibliography

Beer, R. **1909.** *New Phytol.* **8**: 261–266. [Spores, *Equisetum*.]

Berry, E. W. **1920.** *Ann. Rept. Smithsonian Inst.* **1918**: 289–407. 6 pl. 42 figs. [Fossil Pteridophyta.]

Bower, F. O. **1894.** *Phil. Trans. Roy. Soc. London*, Ser. *B*., **185**: 473–572. 11 pl. [Sporangia, *Equisetum*.]

Browne, Isabel M. P. **1922.** *Bot. Gaz.* **73**: 447–468. 7 figs. [Anatomy of *Equisetum*.]

Campbell, D. H. **1918.** The structure and development of mosses and ferns. 3d ed. New York. 708 pp. 322 figs.

——— **1928.** *Ann. Bot.* **42**: 717–728. 1 pl. 10 figs. [Embryo, *Equisetum*.]

Eames, A. J. **1909.** *Ibid.* **23**: 587–601. 1 pl. [Anatomy, *Equisetum*.]

Hirmer, M. **1927.** Handbuch der Paläobotanik. Bd. 1. Munich. 708 pp. 817 figs.

Jeffrey, E. C. **1899.** *Mem. Boston Soc. Nat. Hist.* **5**: 155–190. 5 pl. [*Equisetum*.]

——— **1917.** The anatomy of woody plants. Chicago. 478 pp. 306 figs.

Kashyap, S. R. **1914.** *Ann. Bot.* **28**: 163–181. 45 figs. [Gametophyte, *Equisetum*.]

Kräusel, R., and H. Weyland. **1926.** *Abhandl. Senckenbergischen Naturf. Ges. Frankfurt a/M.* **40**: 115–155. 15 pl. 46 figs. [*Calamophyton*.]

——— **1932.** *Senckenbergiana* **14**: 274–280. 7 figs. [*Hyenia*.]

Sadebeck, R. **1878.** *Jahrb. Wiss. Bot.* **11**: 575–602. 3 pl. [Embryo, *Equisetum*.]

Schratz, E. **1928.** *Biol. Zentralbl.* **48**: 617–639. [Gametophytes, *Equisetum*.]

Scott, D. H. **1920.** Studies in fossil botany. 3d. ed. Vol. 1. London. 434 pp. 190 figs.

Sethi, M. L. **1928.** *Ann. Bot.* **42**: 729–738. 1 pl. 1 fig. [Gametophyte, *Equisetum*.]

Sharp, L. W. **1912.** *Bot. Gaz.* **54**: 89–119. 2 pl. [Antherozoids, *Equisetum*.]

Walker, Elda R. **1921.** *Ibid.* **71**: 378–391. 2 pl. 3 figs. [Gametophyte, *Equisetum*.]

——— **1931.** *Ibid.* **92**: 1–22. 54 figs. [Gametophyte, *Equisetum*.]

Williamson, W. C., and D. H. Scott. **1894.** *Phil. Trans. Roy. Soc. London*, Ser. *B*., **185**: 863–959. 15 pl. [*Calamites, Calamostachys, Sphenophyllum*.]

---

[1] Campbell, 1928.

CHAPTER IX

FILICINAE

The Filicinae have a sporophyte differentiated into root, stem, and leaf. In one or two exceptional genera roots are lacking on mature plants. The vascular cylinder of stems, when siphonostelic, has leaf gaps. The leaves are macrophyllous and spirally arranged on the stem. Sporangia are borne on the margin or on the abaxial face of leaves. A leaf bears many sporangia, and these are generally borne in clusters.

The three general evolutionary lines (Lycopodinae, Equistinae, Filicinae) appear to have diverged from the Psilophytinae fairly early in the Devonian. However, members of the Filicinae were less numerous and a less conspicuous element in the flora of the succeeding geological era, the Carboniferous, than were the Lycopodinae and the Equistinae. This does not mean that the filicinean series evolved at a slower rate. In fact, the reverse was the case; and evolution of the filicinean series progressed beyond the pteridophytic level long before the end of the Carboniferous. In addition to giving rise to seed plants, the dominant element in present-day vegetation, the filicinean series continued evolution at the pteridophytic level. The geological record seems to show that a large majority of these truly pteridophytic plants were post-Carboniferous in origin (Fig. 142). Most of the families of Filicinae with living representatives appeared during the Triassic or Jurassic. The almost complete absence of Polypodiaceae from strata older than the Early Coenozoic indicates that, from the geological standpoint, this family is a distinctly modern one.

Most of the Devonian and Carboniferous Filicinae belong to the Primofilices, a group which shows a much closer resemblance to the Psilophytinae than to other Filicinae. There is direct and indirect evidence showing that all of the Primofilices had a sporophyte differentiated into stem and leaves. Probably, also, these sporophytes bore roots, but this is only known with certainty for one genus (*Botryopteris*).

Evolution of the filicinean plant body with its characteristic stem and leaves appears to have come about through a metamorphosis of certain arms of the branch system comprising the entire psilophytan plant body. It is not improbable that these metamorphosed arms of the psilophytan plant had several dichotomous branchings and a sporangium at the tip of each ultimate dichotomy. The result was a megaphyllous leaf (one with many veins or a single much-branched vein) that bore several isolated marginal sporangia. Certain of the Primofilices, as *Cladoxylon* (Fig. 149) had leaves closely resembling these hypothetical modified branches of a psilophytan plant. A shift from the equal dichotomous branching found in the primitive leaf to a sympodial dichotomous branching in which the two forks develop unequally resulted in the type of leaf found in most Filicinae. The sympodial organization of the leaf is clearly evident in

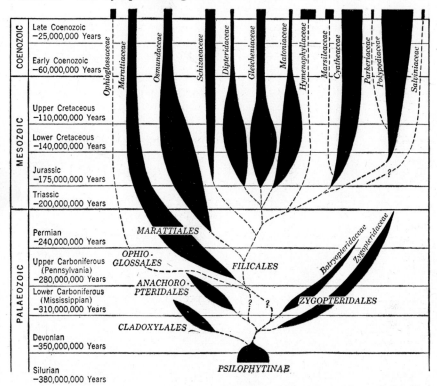

Fig. 142.—Diagram showing the geological antiquity and the suggested interrelationships among the Filicinae.

certain living ferns, as *Hymenophyllum* (Fig. 189), but more often this is obscure. Sporangia of primitive ferns also afford additional evidence that the filicinean leaf is a metamorphosed psilophytan branch. Thus, sporangia of most Primofilices were vertically elongate, with a jacket layer more than one cell in thickness, and opened vertically by a longitudinal splitting of the jacket layer. They were borne singly and terminally on appendages resembling foreshortened branches of Psilophytinae.

Evolution of the filicinean stem from a psilophytan shoot involved but little change. In a majority of Primofilices the stem had the same protostelic organization as shoots of the Psilophytinae.

The Filicinae have a vegetative organ, the root, that was not present in the Psilophytinae. The origin of this new organ is obscure. It may have appeared *de novo*, or it may have arisen by a modification of prostrate branches of the psilophytan shoot.

Evolution from the primitive type of filicinean plant has involved changes in external form and internal structure of the plant body and changes in its sporangial characters. Undoubtedly, also, there have been changes in the gametophytic generation, but these can only be inferred since gametophytes of fossil Filicinae are unknown. A comparison of admittedly primitive and advanced ferns affords a means of determining the general evolutionary tendencies within the class. However, evolutionary advances in various parts of the plant body have not always been at the same rate in the ancestry of any particular genus or family. A fern or group of ferns may be advanced in certain respects and less advanced in others. For example, the highly advanced heterospory of *Marsilea* is associated with a relatively primitive type of vegetative organization in the sporophyte. On the other hand, the Marattiales have an advanced vegetative organization of the sporophyte and primitive features in sporangia and the gametophyte.

When the Filicinae are taken as a whole, the following are among the general evolutionary tendencies evident within the class:[1]

1. *Habit and external morphology of stem.* Stems of ferns show a change from an upright radially symmetrical organization to a prostrate habit and a dorsiventral symmetry.

2. *Vascular organization of stem.* During the evolution of the vascular system there was an advance from a protostelic to a solenostelic or a dictyostelic condition. This was accompanied by a shifting of the protoxylem from an exarch to an endarch position.

3. *Vascular organization of leaf supply.* Primitive ferns generally have a single trace departing to each leaf; advanced ones frequently have the trace dissected into several meristeles. Sometimes, also, the vascular organization of a trace is more primitive than that of a stele.

4. *Leaf blade.* Evolution of leaf blades involved an advance from an equal to an unequal dichotomous branching. An open venation where the forked veins have free ends is considered more primitive than a closed venation where the veins form a reticulum.

5. *Position and protection of sporangia.* Primitive ferns have sporangia borne singly at the ends of dichotomies of a blade or along the blade margin. Advanced ferns have sporangia in groups (*sori*) inward from the margin and on the abaxial face of a leaf. Archaic ferns have unprotected sori; advanced ones frequently have the sorus protected by a covering (*indusium*).

[1] Bower, 1923.

6. *Sequence of sporangial development.* Primitive ferns have a simultaneous development of all sporangia on a leaf; more advanced forms have the sporangia of a sorus developing in basipetalous succession; the most advanced ferns have a sorus in which sporangia of various ages are intermingled with one another.

7. *Mode of sporangial development.* Sporangia of primitive ferns arise from a group of cells (a *eusporangiate* mode of origin); those of advanced ferns arise from a single cell (a *leptosporangiate* mode of origin).

8. *Spore output.* Sporangia of primitive ferns contain a large and indefinite number of spores; those of advanced ferns contain a relatively small number that is some multiple of two.

9. *Differentiation of spores.* The heterospory found in a few of the Filicinae is obviously more advanced than the homospory characteristic of most Filicinae.

10. *Sporangial dehiscence.* Sporangia of archaic ferns have a jacket layer more than one cell in thickness that generally ruptures longitudinally because of hygroscopic changes in a group of cells (the *annulus*) at one side of the sporangial jacket. More highly evolved ferns have a jacket layer one cell in thickness. The more primitive of these have the annulus at one side of the jacket, the more advanced have an annulus consisting of a single vertical row of cells. Sporangia of the latter type rupture transversely.

11. *Gametophyte.* The antheridium is the only gametophytic structure that is of pronounced phylogenetic significance. In the lower ferns it is massive, is embedded in the gametophyte, and contains a large number of antherozoids. In advanced ferns it is small, is emergent, and contains relatively few antherozoids.

12. *Embryology.* As a general rule the more primitive living Filicinae have a massive embryo in which there is a late differentiation of cotyledon, root, stem, and foot. Advanced Filicinae have these organs differentiated early in embryonal development, frequently at the eight-celled stage.

Although all of the foregoing phylogenetic tendencies are indices of evolutionary progress the sporangial characters are of greatest service when it comes to arranging the ferns in a natural system. Sporangial characters of major importance include: the sporangial position, the sequence of sporangial development and the structure of the sporangium itself. It has been held[1] that sporangial position and sequence of sporangial development are features of fundamental significance. According to this interpretation[1] the ferns fall into two major series: *Marginales* with sporangia borne on the leaf margin and *Superficiales* with sporangia borne on the abaxial face of the blade. Each series includes a subseries in

[1] Bower, 1926, 1928, 1935.

which the sporangia develop simultaneously, one in which they develop in basipetalous succession and one in which they develop in an irregular sequence. Such a classification of the Filicinae tends to obscure the differences between Palaeozoic ferns and those of a more recent date. The fundamental significance of the basic criterion (sporangial position) may also be questioned. If there are two major evolutionary series among the ferns, one with marginal sori and the other with abaxial ones, there has been an extraordinary parallelism of the two in such features as soral evolution, sporangial evolution, and evolution of the antheridia.

Sporangia of ferns may develop in a eusporangiate manner (from more than one cell) or in a leptosporangiate manner (from a single cell). Mature eusporangiate sporangia have a jacket layer more than one cell in thickness; leptosporangiate sporangia have a jacket layer one cell in thickness. When first discovered,[1] this distinction was used as a basis for separating all vascular plants into two primary series, the *Eusporangiatae* and the *Leptosporangiatae*, but within a fairly short time these terms became restricted to the Filicinae only. Several systems of classification divide the ferns into the Eusporangiatae and the Leptosporangiatae. Such systems are not so trivial as they appear, since the eusporangiate or leptosporangiate nature of a sporangium is correlated with distinctive antheridial and embryonal characters. The system is applicable to fossil ferns in which sporangial development is unknown because they may be referred to the appropriate subclass according to the type of the mature sporangial jacket. The chief difficulty in accepting this separation of Filicinae into two subclasses is the proper disposition of the ferns that existed during the Devonian and Early Carboniferous. These ferns differed greatly from living eusporangiate and leptosporangiate ferns. A logical escape from this difficulty is the proposal[2] that the primitive Palaeozoic ferns be segregated in a separate series, coordinate in rank with the eusporangiate and leptosporangiate ferns. On such a basis the Filicinae may be divided into the following subclasses:

Primofilices in which the sporangia were generally borne singly at the apex of an ultimate dichotomy of a leaf. The sporangia were elongate, with a jacket layer more than one cell in thickness, and opened by a terminal pore or a longitudinal slit. Known only in the fossil condition and from the Palaeozoic.

Eusporangiatae in which the sporangia are borne on an outgrowth (the fertile spike) from a leaf blade or in sori on the abaxial face of a blade. The sporangia contain many spores and have a jacket layer more than one cell in thickness. The antheridia are embedded in the gametophyte and contain many antherozoids. Known from the Carboniferous to the present.

[1] Goebel, 1880–1881.   [2] Arber, 1906.

Leptosporangiatae in which the sporangia are generally in sori and borne marginally or abaxially on a leaf blade. Sporangia have a jacket layer one cell in thickness and the number of spores is some multiple of two. The antheridia are more or less emergent and contain a relatively small number of antherozoids. Known from the Permian (possibly the Carboniferous) to the present.

SUBCLASS 1. PRIMOFILICES

The Primofilices had sporangia that were generally borne singly at the apex of an ultimate dichotomy of a leaf. The sporangia were elongate, had a jacket layer more than one cell in thickness, and opened by a terminal pore or a longitudinal slit. They are known only in the fossil condition and from the Palaeozoic.

The Primofilices[1] (also known as the *Inversicatenales*,[2] the *Coenopterideae*,[3] and the *Palaeopteridales*[4]) are an ancient extinct group of pteridophytes that practically all paleobotanists[5] relegate to the filicinean series. Although distinctly fern-like in nature, they also show features suggestive of the Psilophytinae. In almost all cases where the fructification is known, the ultimate segments of a leaf had but one sporangium, and this was borne terminally. A sporangium had a jacket layer more than one cell in thickness that opened terminally by an apical pore or dehisced longitudinally by means of a lateral annulus more than one cell in breadth. A majority of the genera had erect stems, a few had prostrate or clambering ones. In only one of the stems did the vascular cylinder evolve to a siphonostelic condition. The leaves, although varied from genus to genus, were distinctly megaphyllous. The leaves were divided, sometimes pinnately, sometimes not. In the relatively few cases where the leaf insertion is known the leaves were borne spirally on a stem.

Taken as a whole, the reproductive portions of these fossil sporophytes show a much greater resemblance to the Psilophytinae than they do to typical Filicinae. The stems were also simpler in structure than those of most other Filicinae. On the other hand, certain of the Primofilices evolved leaves comparable with those of modern ferns.

The geological range of the Primofilices is from the Middle Devonian to the end of the Permian. The subclass includes some 65 species distributed among 24 genera.[6] Stems and leaves are known for about half of the genera, only the stem or only the leaf is known in the remaining genera. Sporangia are known for eight genera.

Even when one excludes discussions[7] antedating the more recent discoveries among the Psilophytinae, there is great diversity of opinion

[1] Arber, 1906.   [2] Bertrand, P., 1913; Bertrand, C. E., and Cornaille, 1904.
[3] Seward, 1910.   [4] Bertrand, P., 1933.
[5] Hirmer, 1927; Potonié, 1921; Scott, 1920; Seward, 1910.
[6] Hirmer, 1927.   [7] Scott, 1920; Seward, 1910.

on the major interrelationships among the subclass.   It is obvious that a classification of the Primofilices based on a consideration of all vegetative and reproductive parts[1] is more logical than one[2] based solely on vegetative structure of leaves.   The major problem in classification is the proper disposition of the Cladoxyloids and Anachoropteroids.   *Cladoxylon* and its immediate relatives have been removed from the Primofilices and placed[3] as a series equal in rank to the lycopodian, filicinean, and other major groups among the Pteridophyta.   This seems to be too drastic a treatment, and it is probably better to follow the customary practice of grouping them among the primitive Filicinae.   The Botryopterids, Zygopterids, and Anachoropterids are usually considered three groups of equal rank.[4]   The distinctiveness of *Anachoropteris* from the Botryopterids and the Zygopterids was pointed out[5] nearly two decades ago, and the recent[6] elevation of the Anachoropterids to a rank equal to that of the Coenopterids (Botryopterids and Zygopterids) seems more logical. Differences between the Coenopterids, Anachoropterids, and Cladoyxloids are of sufficient magnitude to consider each of them an order.

ORDER 1.   COENOPTERIDALES

The Coenopteridales had monostelic stems.   The leaves were of two general categories: those that were not pinnately divided, and those that were pinnately divided with the pinnae at an angle to the plane of a leaf blade.   The sporangia were in pedicellate clusters borne directly on the rachis or on unflattened pinnules.

According to the importance one attached to leaf and sporangial differences, there are two families[5] or two suborders.[3]

SUBORDER 1.   BOTRYOPTERIDINEAE

The Botryopteridineae had monostelic, protostelic to siphonostelic, upright stems with spirally arranged leaves.   With one or two possible exceptions the leaves were not pinnately divided.   The sporangia were borne in tufts on the primary divisions of a leaf.   There are three genera. These are either placed in a single family, the Botryopteridaceae,[7] or in two families.[3]

Botryopteris, the type genus of the Botryopteridineae, is of frequent occurrence in certain Carboniferous deposits in Europe.   The genus has also been found in Pennsylvanian (Upper Carboniferous) material from Illinois.[8]   Very few impressions showing the general habit of the plant have been found.   However, so many sections of various parts of the

---

[1] Hirmer, 1927; Zimmermann, 1930.   [2] Bertrand, P., 1933.
[3] Hirmer, 1927.   [4] Hirmer, 1927; Scott, 1920.   [5] Scott, 1920.
[6] Zimmermann, 1930.   [7] Scott, 1920; Seward, 1910.   [8] Graham, 1935.

plant are known from coal balls that it is possible to visualize its general appearance. It had an upright, more or less branched stem that was 1 to 15 mm. in diameter. The leaves were borne spirally along a stem and sometimes in a definite 2/5 phyllotaxy. The leaves were branched, with the branches given off singly rather than in pairs. Flattened, fleshy, dichotomously branched structures, with stomata restricted to one surface, have been found in association with the leaves. It is uncertain whether these are the tips of leaf branches or are the flattened appendages

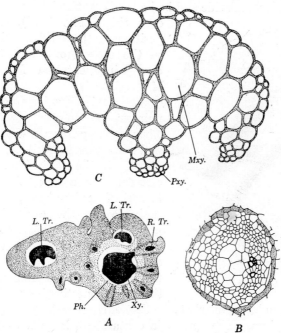

FIG. 143.—*Botryopteris.* *A*, diagram of a transverse section of a stem of *B. ramosa* Williamson. (*Based on Scott*, 1920.) *B*, transverse section of xylem of a leaf trace of *B. cylindrica* Williamson. (*After Scott*, 1920.) *C*, transverse section through the base of a young leaf trace of *B. hirsuta* Williamson. (*L.Tr.*, leaf trace; *Mxy.*, metaxylem; *Ph.*, phloem; *Pxy.*, protoxylem; *R.Tr.*, root trace; *Xy.*, xylem.) (*A*, × 4; *B–C*, × 75.)

(*aphlebia*) sometimes found on fern leaves. The lower part of a stem had numerous adventitious roots, and several of them were borne in the vicinity of each node.

The vascular cylinder of a stem was surrounded by a broad homogeneous cortex (Fig. 143*A*). Cortex and stele were not separated from each other by a well-defined endodermis. The central cylinder was protostelic and with a layer of phloem surrounding a cylindrical mass of xylem. The xylem contained two or more strands of protoxylem some distance in from the surface.[1]

[1] Benson, 1911; Scott, 1920.

The roots had a diarch stele. The general structure of a root resembled that in many present-day ferns.

There was a single trace leading to each leaf. Very close to its departure from a stele, the xylem of a trace was cylindrical and had a small mesarch protoxylem mass toward the adaxial side.[1] At a slightly higher level there was a shifting of the protoxylem so that it was exarch and on the adaxial side (Fig. 143*B*). Higher up, the xylem of certain species [including *B. hirsuta* (Will.) Scott and *B. ramosa* Will.] became three-ridged on the adaxial side and had a small protoxylem mass at the tip of each ridge (Fig. 143*C*). The relative position of these ridges with reference to the stele shows that there was a change in orientation of the upper part of a leaf.

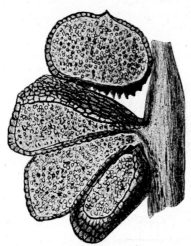

FIG. 144.—Sporangia of *Botryopteris*. (*From Renault, 1875.*)

Sporangia have been described for a number of species of *Botryopteris*.[2] They were pyriform, had small pedicels, and were borne in small clusters attached directly to the rachis (Fig. 144). Such clusters bear a superficial resemblance to sori of modern ferns, but it is very probable that they were similar to the pedicellate clusters in *Etapteris* (page 258). It is uncertain whether the sporangial jacket was one cell or more than one cell in thickness. However, there is no question but that there was a plate-like annulus, somewhat like that of *Osmuda* (page 290), at one side of a sporangium. The sporangia contained a large number of spores, all of them the same size.

SUBORDER 2. ZYGOPTERIDINEAE

The Zygopterids had a unique type of leaf in which the pinnae were in two or in four series inserted at an angle to the plane of a leaf blade. This peculiar arrangement of the pinnae was associated with so distinctive a type of vascular organization in petiole and rachis that it is possible to refer fossils to the zygopterid series when only their leaf bases are known.[3] The stems of the Zygopteridineae were erect, prostrate, or clambering, and had a more or less complicated actinostelic central cylinder. The sporangia were borne in pedicellate clusters on the ultimate segments of a

---

[1] Benson, 1911; Scott, 1920.

[2] Benson, 1911; Graham, 1935; Renault, 1875; Scott, 1910.

[3] Bertrand, P., 1909.

leaf. The jacket layer of a sporangium was more than one cell in thickness and had a definite or indefinite annulus.

The geological range of the suborder is from the Middle Devonian to the end of the Permian. There are approximately 17 genera and 50 species.[1] These have been grouped in a single family, the Zygopteridaceae,[2] and in three families.[1]

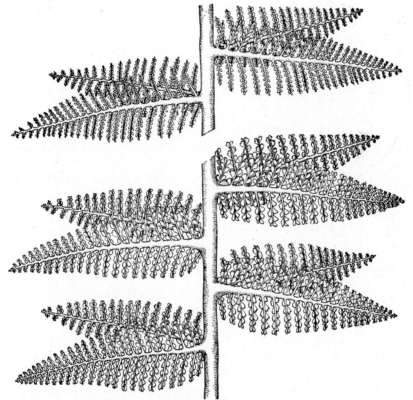

Fig. 145.—Reconstruction of leaf of *Etapteris Lacattei* Renault. (*After Hirmer in Wettstein*, 1933.)

Etapteris, here selected as representative of the Zygopteridineae, is one of the genera in which the stem is unknown. One species is known from from the Lower Carboniferous, three are known from the Upper Carboniferous, and two from the Permian. The leaves of *Etapteris* were fairly large, and those of one species (*E. diupsilon* Will.) had a rachis up to 2 cm. in diameter. The leaves were pinnately divided and had the primary pinnae borne alternately on a rachis. In *E. Lacattei* Renault, the only species in which the external leaf form is known, each pinna immediately

[1] Hirmer, 1927.   [2] Scott, 1920; Seward, 1910.

branched into two pinnules of equal size (Fig. 145).   Both of these pinnules were pinnately divided and had the secondary and tertiary pinnules

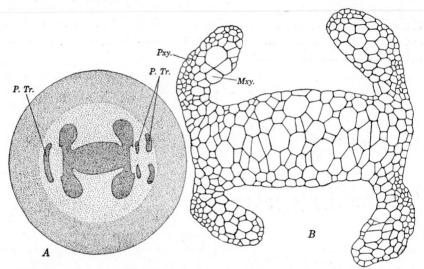

Fig. 146.—*Etapteris Scottii* Renault.   *A,* diagram of a rachis in transverse section.
B, transverse section of the xylem of a rachis.   (*Mxy.,* metaxylem; *P. Tr.,* pinna trace;
Pxy., protoxylem.)   (*A,* × 6; *B,* × 25.)

in the same plane.   Certain pinnules of this species were fertile; others
were sterile.

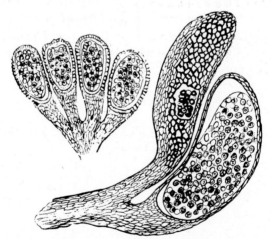

Fig. 147.—Sporangia of *Etapteris.*   (*From Renault,* 1876.)

When seen in cross section, the rachis of *Etapteris* has a very characteristic **H**-shaped xylem mass and one in which the uprights of the **H** may
be curved toward each other (Fig. 146*B*).   In *E. Scottii* P. Bertrand and

E. Lacattei Renault there were two small groups of protoxylem on the outer face of each upright and opposite the cross bar of the **H.** Each protoxylem mass gave off a trace to a pinna. A short distance above the point of departure, the two traces fused to form a strap-like plate (the pinna bar). At a somewhat higher level the bar divided into two **C**-shaped strands, one of which ran to each pinna.[1]

E. Lacattei Renault has been found in a fertile condition.[2] Its sporangia were borne in pedicellate tufts along pinnules that lacked an expanded blade. These fertile pinnules have the vascular structure typical of *Etapteris*.[3] A sporangial tuft had a di- or trichotomously branched pedicel (Fig. 147). The ultimate dichotomies of a pedicel terminated in a single, straight or somewhat curved, ellipsoidal sporangium. The jacket layer of a sporangium seems to have been more than one cell in thickness and to have had a disintegration of all but the outermost cell layer as the sporangium matured. On opposite sides of a sporangial jacket and extending from base to apex there was an annulus several cells in breadth. The sporangia contained a large number of small spores, and there is some indication that they were surrounded by a tapetum.

ORDER 2. ANACHOROPTERIDALES

The Anachoropteridales had pinnately divided leaves with all segments in the same plane and sporangia on the flattened margins of the ultimate pinnules. Stems are unknown for this order.

There is but one family, the Anachoropteridaceae. It consists of a fairly well-known genus (*Anachoropteris*) and another one (*Gyropteris*) known only from fragments of leaf bases. These plants are found in the Lower and the Upper Carboniferous.

The leaf of *Anachoropteris* had a petiole and rachis with a conspicuous **C**-shaped vascular bundle (Fig. 148*A*). The outline of the petiole seems to show that the convex face of the bundle was toward the stem, not away from it as in modern ferns with **C**-shaped bundles.[4] The major portion of a bundle consisted of metaxylem elements. On the convex face there were four cup-shaped projections, each with protoxylem.[5] Vascular strands running to the pinnae arose on the convex side of a bundle and each was connected with a protoxylem group. Nonvascular portions of petiole and rachis were sclerenchymatous toward the exterior, were parenchymatous internal to this, and had a central mass of sclerenchyma encircled by the **C**-shaped vascular strand.

The sporangia were borne in tetrads, one at the apex and others along the lateral margins of flattened leaf-like pinnules.[6] Each tetrad was

---

[1] Bertrand, P., 1909.   [2] Renault, 1876.   [3] Bertrand, P., 1911.
[4] Scott, 1920.   [5] Bertrand, P., 1913; Scott, 1920.   [6] Kubart, 1917.

immediately subtended by a vein of the pinnule (Fig. 148*B–C*). Each tetrad was surrounded by a cup-like sheath of leaf tissue several cells in thickness, and there is also some evidence showing that the sporangia were separated from one another by a delicate parenchymatous tissue. The sporangia had a jacket layer one cell in thickness in which there was no annulus. The sporangia were large, and it has been estimated[1] that they had a potential spore output of over 5,000 spores. It is very probable that the sporangia opened apically and that they spread apart from one another when they opened.[1]

The fertile region of *Anachoropteris* was of a much more advanced type than that in other Primofilices. The Coenopterids had a psilophytan type of fertile region in which a single sporangium terminated an unflat-

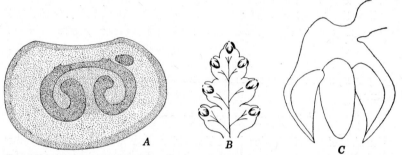

Fig. 148.—*Anachoropteris pulchra* Corda. *A*, diagram of a rachis in transverse section. *B*, fertile tip of a pinnule. *C*, sporangia. (*A, based upon Scott, 1920; B, after Hirmer, 1927; C, after Kubart, 1917.*) (*A*, × 6; *C*, × 30.)

tened ultimate dichotomy of a leaf. In *Anachoropteris*, obliteration of pedicels beneath the sporangia resulted in what may be called a true sorus. Furthermore, several sori were borne marginally on a single pinnule. Irrespective of whether the sori are or are not of a synangial type (page 279), the leaf of *Anachoropteris* shows a close approach to the leaves of more modern ferns, especially those of the Marattiales. If the Anachoropteridales are not along the evolutionary line leading to modern ferns, they at least evolved a type of leaf analogous to that of present-day ferns.

ORDER 3. CLADOXYLALES

The Cladoxylales had dichotomously branched stems that were polystelic, each stele being actinostelic. The stem bore numerous small leaves that were dichotomously branched in one plane. Certain of the leaves were sterile; others were fertile with each ultimate dichotomy terminating in a single sporangium. There is but one family, the Cladoxylaceae.

[1] Kubart, 1917.

The order and family are based upon a single genus, *Cladoxylon*. Two additional genera known only from their stems seem to be related to it.[1] Five species of *Cladoxylon* are known from the Lower Carboniferous and one from the Middle Devonian. The Middle Devonian species (*C.*

FIG. 149.—Reconstruction of shoot of *Cladoxylon scoparium* Kräusel and Weyland. (*After Kräusel and Weyland, 1926.*)

scoparium Kräusel and Weyland) is the only one in which the leaves are known.[2] *C. scoparium* is based upon a single specimen 22 cm. long so embedded in rock that there is a downwardly convergent series of branches. The largest branches are 1.5 cm. in diameter. Their downward convergence suggests that they were borne upon a common axis. The branches were dichotomously forked and leaf-bearing (Fig. 149).

[1] Hirmer, 1927.   [2] Kräusel and Weyland, 1926.

There were numerous spirally arranged leaves on the small upper branches and a few scattered leaves on the thicker lower ones.

Branches of *C. scoparium* had the central area surrounded by a broad homogeneous cortex. The central area was polystelic and, as seen in cross section, had a number of narrow outwardly branched steles (Fig. 150*H–J*). The xylem of a stele contained both scalariform and pitted tracheids. Serial sections cut at 5-mm. intervals on the same branch show that there was a downwardly progressive increase both in the number of steles and in the complexity of their outline. The method by which the number of steles was increased as a branch grew older is

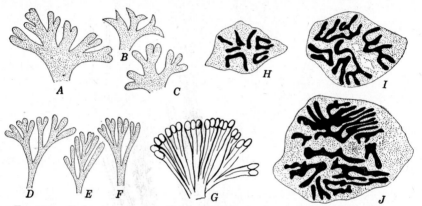

Fig. 150.—*Cladoxylon scoparium* Kräusel and Weyland. *A–C*, sterile leaves from lower branches. *D–F*, sterile leaves from upper twigs. *G*, fertile leaf. *H–J*, transverse sections of the same stem at different levels. (*After Kräusel and Weyland*, 1926.) (*A–G*, × 2½; *H–J*, × 8.)

unknown. Possibly, as in present-day palms, maturation of certain of the vascular elements was long delayed.

Fertile leaves were restricted to certain of the upper branches. Sterile leaves on lower parts of the branch system were 5 to 10 mm. long, broadly cuneate, and dichotomously incised and had a broad or narrow base (Fig. 150 *A–C*). Those on the upper branches were up to 18 mm. in length, narrowly cuneate, and dichotomously branched and had a narrow petiole-like base (Fig. 150*D–F*). The fertile leaves were broadly cuneate, with several dichotomous forkings, and had each of the ultimate dichotomies terminating in a single sporangium that contained many spores (Fig. 150*G*). The structure of the sporangial jacket is unknown.

SUBCLASS 2. EUSPORANGIATAE

The Eusporangiatae produce their sporangia either upon an outgrowth (the fertile spike) from a leaf blade or in sori borne on the abaxial face of a blade. The sporangia contain many spores and have a jacket layer more than one cell in thickness. Antheridia of living species are embedded in the gametophyte and contain many antherozoids. The subclass is known from the Carboniferous to the present.

Sporangia of Eusporangiatae resemble those of Primofilices in that the jacket layer is more than one cell in thickness, but differ in that they are not psilophyte-like in general shape. Sporangia of Leptosporangiatae are immediately distinguishable from those of Eusporangiatae by their jacket layers one cell in thickness and the definite numbers of spores within a sporangium.

The Eusporangiatae fall into two series: one known only in the living condition, the other with a fossil record extending back to the Carboniferous (Fig. 142). The differences between the two are so great that each should be made an order.

ORDER 1. OPHIOGLOSSALES

The Ophioglossales differ from all other Filicinae in that the sporangia are borne on an outgrowth, the *fertile spike*, that projects from the adaxial face of the leaf near the juncture of blade and petiole.

There are three genera of living plants. Two of these, *Ophioglossum* (with 43 species) and *Botrychium* (with 34 species), are world wide in distribution; the third, *Helminthostachys*, is monotypic and found only in the Indo-Malayan area. These three genera are placed in one family, the Ophioglossaceae.

Despite the lack of a fossil record to show their antiquity, there is a very general agreement that the Ophioglossales are a primitive stock. It has been held[1] that they are "an imperfectly modernized relic of the Palaeozoic flora" and a relic that represents a blind evolutionary series from the Primofilices of the Carboniferous and Devonian. They represent a group in which, according to the criteria noted on page 250, there has been considerable progress in evolution of vegetative parts of the sporophyte as against a retention of very primitive characters in the parts concerned with reproduction in both generations. The chief reason for relating the Ophioglossales to the Primofilices of the Palaeozoic is the structure of the spike. It is thought that the lateral branchlets on spikes of *Botrychium* (Fig. 151C), each terminating in a single sporangium, represent a derived condition from a fertile primofilicinean leaf such as that of *Etapteris*.

Ophioglossum, the genus discussed on succeeding pages, is probably a somewhat specialized member of the family. Its fertile spike (Fig. 151A–B) seems to represent a condensation from the branched condition found in the more primitive *Botrychium*. Other reasons for considering *Ophioglossum* more advanced than *Botrychium* are the closed venation of leaves in all species and the division of the leaf trace into several strands

[1] Bower, 1926.

in certain species.[1]　It is a more favorable genus for study of vegetative structure of the sporophyte since there is no obvious secondary thickening as in *Botrychium.*

The sporophyte of most species of *Ophioglossum* has a short, upright, subterranean stem.　A few species (including *O. pendulum* L.) have a markedly dorsiventral stem.　Branching of the sporophyte is generally due to a formation of buds in the axils of leaves.　Occasionally, however, it is due to a dichotomy of the stem apex.[2]　The stem bears numer-

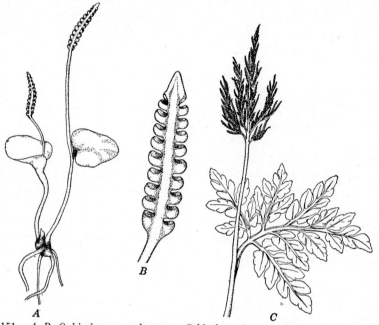

Fig. 151.—*A–B, Ophioglossum moluccanum* Schlecht.　*A*, sporophyte.　*B*, fertile spike. *C*, leaf of *Botrychium silaifolium* Presl.　(*A*, × ⅔; *B*, × 2½; *C*, × ⅓.)

ous adventitious roots (Fig. 151*A*).　As a rule these are borne singly below the leaf scars of previous seasons and the leaf, or leaves, of the current season.　A majority of the species produce but one leaf each year. Some species, especially those growing in the tropics, may produce four or five leaves in a single season.　The leaves are borne in an irregular spiral on the stem.　Sometimes they appear to be in a two-ranked arrangement, but there is no true dorsiventrality in the insertion of these leaves.[3]　The embryonic leaf at a stem apex of species producing but one leaf a year develops slowly for three years and then grows above ground and unfolds the fourth year.　Unfolding leaves of *Ophioglossum* do not have the spiral uncoiling (circinate vernation) so characteristic

[1] Bower, 1926.　　[2] Petry, 1915.　　[3] Petry, 1914.

of Filicinae. A fully expanded leaf is sharply differentiated into blade and petiole. In all but one species there is a single fertile spike at the juncture of blade and petiole. This is usually unbranched, but it may have one or two irregular branchings. *O. palmatum* L. is exceptional in that it has several small fertile spikes in the region where blade and petiole adjoin. The blades of all species but *O. palmatum* are entire and narrowly linear to broadly ovate in outline. In *O. palmatum* the blade is palmately incised into a number of narrow segments. The venation of the blade is always reticulate and, according to the species, is with or without small veinlets ending blindly within the larger meshes (Fig. 154*A*). There is no midrib, but the veins near the central axis of the blade may be more conspicuous than others.

There is a single inconspicuous pyramidal apical cell with three cutting faces[1] at the apex of a stem. Derivatives cut off from the apical cell divide and redivide to form an embryonic tissue that becomes differentiated into stele, cortex, and epidermis when it matures. The first-matured (lowermost) portion of a stem may have an endodermis delimiting stele and cortex;[2] higher up there is no endodermis. Here the innermost cortical cells and the outermost stelar cells are so similar in appearance that it is impossible to tell where one region leaves off and the other begins. Cases have been found[2] where the basal portion of the stem is protostelic and the upper portion siphonostelic. Generally, however, the stem is siphonostelic throughout its entire length.[3] The siphonostele may be solenostelic and may have but one leaf gap when cut at any particular level, but more often there is an overlapping of gaps and a dictyostelic condition (Fig. 152*A–B*). A large majority of the species have a single leaf trace departing at each gap and traversing the cortex without branching. A few species, including *O. palmatum* L.[4] and *O. pendulum* L.[5] have two traces departing at each gap and a division of each trace into several strands before it runs into the leaf base.

The xylem portion of a meristele is endarch in arrangement and has the protoxylem lining the entire inner face of the xylem mass (Fig. 152*C*). The metaxylem is composed of irregularly shaped reticulate tracheids whose length is rarely more than six times the breadth. A small amount of secondary thickening has been observed in the stem of *O. vulgatum* L.[6] All of the phloem lies external to the xylem. Generally it is a layer four or five cells in thickness, but that of *O. pendulum*[5] is uniformly

---

[1] Campbell, 1918.   [2] Bower, 1911*A*.

[3] There are those (Baas-Becking, 1921; Campbell, 1911, 1921; Maheshwari and Singh, 1934) who hold that the vascular organization of the axis in Ophioglossaceae cannot be interpreted according to the stelar theory and that the so-called stele consists exclusively of leaf traces and the vascular supply to roots.

[4] Bower, 1911*B*.   [5] Petry, 1914.   [6] Boodle, 1899.

a single layer of cells separated from the xylem by a layer of parenchyma three to five cells in thickness.   The pith internal to the xylem is usually a homogeneous thin-walled parenchyma of relatively large cells, but sometimes, as in *O. pendulum*, there may be small strands of xylem within the pith.[1]   The cortical portion of the stem is also generally a

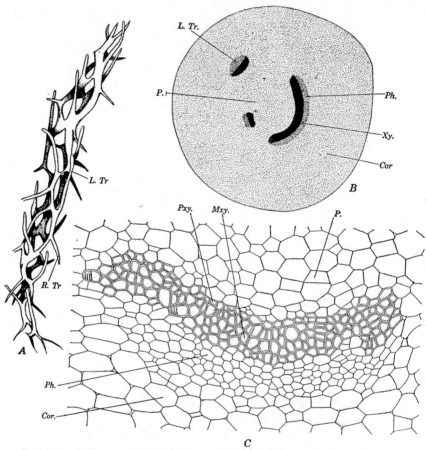

Fig. 152.—*Ophioglossum vulgatum* L.   *A*, vascular skeleton of the stem.   *B*, transverse section of the stem.   *C*, transverse section of a meristele.   (*A*, *after Rostowzew in Bower*, 1908.)   (*Cor.*, cortex; *L. Tr.*, leaf trace; *Mxy.*, metaxylem; *P.*, pith; *Ph.*, phloem; *Pxy.*, protoxylem; *R. Tr.*, root trace; *Xy.*, xylem.)   (*B*, × 21; *C*, × 160.)

uniform thin-walled parenchyma.   In some cases[2] a periderm is differentiated in the superficial portion of the cortex, but this never has a functional phellogen.

The roots of *Ophioglossum* are without root hairs and have the free faces of the epidermal cells thickened and suberized (Fig. 153).   The

[1] Petry, 1914.   [2] Campbell, 1911; Maheshwari and Singh, 1934.

cortex is massive and has the innermost cell layer differentiated into an endodermis with well-defined Casparian strips. The remainder of the cortex consists of two concentric regions of approximately equal thickness. The outer region is composed of angular cells without intercellular spaces, and a mycorhizal fungus is generally present in this portion of the cortex. This fungus is obviously a phycomycete, but, owing to the lack of fruiting bodies, it is impossible to determine whether

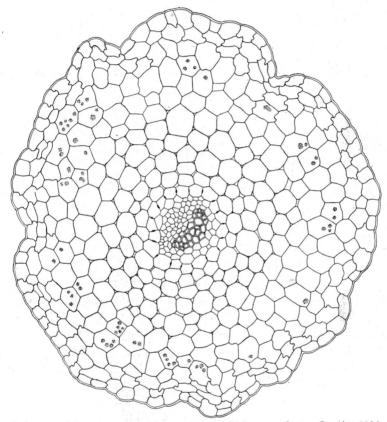

Fig. 153.—Transverse section of a root of *Ophioglossum vulgatum* L. (× 120.)

or not it is identical with the oömycete (*Stigeosporium Marattiacearum* West) found in roots of Marattiales. The inner region of the cortex has rounded cells with intercellular spaces. Cells in this region frequently contain starch grains. The stele of a root is generally monarch or diarch. Tri- and tetrach steles have been observed in a few species. Diarch steles have the usual plate of xylem with a protoxylem mass at each pole. There is a mass of phloem on either side of the xylem. Each of the phloem masses is separated from the xylem by a parenchymatous tissue two to three cells in thickness.   Some monarch roots have the xylem and phloem radial to each other.   Others have the xylem and phloem masses with their broader sides facing each other.   It is very probable that monarch steles of the latter type have been derived from diarch steles by a suppression of one of the phloem masses.   Evidence supporting this assumption is the occasional incomplete suppression of the second phloem mass[1] and the occurrence of two protoxylem points on the xylem mass.

The trace, or pair of traces, departing to a leaf always become divided into strands that lie parallel to one another throughout the length of the petiole.   Certain of these strands in a petiole run to the fertile spike; others run to the sterile blade.   Exclusive of the vascular strands, the

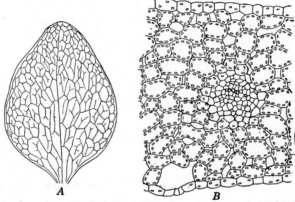

A   *B*

Fig. 154.—*A*, surface view of leaf blade of *Ophioglossum Moluccanum* Schlecht.   *B*, transverse section of a leaf of *O. pendulum* L.   (*A*, × ¾; *B*, × 80.)

interior of a petiole is composed of a spongy parenchyma that may or may not have conspicuous cavities in the central region.   Parenchyma cells just beneath the epidermis frequently contain numerous chloroplasts. The epidermal layer of a petiole is not heavily cutinized.   The sterile blade has a structure resembling that of a petiole.   If the species is one with erect leaves, stomata are present in equal numbers on both faces of the blade; if, as in *O. reticulatum* L., the leaf lies more or less horizontally, there are more stomata in the upper epidermis.[2]   The mesophyll of a blade is composed of vascular tissue and a spongy parenchyma in which all of the cells contain chloroplasts (Fig. 154*B*).

A very young fertile spike is a conical hump of meristematic tissue which grows by means of a pyramidal apical cell with four cutting faces. The four quadrants recognizable in transverse sections cut just back of the apex of the spike correspond to the four cutting faces of the apical

[1] Boodle, 1899.   [2] Campbell, 1911.

cell.[1] They are so oriented that two lie in a plane perpendicular to the sterile blade, and two in a plane parallel to it. As development continues, there is the differentiation of a vertical strip of cells in the epidermal layer of the two quadrants in the plane parallel to the leaf blade. Each strip, which is two to three cells broad and several cells tall, is a *sporangiogenic band.*[1] The two bands become three or four cells in thickness soon after they are recognizable (Fig. 155*A*). At this time there is a differentiation of the hypodermal region of the band into alternate superimposed blocks of archesporial cells and sterile cells (Fig. 155*B*).

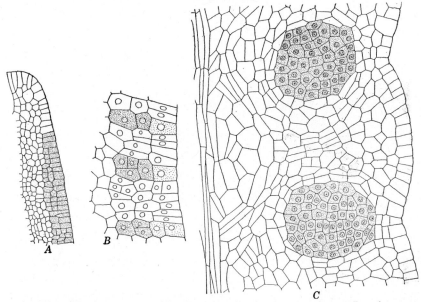

Fig. 155.—Vertical sections of fertile spike of *Ophioglossum vulgatum* L. *A*, a very young spike with a sporangiogenic band. *B–C*, after the differentiation of the sporangia. (*A–B, after Bower*, 1896.) (*A*, × 75; *C*, × 160.)

Each group of archesporial cells divides and redivides to form a large number of sporogenous cells. The portion of the band external to each archesporium divides periclinally to form a jacket layer that is several cells in thickness when the sporangium is mature (Fig. 155*C*). There is also a division and redivision of the sterile cells vertically separating the sporangia one from another and the ultimate maturation of an irregularly branched vascular strand within each sterile mass. As the sporogenous tissue continues development, it becomes surrounded by a poorly defined tapetum (Fig. 156). This has been described as arising from the outermost sporogenous cells,[2] but it seems more probable that it comes from cells immediately external to the sporogenous mass. The tapetum

---

[1] Bower, 1896.   [2] Bower, 1908.

ultimately breaks down into a plasmodial mass, with persistent nuclei, that invades the space between the isolated spore mother cells.[1]   Each sporangium of the spike opens by a transverse cleft after the spores are mature (Fig. 151B), but there is no special mechanism (annulus) causing an opening of the sporangial jacket.   Dehiscence seems to result from a drying out and shrinking of the sterile tissues within the spike.

The morphological nature of the fertile spike has been argued at length.   There is no need of discussing whether or not it is a single septate sporangium,[2] since this hypothesis has been rejected by its pro-

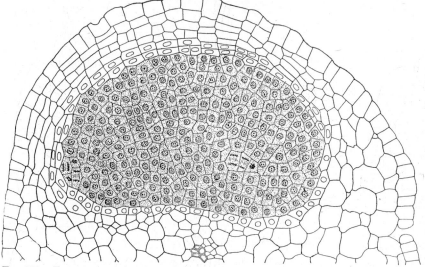

Fig. 156.—Transverse section through portion of a fertile spike of *Ophioglossum vulgatum* L. (× 160.)

ponent.[3]   During recent years practically all of those considering the question are in agreement that it is pinna-like in nature.   The pinna-like nature is more evident in *Botrychium*, where the sterile blade is pinnately divided, than it is in *Ophioglossum*, where the blade is entire. It has been held[4] that the spike represents a single pinna, but it is more probable that it represents the fusion of the two basal pinnae of a leaf.[5] One of the reasons for the latter interpretation is that the fertile spike has the same vascular supply as would go to a pair of pinnae.   If the plant is abnormal and has a pair of fertile spikes instead of one, each spike has the vascular supply that would ordinarily go to a single pinna. The pinna-nature of the spike is shown most strikingly by *Botrychium lanuginosum* Wall., a species found in southeastern Asia.   Here[6] the

[1] Bower, 1896; Burlingame, 1907.   [2] Bower, 1896, 1908.
[3] Bower, 1911A, 1926.   [4] Goebel, 1915.   [5] Chrysler, 1910.
[6] Chrysler, 1925.

spike is inserted in the middle of the blade and in the position of the third to the sixth leaflet from the base.

The gametophyte of *Ophioglossum* may be wholly subterranean in habit and obtain all of its food through the agency of a mycorhizal fungus, or it may have small green lobes above ground. Germination of spores to form gametophytes may take place immediately or may be greatly delayed.[1] In either case, the young gametophyte does not develop beyond the three- or four-celled stage unless it becomes infected with the mycorhizal fungus. The spore divides transversely into a lower and an upper cell. Subsequent development is chiefly by division and redivision of the lower cell, but there is a certain amount of division in the upper cell. The fungus which becomes the mycorhizal endophyte always enters through the lower cell (Fig. 157*A*). The largest gametophytes that have been grown from spores consisted of but 13 cells.[2] They were globose and without rhizoids. Possibly there was an apical cell at this stage, but this could not be determined with certainty. Mature gametophytes[3] are irregularly cylindrical to conical and, according to the species, unbranched or profusely branched (Fig. 157*B*). In most species the gametophyte is perennial, but in *O. moluccanum* Schlecht. it seems to be an annual.[2] The growing apex of a prothallus has a single apical cell with three or four cutting faces. The region immediately posterior to the apical cell is colorless; the remainder of the prothallus is brownish. According to the species, the gametophyte has numerous rhizoids in the older portion[2] or lacks them.[4] There is little differentiation of tissue within a gametophyte, except that cells toward the interior may be somewhat elongate. The apical portion of the thallus and the outer cells in older portions are free from fungi. Interior cells in older parts of a gametophyte are sparingly or abundantly infected with a mycorhizal fungus. These interior cells may also contain numerous starch grains.

Sex organs generally begin to develop near the growing tip; sometimes even in a segment but once removed from the apical cell. In *O. pendulum* L. most of them arise in acropetalous succession. Antheridia and archegonia are formed in irregular sequence, and the two are gener-

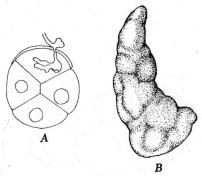

Fig. 157.—*Ophioglossum pendulum* L. *A*, four-celled gametophyte. *B*, mature gametophyte. (*A*, *after Campbell*, 1907.) (*A*, × 265; *B*, × 5.)

[1] Campbell, 1911.　[2] Campbell, 1907.
[3] Bruchmann, 1904; Campbell, 1907; Lang, 1902.　[4] Bruchmann, 1904.

ally indiscriminately intermingled on the lobes of a thallus. The ratio between the two is quite variable, and it is not uncommon to find either antheridia or archegonia markedly predominating on a particular gametophyte.

The antheridium arises from a superficial cell of the gametophyte.[1] This initial divides periclinally into an outer cell (the jacket initial) and an inner cell (the primary androgonial cell). The jacket initial always divides anticlinally and generally into two daughter cells of equal size (Fig. 158A). One of these daughter cells, by anticlinal division in a plane diagonal to the first wall, forms two daughter cells—one approximately triangular, the other approximately rectangular. The triangular cell functions in the same manner as an apical cell and successively cuts off a series of cells from each of its three sides. After it

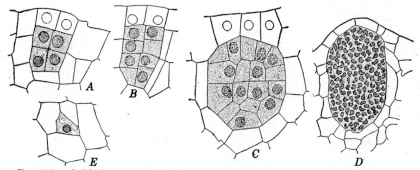

Fig. 158.—*Ophioglossum pendulum* L.   *A–D*, vertical sections of antheridia at various stages of development.   *E*, transverse section through the jacket of an antheridium showing the opercular cell.   (*A–C, E,* × 215; *D,* × 140.)

has stopped cutting off segments it is known as the *opercular cell* (Fig. 158E). As the antheridium approaches maturity the opercular cell becomes brownish and ultimately disintegrates. Eventually there is an escape of the antherozoids through this triangular pore. Division of the primary androgonial cell to form two androgonial cells may be anticlinal or periclinal. In either case the next division is in the opposite plane so that the four androgonial cells lie in two tiers (Fig. 158A). Division and redivision is long continued in the androgonial tissue (Fig. 158B–D), and it has been estimated[2] that an antheridium contains several thousand androgonial cells. Members of the last cell generation of androgonial cells, the androcyte mother cells, have two blepharoplasts at one side of the nucleus.[2] When an androcyte mother cell divides to form two androcytes, each receives one of the blepharoplasts. The first noticeable change in the metamorphosis of an androcyte into an antherozoid is an elongation of the blepharoplast. As metamorphosis continues

---

[1] Bruchmann, 1904; Campbell, 1907; Lang, 1902.   [2] Campbell, 1907.

the blepharoplast becomes coiled into two or more turns and the nucleus also becomes coiled. Shortly after this there is a development of several flagella at the anterior portion of the blepharoplast. The end result is the coiled multiflagellate antherozoid characteristic of all Filicinae. The narrowly coiled anterior portion of the antherozoid consists mainly of blepharoplast and cytoplasm; the broad, loosely coiled posterior portion is mainly nucleus.

Archegonia also arise from a single superficial cell of the prothallus. Division of an archegonial initial is periclinal and into a primary cover cell and an inner cell (Fig. 159A). This is followed[1] by a periclinal division of the inner cell into a central cell, which lies next the primary cover cell, and a basal cell (Fig. 159B). Next to follow is an anticlinal division of the primary cover cell, after which the two daughter cells

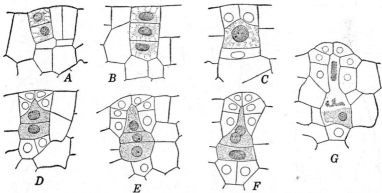

Fig. 159.—Vertical sections showing stages in development of archegonia of *Ophioglossum pendulum* L. (× 215.)

divide anticlinally to form the four quadrately arranged neck initials (Fig. 159C). Diagonally transverse division of each of the neck initials results in a neck composed of two tiers of four cells each (Fig. 159D). Accordingly as the cells in one or both tiers divide transversely, the mature neck is three or four cells in height (Fig. 159E–G). In either case it is a structure that projects but slightly above the surface of the gametophyte. As the neck is developing there is a periclinal division of the central cell into a primary canal cell and a primary ventral cell (Fig. 159D). The primary canal cell elongates vertically and pushes out into the neck. Its nucleus generally divides, but this is rarely followed by a division into two canal cells. Shortly before the archegonium is mature there is a division of the primary ventral cell into a ventral canal cell (which immediately disintegrates) and an egg (Fig. 159E). The ventral canal cell is such a transitory structure in the

[1] Bruchmann, 1904; Campbell, 1907; Lang, 1902.

ontogeny of an archegonium that it is rarely demonstrable.[1] The last step in archegonial development is a disintegration of the canal cell (or cells) and an opening of the archegonial neck (Fig. 159G).

Development of an embryo into a self-sustaining sporophyte with cotyledon and primary root may take a single year (O. moluccanum Schlecht.),[1] or it may require several years (O. vulgatum L.).[2] Early

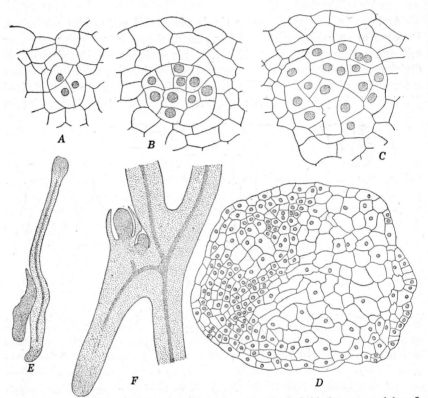

Fig. 160.—A–D, vertical sections through embryos of Ophioglossum pendulum L. E, vertical section through gametophyte and a young sporophyte of O. moluccanum Schlecht. F, vertical section through an older sporophyte of O. moluccanum: reconstructed from several successive sections. (A–C, × 160; D, × 80; E, × 10; F, × 20.)

stages in embryonal development are best known in O. pendulum L.,[1] but even here there are many gaps in the developmental history. All species investigated have an approximately transverse division of the zygote (Fig. 160A). The meager evidence at hand makes it uncertain whether the hypobasal cell (that farthest from the archegonial neck) develops only into the foot[1] or into the foot and primary root.[2] Irrespective of its precise point of origin, there is an early differentiation of an apical

[1] Campbell, 1907.   [2] Bruchmann, 1904.

cell in the root portion of an embryo (Fig. 160*B–D*). In some species, including *O. vulgatum*,[1] development of root and foot so overshadows that of cotyledon and stem that the young sporophyte appears to be all root for a considerable time after it protrudes from the gametophyte. In other species, including *O. moluccanum* Schlecht.,[2] the cotyledon and primary root grow at an equal rate (Fig. 160*E*). The method of formation of the cotyledon from the epibasal (upper) half of the embryo is unknown. Cotyledonary growth is due to an apical cell, but it is uncertain whether this is differentiated early or late in the ontogeny of the epibasal half. After the primary root and cotyledon are well along in development, there is an appearance of the apical cell of the stem in the region where they adjoin each other. This cell seems to be a superficial cell of the young sporophyte. Development of the stem from this apical cell takes place very slowly. The first, second, third, and successive leaves of the sporophyte appear to originate in the same manner as do leaves of other pteridophytes, that is, as meristematic outgrowths slightly posterior to the apical cell.[3] However, the growth and maturation of leaf tissues greatly overshadow those of stem tissue. Thus the young stem is composed mainly of leaf bases and the tissues of adventitious roots formed in association with these leaves (Fig. 160*F*). Later on, when the sporophyte has formed several leaves, there may be a less marked predominance of the leaf portion over the stem portion of the plant.

ORDER 2. MARATTIALES

The Marattiales include all the Eusporangiatae in which the sporangia are borne in sori on the abaxial face of a leaf blade. Sometimes the sporangia are laterally adherent to form a synangium, but this character is not universal throughout the order. Marattiales also differ from other living ferns in the structure of the stem and in having stipules at the leaf bases. They differ from all living ferns, except the Ophioglossales, in the eusporangiate origin of the sporangia and in the structure of the antheridia.

There are seven genera of living Marattiales, all of them tropical in distribution. Three of the genera are monotypic, the remaining four have 25 to 62 species each. In addition to the living representatives there are a number of fossil genera that have been referred to the order, either because of the synangial nature of their sori or because of the stem structure. While the systematic position of certain of these genera may

---

[1] Bruchmann, 1904.   [2] Campbell, 1907.

[3] It has also been held (Campbell, 1911) that all parts of the sporophyte but the cotyledon and primary root are formed from an adventitious bud that arises endogenously in the primary root.

be dubious, that of others seems to be sufficiently well established to warrant the statement that members of the order are found as far back as the Middle Carboniferous.[1]

The Marattiales have a number of features in common with the Ophioglossales. These include: the eusporangiate formation of sporangia, similarities in ontogeny and structure of sex organs, and late differentiation of cotyledon, root, and stem in the embryo. The presence of

Fig. 161.—Young sporophyte of *Marattia alata* Smith from which all but one of the leaves have been removed. ($\times \frac{1}{3}$.)

so many common features indicates that the two have a mutual ancestry. On the other hand, the marked differences in structure of the mature sporophyte and in the method in which the sporangia are borne seem to indicate that they diverged from each other long ago. The seven living genera of Marattiales are so alike that they are placed in a single family, the Marattiaceae.

[1] Hirmer, 1927; Scott, 1920; Seward, 1910.

Marattia, the type genus of the family and order, ranges widely throughout tropical regions of both hemispheres. There are some 26 species. Although none of these occurs in the United States, six species are known from Mexico, Central America, and the West Indies.[1]

The adult sporophyte of *Marattia* possesses an upright, tuberous, conical, fleshy stem which bears a crown of pinnately divided leaves at

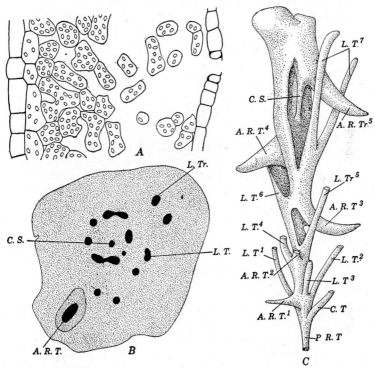

Fig. 162.—*A,* transverse section of leaf of *Marattia fraxinea* Smith. *B,* transverse section of stem of *M. alata* Smith. *C,* stereodiagram of vascular system of stem of *Danaea alata* Smith. (*C, after West,* 1917*A.*) *A.R.T.,* adventitious root trace; *C. S.,* commissural strand; *C.T.,* cotyledonary trace; *L.T.,* leaf trace; *P. R. T.,* primary root trace.) (*A,* × 215; *B,* × 3.)

its apex (Fig. 161). Each leaf has a pair of stipules at its base and the stem surface below the leaves is covered with leaf scars, each with two persistent stipules. The stem has numerous long adventitious roots, each inserted below a leaf or a leaf scar. In the largest species of *Marattia* the stem may be half a meter or more in diameter and the leaves 3 or 4 meters in length.

The growing apex of a young stem has a single apical cell. Later on this is replaced by a group of meristematic initials.[2] Young stems and

[1] Underwood and Benedict, 1909.   [2] Charles, 1911.

the first-matured portions of old stems generally have an endodermal layer at the inner face of the cortex; later-matured parts of a stem rarely contain an endodermis.[1]   The cortex in both old and young stems is wholly parenchymatous.   The cortex of *Marattia*, similar to that in all other members of the family, contains numerous mucilage canals and tannin-filled cells.[2]

The vascular cylinder in the first-formed portion of a stem is protostelic.   At the level of the third or the fourth leaf, there is an abrupt transition to a siphonostelic organization.[3]   The protostelic and lowermost siphonostelic portions of the vascular cylinder have a single trace departing to each leaf.   In the later-formed portions of the siphonostele there are two traces to each leaf.   Shortly above the level where the stem has become siphonostelic, there is a strand of vascular tissue (the *commissural strand*) that runs diagonally across the pith at each node. The relationship of this strand to the vascular skeleton appears to better advantage in *Danaea* (Fig. 162C), a member of the family that has longer internodes than does *Marattia*.   Stems of older plants of *Marattia* have the commissural strand broken up into strands that lie in a ring internal to the vascular cylinder.   It is the presence of this ring of strands, as well as the numerous leaf traces and root traces, that makes transverse sections of old stems so difficult of interpretation (Fig. 162B).   It is not improbable that very old stems may have the vascular tissues in three or more concentric rings.[4]

The root system of *Marattia* is composed of a number of adventitious roots, one of which is generally formed below each leaf.   The vascular tissue of a root may connect with the vascular cylinder of the stem just below departure of a leaf trace, or it may connect with the system of commissural strands internal to the main vascular cylinder.[4]   Each of the roots may bear several irregularly distributed lateral roots.   The chief difference between the internal organization of older roots in Marattiales, of which *Marattia* (Fig. 163) is quite typical, and that of roots in other Filicinae is the polyarch actinostelic organization of the vascular cylinder. In *Marattia* the number of protoxylem points may be as high as twelve.[5] The cortex is a uniform parenchyma with numerous mucilage canals. The first-formed roots generally contain a mycorhizal oömycete (*Stigeosporium Marattiacearum* West) within their cortices.   Later-formed roots generally lack the endophyte.[6]

Very young leaves have a precocious growth of their stipules to form a protective sheath around the young blade and petiole; later on there is an elongation of the leaf tip beyond the stipulary sheath.   This elongation is by the spiral uncoiling (circinate vernation) characteristic of most

[1] Charles, 1911.   [2] West, 1915.   [3] Brebner, 1902; Charles, 1911; West, 1917A.
[4] West, 1917A.   [5] Campbell, 1911.   [6] West, 1917.

Filicinae. Well-developed leaves of *M. alata* Smith may be 2 to 3 meters in length and have a petiole 5 to 6 cm. in diameter. The blade of *M. alata* is three to five times pinnately compound and has the ultimate pinnules about 2 cm. long. A pinnule has a conspicuous main vein (midrib) and alternately disposed lateral veins. Certain of the lateral veins are simple; others are dichotomously forked. In either case their apices end blindly near the margin of the pinnule. The internal organization of a blade resembles that of an angiosperm in that there is a compact

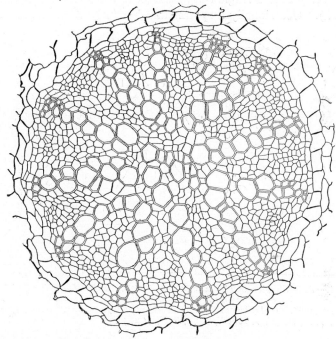

Fig. 163.—Transverse section of stele and inner portion of cortex of root of *Marattia alata* Smith. (× 160.)

palisade-like tissue beneath the upper epidermis and a loose spongy tissue next the lower epidermis (Fig. 162*A*). Stomata are restricted to the lower epidermis. Sooner or later there is the formation of an abscission layer at the base of the petiole. When the leaf falls away, it leaves a clean-cut leaf scar, flanked on either side by a persistent stipule.

The sporangia of *Marattia* are borne in more or less linear sori. These lie below the lateral veins, on the lower side of a pinnule, and some distance in from the margin of the pinnule (Fig. 164*A*). The sporangia in each sorus are in two rows and laterally fused with one another to form a *synangium* (Fig. 164*F–H*). The number of sporangia in a synangium ranges from 12 to 36.

The first evidence of sporangial development is a greater accumulation of cytoplasm in certain epidermal cells lying in localized areas on the underside of a pinnule.[1] At first each area, the receptacle of a sorus, is flush with the leaf surface; soon the sides of the receptacle, but not the axial portion, become somewhat elevated (Fig. 164*B–C*). Elevation of the receptacle above the leaf surface is accompanied by a development of unbranched multicellular hairs from immediately adjoining epidermal cells. Development of the individual sporangia generally begins with a periclinal division of a single cell in the receptacle, the sporangial initial (Fig. 164*C*). Occasionally a sporangium has more than one initial cell.

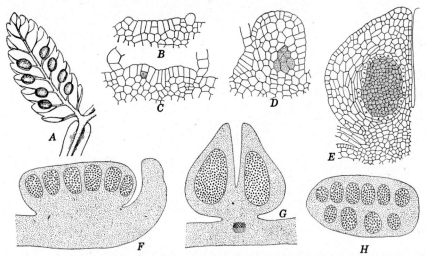

Fig. 164.—*A*, fertile pinnule of *Marattia alata* Smith. *B–H*, *M. fraxina* Smith. *B–E*, stages in development of synangium. *F–G*, longitudinal and transverse vertical sections of mature synangia. *H*, horizontal section of a mature synangium. (*B–E*, *after Bower*, 1897.) (*A*, × 1½; *B–D*, × 150; *E*, × 75; *F–H*, × 21.)

The outer daughter cell formed by periclinal division of an initial cell is the jacket initial; the inner cell is the archesporial cell. Division and redivision of the archesporial cell eventually result in a sporogenous tissue of some 650 spore mother cells (theoretically 664).[1] Since all spore mother cells are functional, there is a potential output of 2,656 spores in a sporangium. Formation of the sporogenous tissue is accompanied by periclinal and anticlinal division of the jacket initial to form the apical portion of the jacket layer (Fig. 164*D–E*). The remainder of the jacket layer is derived from cells lateral to the sporangial initial. Sporangial development in *Marattia*, as in all other Marattiales, is, therefore, of the eusporangiate type. The jacket eventually becomes a tissue several cells in thickness and one in which the jacket cells immediately next the spo-

[1] Bower, 1897.

rogenous mass function as a tapetum. The outer cells in the free face of the jacket layer become thick-walled. Drying out of these cells causes the two halves of the synangium to spread apart in a manner very much like the opening of a book. Spreading apart of a synangium is followed by a vertical dehiscence of each of the exposed sporangia.

Gametophytes of Marattiales (Fig. 165*A–C*) are dark green in color, are fleshy in texture, and have an external appearance resembling that of such liverworts as *Pellia* and *Riccardia*. They are among the largest

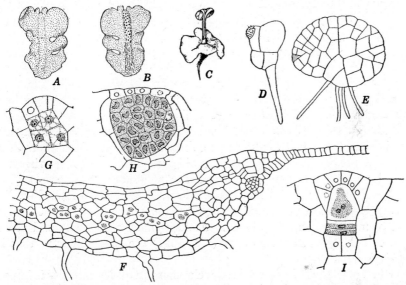

Fig. 165.—*A–B*, dorsal and ventral views of a gametophyte of *Marattia Douglasii* Baker. *C*, gametophyte and young sporophyte of *Danaea elliptica* Smith. *D–E*, early stages in development of gametophyte of *Marattia fraxina* Smith. *F*, transverse vertical section of a mature gametophyte of *M. Douglasii*. *G–H*, antheridia of *M. Douglasii*. *I*, archegonium of *M. Douglasii*. (*D–E*, after *Jonkman*, 1880.) (*A–C*, × 1½; *F*, × 80; *G–I*, × 325.)

found in the Pteridophyta, and those of *Christensenia* (*Kaulfussia*) may attain a length of more than 2.5 cm.[1] Spores of *Marattia* germinate within a few days after they are sown. Germination begins[2] with an enlargement of a spore to several times its original diameter, and an appearance of numerous chloroplasts within the spore. During this enlargement there is a rupture of the two outer layers of the spore wall. The first cell division, which is transverse, takes place about a month after spores are sown. The next cell division is in a plane at right angles to that of the first (Fig. 165*D*). The time of formation of the first rhizoid on a gametophyte is variable. It may appear at the two-celled stage, the four-celled stage, or considerably later. One of the cells of the four-celled

[1] Campbell, 1908.   [2] Jonkman, 1880.

stage begins to function as an apical cell and alternately cuts off segments right and left.   The remaining three cells divide in irregular sequence for a few times.   Because of the rapid growth of the apical cell during the early stages, the young gametophytes are more or less spatulate in shape (Fig. 165E).   Older gametophytes are heart-shaped because of a more rapid growth of portions lateral to the apical region.   These older gameto-phytes have a group of initials instead of a single apical cell.   A mature prothallus is more than one cell in thickness, except at the extreme margins, and has a conspicuous midrib extending the whole length of the thallus.   The gametophyte of *Marattia*, similar to roots of the sporo-phyte, contains an endophytic fungus (Fig. 165F).   In the case of the gametophyte this seems to be more of a parasite than a mycorhizal symbiont.[1]

Antheridia and archegonia are borne on the same thallus, but the former are produced before the latter.   Small gametophytes may bear antheridia only.   Most of the antheridia are formed on the ventral side and along the midrib, but occasional ones are formed on the dorsal side. Archegonia are formed only on the ventral side and along the midrib. They are present in large numbers on old gametophytes and are visible to the naked eye as small brown flecks.   Antheridial development (Fig. 165 G–H) is similar to that in *Ophioglossum*.[2]   A mature antheridium lies deeply embedded in the gametophyte, contains many antherozoids, and opens by an opercular cell.   Archegonial development and struc-ture of the mature archegonium (Fig. 165I) are also similar to that in *Ophioglossum*.[2]

Our knowledge of embryonal development in all Marattiales is imper-fect because "a very large number of prothallia must be examined before even a small series of embryos can be secured."[3]   Division of the zygote of Marattiales is transverse instead of vertical as in the Filicales.   Such early stages of embryonal development as are known for *Marattia* show[3] that the epibasal cell of the zygote (that nearest the archegonial neck) gives rise to the foot of an embryo, and the other (hypobasal) daughter cell gives rise to the primary root, cotyledon, and stem.   The first two or three succeeding divisions are in fairly regular sequence but there is soon a disappearance of any regularity of division (Fig. 166A).   Differentiation of root, cotyledon, and stem is not apparent until the embryo has become a massive many-celled structure.   The cotyledon arises in the portion of the embryo farthest from the neck of the archegonium, that is, from the free face of the hypobasal half.   Early stages in cotyledonary develop-ment may possibly have an apical cell, but this cell is not definitely recognizable until the cotyledon has attained a considerable size.   Unlike the cotyledon of Filicales (which curves around the growing point of its

[1] West, 1917.   [2] Campbell, 1894.   [3] Campbell, 1911.

gametophyte), the cotyledon of *Marattia* and other Marattiales grows through the middle of the gametophyte (Fig. 166*B*). The two sides of a cotyledon pushing through the gametophyte grow at unequal rates. Thus, similar to young foliage leaves, it has a curved apex. Development of the primary root is due to an apical cell differentiated endogenously along the plane where epibasal and hypobasal halves adjoin.[1] The primary root developed from this apical cell grows directly downward into the soil. The cotyledon and primary root are well-matured structures, with a single continuous vascular strand, before there is any produc-

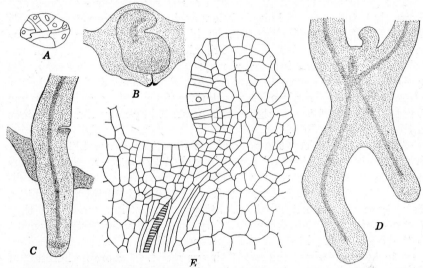

Fig. 166.—*Marattia Douglasii* Baker. *A–B*, embryos. *C–D*, young sporophytes. *E*, stem apex of sporophyte in Fig. *D*. (*A, after Campbell*, 1911; *B, after Campbell*, 1894.) (*A*, × 100; *B*, × 45; *C–D*, × 21; *E*, × 160.)

tion of stem tissue. These are formed through the agency of an apical cell, differentiated in the epidermis and at the juncture of cotyledon and primary root. Development of the young stem is overshadowed by that of the leaves borne on it, but, by the time the second or third leaf has matured, there is an evident protostele within the stem (Fig. 166*C–E*).

SUBCLASS 3. LEPTOSPORANGIATAE

There are several features separating the Leptosporangiatae from other ferns. The most readily demonstrable of these is the sporangial jacket one cell in thickness. This results from the fact that the capsule portion of a sporangium is referable to a single initial cell. Another distinctive sporangial feature is the early differentiation of the tapetal layer from a single internal cell of a developing sporangium. Antheridia of Lepto-

[1] Campbell, 1894.

sporangiatae differ from those of other living ferns in that they are small, are more or less emergent, and contain relatively few antherozoids. Archegonia of most leptosporangiate ferns have necks that protrude a considerable distance beyond the gametophyte. Most Leptosporangiatae also have a distinctive type of embryonal development in which the foot, primary root, cotyledon, and stem of a young sporophyte are each referable to a cell of the four-celled embryo. There are no characteristic vegetative features distinguishing sporophytes of Leptosporangiatae from those of other Filicinae.

The geological record of the subclass is remarkably complete and shows that, taken as a whole, it is less ancient than other Pteridophyta (Figs. 77, 142). A majority of the families are not known from horizons earlier than the Permian or the Triassic. With the exception of the Polypodiaceae (which include a majority of the living species), the Leptosporangiatae appear to have reached their climax during the Lower Cretaceous. However, no family known from this era has become extinct, and all but two of them are represented by more than one genus in the present-day flora.

According to a recent survey of the ferns,[1] there are 132 genera of living leptosporangiates and approximately 3,975 species. Ninety-nine of these genera, with more than 2,600 species, are referred to the Polypodiaceae. Leptosporangiate ferns are found in all parts of the world, but a majority of them are tropical or subtropical in distribution. Here they may occur in such abundance that they constitute an important element in the vegetation. Most of the leptosporangiates of temperate regions grow in habitats where the soil is always moist. Favorable habitats of this type include swamps and marshes, deep woods, and rocky ravines not subject to summer drought. However, certain species of temperate regions are xerophytic in habit and grow on rocky cliffs or dry hillsides. In sharp contrast with them are the hydrophytic species that grow only in water. Hydrophytic ferns may be free-floating (*Azolla*) or may grow with their rhizomes embedded in mud at the bottom of shallow pools (*Marsilea*). The size of the sporophyte varies greatly from genus to genus. At one extreme are the small, delicate "filmy ferns" (Hymenophyllaceae) that resemble leafy liverworts in size and appearance. At the other extreme are the tree ferns whose erect cylindrical stems may be 15 meters in height.

Comparisons of the various living genera show that there are certain well-marked evolutionary tendencies within the subclass. Beginning with a sorus in which sporangia develop simultaneously (the *simple sorus*),[2] there has been an evolution of one in which sporangia are formed in basipetalous succession (the *gradate sorus*). This, in turn, has led to

---

[1] Bower, 1926, 1928.   [2] Bower, 1899.

one in which sporangial development is in an irregular sequence (the *mixed sorus*). Evolution of the sorus has been accompanied by changes in the sporangia. Conspicuous among these is a shifting of the annulus from a lateral to a vertical position and a consequent change from a vertical to a transverse dehiscence. Sporangial evolution has also been accompanied by a reduction in spore output per sporangium. The antheridium also shows well-marked evolutionary tendencies. The antheridial initial of primitive leptosporangiates functions as an apical cell that successively cuts off one or more jacket cells from each of its three cutting faces. The initial of an advanced leptosporangiate divides vertically by means of an unique "funnel wall" (page 346). The external morphology and vascular organization of a stem, the vascular organization of the leaf supply, and the venation of a leaf blade are also of service in helping to differentiate between primitive and advanced members within the subclass.

There remains the question of the phylogenetic value of sporangial position. This has been held to be a point of fundamental significance.[1] It has been argued that there are two major evolutionary series within the Leptosporangiatae. In one series the sporangia are restricted to the leaf margins; in the other they are borne superficially on the leaf blade. If one adheres to this diphyletic theory, one must accept a parallel evolution of several distinctive features. Among these are the simple-gradate-mixed evolution of the sorus, the shift in position of annulus and dehiscence, and the evolution of the peculiar "funnel wall" of antheridia. One would also have to admit the parallel evolution of a distinctive annulus in sporangia of Schizaeaceae since sporangia of this family[2] may be marginal or superficial. The presence of so many features common to the "Marginales" and the "Superficiales" indicates that the two have not evolved independently. It is more probable that the Leptosporangiatae constitute a single phylogenetic series, with many side branches, rather than two series paralleling each other in evolutionary progress.

Phylogenetic progress within the subclass has also included an evolution of heterospory. There are two heterosporous families: the Marsileaceae and the Salviniaceae. Both of them have individual sori or groups of sori enclosed by a many-celled envelope, the whole constituting what is known as a *sporocarp*. Members of both families differ from most other ferns in that they are aquatic or are semiaquatic mud-dwellers. Because of the distinctive heterospory and the formation of sporangia within sporocarps, the two are often placed in a separate order or subclass, variously called the Salviniales, the Hydropteridineae, or the Rhizocarpeae. The last of these three names is based upon the erroneous idea that the sporocarps are borne directly on the roots. There has long been a realization[3]

[1] Bower, 1913, 1926, 1928, 1935.   [2] Diels, 1898.   [3] Campbell, 1895.

that the two families are not closely related to each other and that sporo-carps of the two are quite different in nature. An evaluation of them according to various phylogenetic indices shows that the Marsileaceae are lower in the evolutionary scale than are the Salviniaceae.[1] The unique features common to the two (heterospory and formation of a sporocarp) are due to parallel evolution instead of a common origin.

The number of orders that one recognizes among the Leptospo-rangiatae depends upon the treatment accorded the Osmundaceae and the heterosporous families. Sporangia of Osmundaceae differ from those of other leptosporangiates in that they are not derived in entirety from a single initial. However, formation of the capsule portion is typically leptosporangiate. The early embryology of *Osmunda* is also more like that of a eusporangiate fern. The family has been placed in a separate order,[2] but such a disposition of it minimizes the fact that Osmundaceae resemble typical leptosporangiates in most other respects. It is better, therefore, to follow the usual practice of placing it in the same order as other homosporous leptosporangiates. The two heterosporous families are not related to each other. If they are to be segregated because of their heterospory, they should be placed in separate orders or suborders. Since this would overemphasize one character (heterospory), it is better to group them with the homosporous forms. Relegation of the Osmund-aceae and the heterosporous families to the same rank as other Leptospo-rangiatae results in but one order, the Filicales.

The number of families that one recognizes among the Filicales depends upon the disposition one makes of the polypods and of the tree ferns and their allies. The segregation of each group into several families[3] is undoubtedly correct, but for purposes of convenience these are here included in two families, Polypodiaceae and Cyatheaceae.

The only constant characters distinguishing families one from another are those of sori and sporangia. Some families are also characterized by distinctive vegetative features; others are not. However, the vegetative organization is of considerable importance in helping to distinguish between primitive and advanced members of the order, and in establishing interrelationships between the various families.

FAMILY 1. OSMUNDACEAE

The Osmundaceae have all sporangia on a leaf developing simultane-ously and either in distinct or in indistinct sori that are without indusial protection. The sporangia are massive and dehisce longitudinally by means of a shield-shaped annulus at one side of the sporangial jacket.

Leptosporangiatae with a simultaneous development of all sporangia on a leaf or leaflet are considered more primitive than those in which the

[1] Bower, 1926, 1928.   [2] Zimmermann, 1930.   [3] Bower, 1926.

sporangia develop in basipetalous succession or in an irregular sequence. There are several reasons for regarding the Osmundaceae as the simplest of those Leptosporangiatae which have a simultaneous development of sporangia. Among these reasons are: (1) the pseudo-eusporangiate nature of the sporangium; (2) the shield-shaped lateral annulus of the sporangium; (3) the relatively large number of antherozoids in an antheridium and their escape through a pore formed by an opercular cell; (4) the shape of the mature gametophyte; and (5) the relatively late differentiation of parts in an embryo.

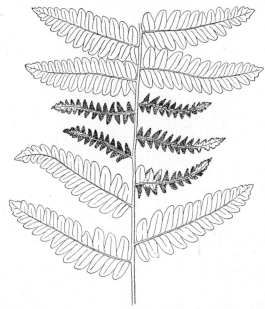

Fig. 167.—Portion of a leaf of *Osmunda Claytoniana* L. ($\times \frac{1}{2}$.)

There are two genera of living Osmundaceae, *Osmunda* and *Todea*. *Osmunda*, with nine species, is cosmopolitan in distribution. *Todea*, whose eight species are sometimes placed in two genera, is South African and Australasian. There are also several Mesozoic fossil genera whose anatomical structure shows that they unquestionably belonged to the family.[1]

The sporophyte of *Osmunda* has a short, upright or creeping stem that is invested with persistent remains of old sclerenchymatous leaf bases. The stem has numerous adventitious roots, two of which arise at each leaf base. Stems usually bifurcate into two branches of equal size; occasionally one of the branches bifurcates again.[2] The apex of each branch bears a crown of pinnate or bipinnate leaves. Some species have two kinds of

[1] Kidson and Gwynne-Vaughan, 1907, 1908, 1909, 1910.   [2] Faull, 1901.

leaves, fertile and sterile. If the leaves are dimorphic, the fertile ones appear before the sterile ones when a new set of leaves is unfolded. Other species have all leaves fertile and the production of sporangia restricted to pinnae at the middle (Fig. 167) or at the apex of a blade.

The first-developed portion of a stem may have a central cylinder with a protostelic organization;[1] later-developed portions of the central cylinder are always dictyostelic and have numerous overlapping narrow

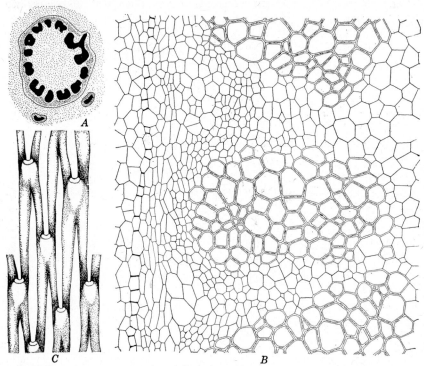

C   B

Fig. 168.—*A*, transverse section of the stele and inner cortex of *Osmunda Claytoniana* L. *B*, enlarged portion of the stele in Fig. *A*. *C*, stereodiagram of the vascular cylinder of *O. regalis* L. (*C, after Lachmann in Kidston and Gwynne-Vaughan*, 1907.) (*A*, × 5; *B*, × 120.)

leaf gaps (Fig. 168*C*). Cortex and stele are delimited from each other by a well-defined endodermis. This is unusual because it is not interrupted at the leaf gaps. The outer portion of the cortex is dark brown in color and has highly sclerified cells; the inner portion is colorless and parenchymatous. Both portions of the cortex contain numerous spirally arranged, **C**-shaped leaf traces, each surrounded by an endodermal layer (Fig. 168*A*). The outermost region in the dictyostelic portion of stele is a pericycle that is two to four cells in thickness (Fig. 168*B*). Internal to

[1] Gwynne-Vaughan, 1911.

the pericycle is a continuous sheath of phloem that is thicker in portions external to the leaf gaps. The inner portion of the phloem differs from that in most ferns in having its cells with their long axes diagonal or tangential to the long axis of the stele.[1] Between phloem and xylem is the so-called xylem sheath, a layer four to six cells in thickness. The meristeles of the xylem ring are oval to U-shaped in outline, and each generally has a small protoxylem mass that is mesarch in position. The metaxylem is composed of large scalariform tracheids. Some species have a homogeneous pith internal to the xylem; others, including *O. cinnamomea* L., have one or more strands of sclerenchyma in the pith. *O. cinnamomea* may also have an endodermal layer internal to the xylem,[1] but this is not always clearly distinguishable.

The two adventitious roots formed below each leaf arise endogenously and at the base of the leaf trace or immediately below it. A root has a broad cortex with small thick-walled cells at the exterior and progressively larger and thinner-walled cells inward to the endodermis. In most cases the vascular cylinder is diarch but occasionally it is triarch.[1]

The single trace departing to a leaf runs diagonally upward through the cortex without branching and without a disappearance of the ensheathing endodermal layer. The xylem of a leaf trace is C-shaped in cross section and has a small protoxylem mass in the concave side toward the stele. It is surrounded on all sides by a layer of phloem. The petiole of an *Osmunda* leaf differs from those of most other Leptosporangiatae in the stipule-like expansions at its base. The single bundle running the length of a petiole is similar in shape to a leaf trace but is without a conspicuous endodermal layer. The blade of the leaf may be pinnately or bipinnately divided. Pinnae have the open venation typical of primitive ferns. The internal structure of a pinna is much like that in other Leptosporangiatae.

Sporangia of *Osmunda* are first recognizable as small convex protuberances on the pinnae or pinnules.[2] There is one conspicuous cell (the sporangial initial) in each protuberance. *Osmunda* differs from typical Leptosporangiatae in that the whole sporangium is not referable to this initial. Instead, the massive stalk is formed in whole or in part from cells adjoining the initial. The sporangial initial divides periclinally into an outer cell (the jacket initial) and an inner cell (the archesporial cell). The shape of the archesporial cell is variable; most frequently it is a truncate pyramid (Fig. 169*A*). Division of the jacket initial and its daughter cells is always anticlinal. Thus the tissue derived from it is a layer one cell in thickness. The archesporial cell functions as an internal apical cell and cuts off a flat cell from each of its faces, including that next to the jacket initial (Fig. 169*B–C*). After cutting off these flat cells, the

[1] Faull, 1901.   [2] Bower, 1889.

archesporial cell functions as the primary sporogenous cell. The flat cells cut off by the archesporial cell have been called tapetal cells[1] because they have been thought to be similar to the tapetal initials of typical leptosporangiatae. In the case of *O. Claytoniana* L. the layer of flattened cells internal to the jacket layer never develop the dense protoplasts typical of tapetal cells (Fig. 169*E–F*). Instead, they have more watery protoplasts from early spore mother cell stages onward. Furthermore, they do not

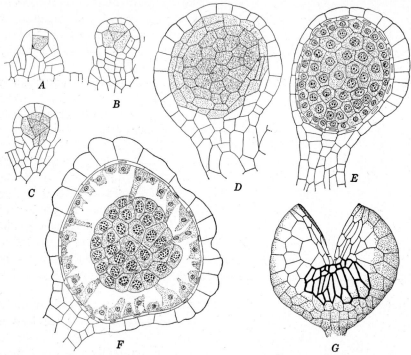

Fig. 169.—*A–D*, early stages in the development of sporangia of *Osmunda regalis* L. *E–F*, late stages in development of sporangia of *O. Claytoniana* L. *G*, surface view of mature sporangium of *O. Claytoniana*. (*A–D, after Bower*, 1889.) (*A–D*, × 160; *E–G*, × 215.)

disintegrate even after the spores have well-developed walls. On this account these cells are to be interpreted as a thin-walled layer of the jacket, but a layer that is of no importance in spore protection or sporangial dehiscence. The primary sporogenous cell undergoes a series of divisions to form a large number of sporogenous cells, theoretically 64 or 128. In *O. Claytoniana* L. the outer layer of sporogenous cells functions as a tapetum after the cessation of division, and the remaining sporogenous cells function as spore mother cells (Fig. 169*F*). During meiosis the tapetal cells elongate greatly and their walls disappear. Eventually

[1] Bower, 1889, 1899.

the elongating tapetal cells push between the dividing spore mother cells and fuse with one another to form a plasmodial reticulum that eventually disappears during the course of spore-wall formation. Late in sporangial development there is a thickening of the walls in a group of jacket cells at one side of the sporangium. This annulus may be a plate, or it may be a transverse band (several cells broad and two to three cells tall) that extends a considerable distance around the circumference of the sporangium.[1] Perpendicular to the annulus, and extending over the sporangial apex and nearly down to the stalk, is a band of elongate thin-walled cells—the future zone of vertical dehiscence of the sporangium (Fig. 169*G*).

Spores of *Osmunda* contain chloroplasts when they are ripe. This accounts for their rapid germination when sown, and may possibly account for the short time they remain viable when stored. When germination takes place there is a bursting of the outer spore-wall layer (the exospore) along the three ridges of the spore wall and a protrusion of the spore contents, still enclosed by the two inner spore-wall layers. The first division, generally at right angles to the long axis, forms two daughter cells of unequal size. The larger cell develops into the gametophyte, the smaller elongates and becomes the first rhizoid.[2] This rhizoid, unlike rhizoids of most other ferns, contains chloroplasts. The larger cell divides transversely to form a file of three or four cells whose terminal cell, by two successive diagonal divisions, then differentiates an apical cell that alternately cuts off derivatives right and left for some time. The apical cell projects ahead of the rest of the thallus during early stages of prothallial growth. Later on, because of rapid cell division in its derivatives, the apical cell comes to lie in a depression at the anterior end of the gametophyte (Fig. 170*A*). The two-sided apical cell is eventually replaced by one with four cutting faces or is replaced by a group of two or three initials that cut off daughter cells dorsally and ventrally as well as laterally. This results in a gametophyte with a longitudinal midrib and one similar in appearance to those of Marattiales.

Young gametophytes have antheridia only and produce them either marginally or terminally. Antheridia are also formed on mature gametophytes with archegonia. Here they are formed on the ventral side of the lateral wings. Antheridial development[2] begins with a protrusion of a cell above its neighbors and the cutting off of a small cell, the antheridial initial, by a diagonal wall (Fig. 170*C*). By two successive diagonal divisions, the initial forms a pyramidal cell and two flattened cells. The pyramidal cell functions in the manner of an apical cell with three cutting faces and cuts off tabular cells on the side toward the gametophyte. The cells thus cut off constitute the basal part of the antheridium. If several

[1] Williams, 1928.   [2] Campbell, 1892.

tabular cells are cut off, a pedicel is formed, and the mature antheridium stands considerably above the surface of the gametophyte. After cutting off one or more segments from each basal face, the pyramidal cell divides periclinally into a jacket initial and a primary androgonial cell that are separated from each other by a curved wall. The jacket initial divides anticlinally (Fig. 170D). Its daughter cells also divide anticlinally and by oblique walls. The last-formed jacket cells meet to enclose a triangular cell that lies either at the top or at the side of the antheridium. This cell is thrown off when the antheridium is mature and is very sugges-

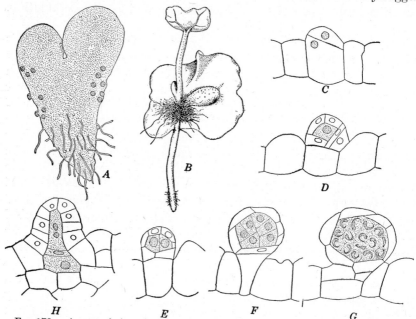

Fig. 170.—A, ventral view of gametophyte of *Osmunda cinnamomea* L. B, gametophyte and young sporophyte of *O. Claytoniana* L. C–G, stages in development of antheridia of *O. cinnamomea*. H, archegonium of *O. cinnamomea*. (B, after Campbell, 1892.) (A, × 21; B, × 6; C–H, × 325.)

tive of the opercular cell in Eusporangiatae. Coincident with the first division of the jacket initial, there is a vertical division of the primary androgonial cell (Fig. 170E). The two androgonial cells thus formed divide, and their daughter cells redivide to form a hundred or more androcytes (Fig. 170F–G). This number is very high for a leptosporangiate fern. Metamorphosis of the androcytes into antherozoids is essentially as in *Ophioglossum*.

Archegonia are formed on the ventral side of old gametophytes and over the entire midrib (*O. Claytoniana* L.) or only along its edges (*O. cinnamomea* L.)[1] The general sequence of archegonial development is

[1] Campbell, 1892.

quite similar to that in *Ophioglossum*. In fact, there are but minor differences between archegonial development in Eusporangiatae and in Leptosporangiatae. The chief differences in the two are in the length of the neck and the amount of its curvature. *Osmunda* has an archegonial neck eight cells in height, which stands erect from the prothallus (Fig. 170*H*).

Division of the zygote is vertical and in a plane parallel to the neck of the archegonium.[1] The two daughter cells also divide vertically, but in a plane at right angles to the first plane of division. Transverse division of each cell results in an eight-celled embryo with the cells in two tiers of four (Fig. 171*B*). *Osmunda* differs from most other Leptosporangiatae in

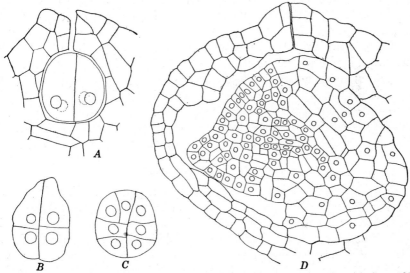

Fig. 171.—Stages in development of embryos of *Osmunda Claytoniana* L. (*A–C*, × 325; *D*, × 215.)

that the cotyledon, stem, primary root, and foot are not each referable to a specific cell of the four-celled embryo.[2] Instead, cotyledon, stem, and primary root of *Osmunda* are derived from one half of the eight-celled embryo, and the foot from the other half. In *O. cinnamomea* L. the half of the eight-celled embryo next the archegonial neck develops into cotyledon, stem, and primary root, and the other half develops into the foot.[2] *O. Claytonia* L. may have cotyledon, stem, and root, derived from one daughter cell of the zygote and the foot derived from the other daughter cell. In either case the embryo is far advanced beyond the octant stage before its various parts are clearly recognizable (Fig. 171*C–D*). The cotyledon and stem are each due to the activity of a special apical cell. These cells are superficial (epidermal) and lie closely to each other. The

---

[1] Campbell, 1892; Cross, 1931.   [2] Cross, 1931.

root initial arises in the same half of the embryo, but endogenously and near the foot half.[1]   Up to this time enlargement of the embryo has been accompanied by an enlargement of the old archegonium and adjoining tissues into an enclosing sheath, the calyptra.   Shortly after this the root and the cotyledon burst through the calyptra; one growing upward, the other downward.   The cotyledon grows out to the side of the gameto-phyte after it bursts through the calyptra, and then it grows upward.[2] This curvature of the cotyledon around the gametophyte, instead of an upward growth through it, is a feature distinguishing Leptosporangiatae from Eusporangiatae with thallose gametophytes (Marattiales).   How-ever, *Osmunda* differs from other Leptosporangiatae in that the cotyledon curves around the side of the gametophyte instead of around the apical notch (Fig. 170*B*).

Gametophytes grown from spores may form sporophytes apogamously instead of by a union of gametes.[3]   A sporophyte of an apogamous game-tophyte arises as a meristematic outgrowth along the central axis of the thallus.   Apospory has also been observed in *Osmunda*, but only when young sporophytes are wounded or are growing under unfavorable condi-tions.   Cytological studies show[4] that the aposporously produced gameto-phytes have the diploid number of chromosomes.

FAMILY 2.   SCHIZAEACEAE

The Schizaeaceae have all sporangia on a leaf developing simultane-ously and the sporangia borne singly.   The sporangia are generally protected by an indusial outgrowth from the leaf margin.   The sporangia dehisce longitudinally by means of a transverse, ring-shaped annulus at the distal end of the sporangial jacket.

There are several reasons for placing the family at a low level in the leptosporangiate series.   These include: the simple leaf trace, the open venation of the blade, the simultaneous development of sporangia, the terminal annulus, the solitary sporangia, the relatively large spore output, structure of the gametophyte, and structure of the antheridia.

The family has four living genera: *Schizaea*, with 25 species; *Lygodium*, with 26 species; *Anemia*, with 64 species; and *Mohria*, with three species. Most species are tropical or subtropical in distribution.   The first three genera are widespread; *Mohria* is South African.   The family also includes several genera known only in the fossil condition.   Although there is some question as to whether or not the family existed during the Carboniferous, it is known with certainty from as far back as the Jurassic.[5]

One species of the type genus (*Schizaea*) occurs in the United States. This species, *S. pusilla* Pursh (Fig. 172), is found only in *Sphagnum*

---

[1] Cross, 1931.   [2] Campbell, 1892.   [3] Brown, 1920.   [4] Manton, 1932.
[5] Seward, 1910.

swamps in the Pine Barrens of New Jersey. It is considered[1] a stranded relic from preglacial ages when tropical plants grew far to the north.

Most species of *Schizaea* have a short upright rhizome but a few of them have a horizontal one. Occasional individuals of various species have one or two dichotomous branchings of the rhizome.[2] Leaves and adventitious roots are borne spirally on the stem. Very young leaves may be in a 1:3 spiral arrangement, corresponding to the three cutting faces of the apical cell, but there is soon an obliteration of any definite phyllotaxy. Some species, including *S. pusilla* Pursh.[3] and *S. rupestris* R. Br.,[4] have two sorts of leaves, sterile and fertile. Sterile leaves of

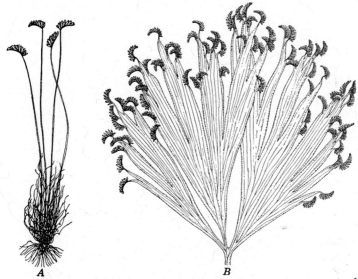

Fig. 172.—*A*, *Schizaea pusilla* Pursh. *B*, leaf of *S. elegans* (Vahl.) Sw. ($\times \frac{1}{2}$.)

these species have a few crowded pinnae at their apices, the two rows of pinnae lying parallel to each other and approximately perpendicular to the axis of the leaf. The pinnate portion of a fertile leaf looks much like a double comb. Other species have all leaves fertile. Leaves of these species may be like the fertile leaves of dimorphic species, or they may have one or more dichotomous branchings and a comb-like double row of pinnae at the tips of the ultimate dichotomies (Fig. 172*B*).

The vascular organization of the stem in the Schizaeaceae ranges from a simple protostele (*Lygodium*) to a dictyostele (*Mohria*). The first-formed portion of the vascular cylinder of *Schizaea* may be protostelic;[5] later-formed portions are always siphonostelic and ectophloic. The pith

[1] Maxon, 1925.   [2] Bartoo, 1930; Boodle, 1903; Tansley and Chick, 1903.
[3] Bartoo, 1930.   [4] Bartoo, 1929*A*.
[5] Bartoo, 1930; Boodle, 1903; Thompson, 1920.

internal to the ring of xylem may be homogeneous or heterogeneous. In the latter case[1] it contains small spindle-shaped masses of tracheids with or without a surrounding endodermal layer (Fig. 173). The cortex is generally but a few cells in diameter.[2] Cortical cells are usually sclerified and they may contain considerable starch. There is a well-defined

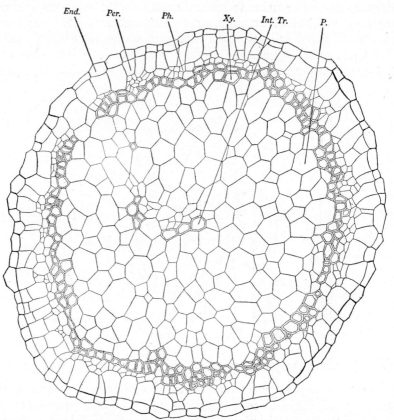

Fig. 173.—Transverse section of the stele and endodermis of *Schizaea malacceana* Bk. (*End.*, endodermis; *Int. Tr.*, internal tracheids; *P.*, pith; *Per.*, pericycle; *Ph.*, phloem; *Xy.*, xylem.) (× 160.)

endodermal layer toward the inner face of the cortex. A study[3] of the histogenesis of this layer in *S. pusilla* Pursh shows that it and the pericyclic layer internal to it are derived from the innermost layer of the cortex. Thus, in this species both endodermis and pericycle are cortical in nature. Among species where the pericycle is more than one cell in thickness, as *S. dichotoma* J. Sm.,[4] the endodermis seems to be the innermost cortical layer. Whatever its nature, the endodermis is similar to

[1] Boodle, 1903; Thompson, 1920.   [2] Boodle, 1901; Tansley and Chick, 1903.
[3] Bartoo, 1930.   [4] Thompson, 1920.

that of *Osmunda* in that it is not interrupted when a leaf trace departs from the stele.

Adventitious roots of *Schizaea* arise endogenously. In *S. pusilla* Pursh they originate from a single cell of the innermost layer of the cortex.[1] This cell soon gives rise to an apical cell with three lateral cutting faces. The formation of cortical and stelar tissues from segments cut off by the apical cell is in diagrammatic sequence.[2] The stele of a root is very small and diarch, phloem and xylem each containing only four to six elements when seen in cross section (Fig. 174). Phloem and xylem are surrounded by a ring of six pericyclic cells. This is successively enclosed by a ring of

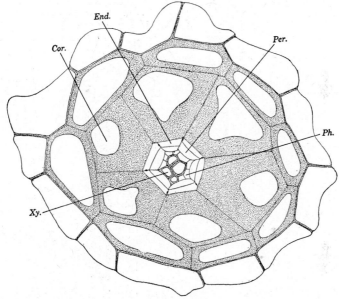

Fig. 174.—Transverse section of root of *Schizaea malacceana* Bk. (*Cor.*, cortex; *End.*, endodermis; *Per.*, pericycle; *Ph.*, phloem; *Xy.*, xylem.) (× 215.)

six endodermal cells and a ring of six cortical cells. The radial arrangement of cells in the pericyclic, endodermal, and innermost cortical layers shows that they have been derived from a common mother-cell layer. The cortex, including the endodermis, is generally three cells in thickness. One peculiar feature of the root is the conspicuous thickening of radial and inner tangential walls in the cell layer immediately external to the endodermis. The epidermal layer in young parts of a root has root hairs. Some species have a persistence of the epidermis and its hairs;[1] others have an eventual sloughing off of the epidermis.[3]

Leaves are formed from a single superficial cell three or four removed from the apical cell of the rhizome. This cell gives rise to a leaf initial

[1] Bartoo, 1930.   [2] Bartoo, 1929*A*, 1930.   [3] Boodle, 1901.

with two cutting faces.   Developing leaves have the spiral uncoiling
(circinate vernation) typical of most ferns.   The petiole of an unfolding
leaf has a single vascular bundle, continuous with a single trace running
through the cortex to the stele.   Both the trace and the petiolar bundle
are surrounded by a pericycle and an endodermis derived from a common
cell layer.[1]   Sterile leaves of some dimorphic species have no expansion of
the distal portion into a blade (*S. pusilla* Pursh); those of other species
have an expanded blade with an open venation (*S. rupestris* R. Br.).

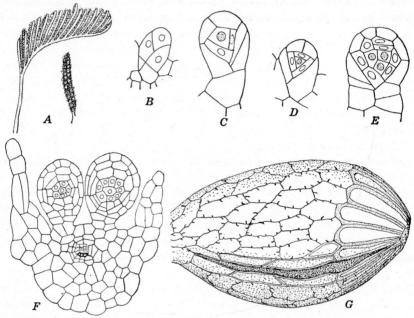

Fig. 175.—*A*, leaf and pinnule of *Schizaea pusilla* Pursh.   *B–E*, stages in development
of sporangia of *S. rupestris* R. Br.   *F*, transverse section of fertile leaf of *S. rupestris*.   *G*,
surface view of mature sporangium of *S. bifida* Sw.   (*B–E, after Bartoo*, 1929*A*; *F, after
Bower*, 1918.)   (*A*, × 1½; *F*, × 60; *G*, × 180.)

Species in which all leaves are fertile have a similar expansion or lack of
expansion in the sterile portion beneath the fertile pinnules.

Fertile leaves of *Schizaea* (Fig. 175*A*) look as if the sporangia were
borne on the upper (adaxial) sides of pinnules that face one another, but
the relative position of xylem and phloem in the pinnules (Fig. 175*F*)
shows that in reality the pinnules are apposed back to back and that the
sporangia are borne on the lower (abaxial) face.   Sporangial development in *Schizaea* is strictly leptosporangiate, and each sporangium and its
stalk is referable to a single initial cell.   These initials lie in two rows,
one along either margin of a pinnule.   The sporangia matured from a file

[1] Bartoo, 1930.

of marginal initials generally lie in a single row, but in some species they are alternately pressed right and left to form a double row.[1] Sporangial development[2] begins with a protrusion of an initial and its transverse division into an inner and an outer cell. The inner cell, which contributes to the base of the stalk, may divide once or twice. The outer cell, by three successive diagonal divisions, gives rise to a pyramidal apical cell that cuts off a variable number of segments from each of its three lateral cutting faces (Fig. 175*B*). The last three segments cut off contribute to the sporangial jacket; those cut off previously go to form the stalk. Apical growth terminates with a periclinal division that forms a flat outer cell (a jacket initial) and an inner pyramidal cell (the archesporial cell). The archesporial cell functions as an internal apical cell and successively cuts off a tabular tapetal initial from each of its four cutting faces (Fig. 175*C–D*). Division of the tapetal initials is both periclinal and anticlinal, and produces a tapetal layer two cells in thickness. The cell remaining after cutting off of the tapetal initials is the primary sporogenous cell. Cell divisions in development of the sporogenous tissue from the primary sporogenous cell are always simultaneous, and, accordingly as there are four or five successive divisions, there are 16 or 32 spore mother cells. During the meioses to form the 64 or 128 spores, there is a disintegration of the tapetum into a plasmodial mass that gradually disappears as the spores ripen. Similar to other Leptosporangiatae, the jacket initials develop into a jacket layer one cell in thickness. The cells at the distal end of the jacket are so oriented that their long axes are radial to a single central cell. There are about 15 of these cells, and the thickening of their walls results in the distal annulus that causes a longitudinal dehiscence of a sporangium (Fig. 175*G*). Although the sporangia are strictly marginal in origin, they appear to lie some distance in from the margin when mature. This apparently nonmarginal position results from the proliferation of a protective flap (indusium) as the sporangia are developing (Fig. 175*F*).

Gametophytes of *Schizaea* are atypical in that they are protonemalike branched filaments.[3] Gametophytes of many ferns show a filamentous tendency when growing in moist habitats and under faint illumination, but environmental conditions do not account for the filamentous gametophyte of *Schizaea*.[4] The filamentous prothallus of *Schizaea* might be interpreted as a primitive type in which there has been a persistence of the filamentous body of the ancestral algae. The fact that other members of the family, *Anemia*[5] and *Lygodium*,[6] have a thallose gametophyte with a longitudinal midrib shows that this is not the case. A more attractive

[1] Bower, 1918.   [2] Bartoo, 1929*A*; Bower, 1918.
[3] Britton and Taylor, 1901; Thomas, 1902.   [4] Thomas, 1902.
[5] Twiss, 1910.   [6] Rogers, 1923; Twiss, 1910.

interpretation of the filamentous gametophyte of *Schizaea* is the hypothesis[1] that it represents a permanent retention of a juvenile stage that is of but short duration in most ferns.

The filamentous gametophytes of *S. pusilla* Pursh[2] have unicellular colorless rhizoids that arise from short branches with swollen cells containing an endophytic fungus (Fig. 176). The pale color of chloroplasts in the remainder of the plant suggest that the fungus is mycorhizal in nature. Antheridia and archegonia, both of which develop on the same gametophyte, are formed on one-celled lateral branches. Mature antheridia have a one-celled pedicel; archegonia may be sessile or may have a basal

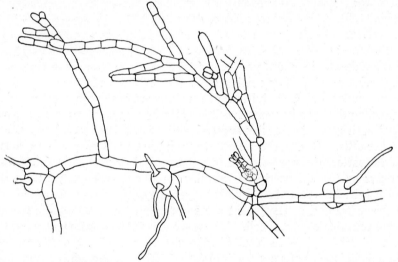

FIG. 176.—Gametophyte of *Schizaea pusilla* Pursh. (*After Britton and Taylor*, 1901.) (× 30.)

cushion of a few cells. The details of development of sex organs have been worked out more thoroughly in *Lygodium* than they have in *Schizaea*. Antheridia of *Lygodium*[3] are emergent and generally contain 128 antherozoids. This is a large number for a leptosporangiate fern and is to be considered a primitive character. Archegonia of *Lygodium*[4] have necks four to five cells in height that curve away from the apical notch of a prothallus. One primitive feature in an archegonium is the rather frequent occurrence of four nuclei within the neck canal cell.

The only studies on the early embryogeny of Schizaeaceae have been on *Lygodium*.[4] Here the first two divisions of a zygote are vertical. Development of the foot, primary root, cotyledon, and stem from one quadrant each of the four-celled embryo is similar to that in most leptosporangiate ferns.

[1] Goebel, 1930.   [2] Britton and Taylor, 1901.   [3] Twiss, 1910.   [4] Rogers, 1927.

FAMILY 3. GLEICHENIACEAE

The Gleicheniaceae have all sporangia on a leaf developing simultaneously and have them produced in sori that are without indusial protection. The sporangia are subsessile and dehisce longitudinally by means of an obliquely transverse annulus. Different from other families in which sporangia develop simultaneously and are in unprotected sori, the Gleicheniaceae have practically sessile sporangia with an obliquely transverse annulus.

There are numerous features indicating that the family stands at a low level among the Leptosporangiatae. Among these are: the vascular organization, the simple leaf trace, the open venation, the simultaneous development of sporangia, the unprotected sori, the vertical dehiscence of sporangia, the relatively large spore output, gametophytes with a longitudinal midrib, the large number of antherozoids in an antheridium, and the escape of antherozoids through a triangular opercular cell.

The family contains two genera with living species. *Gleichenia*, with some 80 species, is widely distributed throughout tropical and subtropical regions. *Stromatopteris* is monotypic and known only from New Caledonia. Fossils from the Carboniferous have been assigned to the family, but this is very questionable.[1] The Gleicheniaceae were conspicuous in the flora of the Late Mesozoic and appear to have reached their greatest distribution during the Cretaceous. At this time they ranged as far north as the western coast of Greenland. Changes in climatic conditions toward the close of the Cretaceous drove them toward the equator where the environment more nearly coincided with conditions of life that had ceased to exist in the higher latitudes.

Sporophytes of *Gleichenia* generally have creeping, dichotomously branched rhizomes with long internodes between the leaves. The leaves are restricted to the upper side of a rhizome and appear to be borne in a single row. In some species this is really a three-ranked (tristichous) arrangement. Adventitious roots are borne on the underside of a rhizome and either in three rows or irregularly distributed along the rhizome. The leaves of certain species are repeatedly forked and capable of indefinite apical development. Growth of the clambering vine-like leaves over the other vegetation results in an impenetrable thicket. The encroachment of *Gleichenia* upon cultivated fields often makes it a serious nuisance to agriculture in the tropics. The forking of a leaf appears to be a dichotomous branching. Actually, there is a terminal arrestation of development in a leaf with sympodial pinnae and continued growth of the two lowermost pinnae (Fig. 177). Some species have no terminal arrestation of development in the two pinnae; others have the pinna apices ceas-

[1] Seward, 1910.

ing to develop and the two lowermost pinnules continuing to grow. Pinnules of the latter type may have an indefinite number of forkings, but there eventually comes a time when they, also, have no terminal arrestation of development. The ultimate pinnules are sympodially arranged and have an open venation.

Stems of all but two species have protostelic vascular cylinders. These protosteles may be incipient actinosteles (Fig. 178*A*). *G. microphyllum* (R. Br.) F. v. M. and *G. pectinata* Presl. have siphonosteles; the former with an internal endodermis, the latter without one.[1] Protostelic stems[2] have a massive central core of xylem which is composed of tracheids intermingled with thin-walled parenchyma (Fig. 178*B*). A short distance

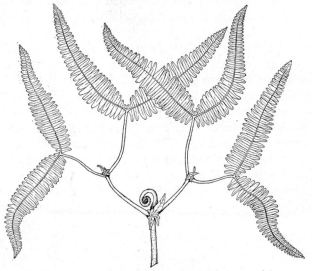

Fig. 177.—Leaf of *Gleichinia pectinata* Presl. (× ⅓.)

inward from the periphery of the xylem, and hence in a mesarch position, are a variable number of small protoxylem masses. There is frequently a pulling apart of cells in the region of the protoxylem to form small cavities similar in nature to the carinal canals in *Equisetum*. The xylem is completely encircled by a layer of phloem, and this, in turn, is encircled by a narrow belt of pericyclic cells. An endodermis with typical Casparian strips surrounds the pericycle. The cortex of a rhizome may be wholly sclerenchymatous, or it may have a narrow layer of thin-walled parenchyma just outside the endodermis. Leaf traces departing from the stele are C-shaped and undivided until after they enter a petiole. Traces of most species have three protoxylem masses on the concave side facing the stele, but some species have more protoxylem masses.

[1] Boodle, 1901*A*; Boodle and Hiley, 1909.   [2] Boodle, 1901*A*.

Roots of *Gleichenia* are freely branched. They have di- to tetrarch vascular cylinders.[1]

Sporangia are borne in unprotected sori that lie in two rows along a pinnule. The soral rows are on either side of, and a short distance out from, the midrib (Fig. 179*A*). The margin of the somewhat elevated soral receptacle bears a ring of four to seven or eight sporangia. According to the species, the central portion of a receptacle is without sporangia or bears one to six of them. When examined superficially, a sorus looks

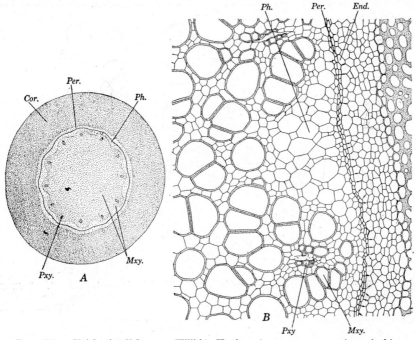

Fig. 178.—*Gleichenia dichotoma* (Willd.) Hook. *A*, transverse section of rhizome *B*, enlarged portion of outer stele and inner cortex of Fig. *A*. (*Cor.*, cortex; *End.*, endodermis; *Mxy.*, metaxylem; *Per.*, pericycle; *Ph.*, phloem; *Pxy.*, protoxylem.) (*A*, × 11; *B*, × 120.)

like a synangium, but this is not the case since the individual sporangia are not fused with one another.

Sporangial development is preceded by an elevation of the receptacle above the surface of the pinnule.[2] The sporangial initials are not evident until the receptacle has attained a height almost equal to the thickness of the young pinnule (Fig. 179*B*). Sporangial initials are differentiated only on the top of a receptacle, either over the entire top or only along the margin. Development of a sporangium is strictly leptosporangiate (Fig. 179*C–E*). The tapetal initials develop into a tapetum two cells in

[1] Boodle, 1901*A*.   [2] Bower, 1899.

thickness, but one in which only the inner cell layer contributes to the nutrition of developing spores.   The outer layer from the tapetal initials develops into a tissue that seems to be a portion of the sporangial jacket. In this latter respect sporangia of *Gleichenia* resemble those of *Osmunda*, but there is a strong probability that the spore-nourishing tissue in the two is not similar in origin.   Accordingly as there are five, six, seven, or eight cell generations in the sporogenous tissue, there may be a formation of 128, 256, 512, or 1,024 spores in a sporangium.   Such a high spore output in a sporangium is a primitive feature.   During the maturation of the

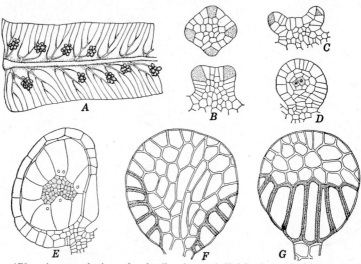

Fig. 179.—*A*, ventral view of a fertile pinna of *Gleichenia pectinata* Presl. *B–E*, *G*. *flabellata* R. Br. *B–C*, young receptacles. *D–E*, stages in development of sporangia. *F–G*, ventral and dorsal surface views of a mature sporangium of *G. pectinata* Presl. (*B–E*, *after Bower*, 1899.) (*A*, × 4; *B–D*, × 150; *E*, × 75; *F–G*, × 120.)

jacket layer, there is the formation of a linear, obliquely transverse annulus (Fig. 179*F–G*) that causes a vertical dehiscence of the sporangium. Species with sporangia arranged in a ring on the receptacle always have the sporangia dehiscing toward the center of the ring.   This is not always the case with species in which there are also sporangia on the central portion of the receptacle.

Except for a lack of chloroplasts in the spores and a slower rate of progress, early stages in development of gametophytes of *Gleichenia* are quite similar to those in *Osmunda*.[1]   Mature prothallia also resemble those of *Osmunda* in having an elongate midrib, flanked on either side by a thin wing (Fig. 180*A*).   Some species have irregularly folded and crinkled wings that partly or completely obscure the midrib.   In the case

[1] Rauwenhoff, 1891.

of *G. laevigata* Hook. the folding is so extensive that the gametophytes look like those of *Fossombronia*.[1]

Sex organs are usually formed only on the ventral face of a gameto-phyte, but in *G. laevigata* antheridia may be formed on both faces of it. Early stages of antheridial development (Fig. 180*B–D*) are quite similar

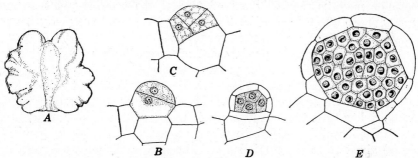

Fig. 180.—*A*, ventral view of gametophyte of *Gleichenia dichotoma* (Willd.) Hook. *B–E*, stages in development of antheridia of *G. pectinata* Presl. (*A*, × 3; *B–E*, × 325.)

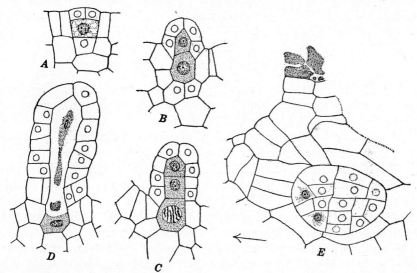

Fig. 181.—*Gleichenia pectinata* Presl. *A–D*, stages in the development of archegonia. *E*, embryo; the arrow points to the apex of the gametophyte. (× 325.)

to those in *Osmunda*.[1] Development of the antheridial jacket is also similar, and the last cell division results in a small triangular opercular cell at the apex of the jacket. The number of androgonial cells formed from the primary androgonial cell may be even greater than in *Osmunda* (Fig. 180*E*), and in the case of *G. pectinata* Presl. there may be more than 500 androcytes. Archegonia are produced in large numbers on the

[1] Campbell, 1908.

ventral side of a midrib and in acropetalous succession. Archegonial initials are differentiated close to the apical initials of a gametophyte. The sequence of their development is quite similar to that in other ferns (Fig. 181*A–C*). Mature archegonia (Fig. 181*D*) have long necks, 8 to 12 cells in height, that may stand erect from the gametophyte (*G. pectinata*) or may be markedly curved toward the growing point of the gametophyte (*G. polypodioides* Sm.). Most species have the primary canal cell dividing into two neck canal cells.[1]

Stages in embryonal development are exceedingly rare despite the fact that most gametophytes produce archegonia in abundance. The few early stages that have been observed[1] seem to show that the first two cell divisions in an embryo are parallel to the long axis of the archegonium but at right angles to one another. As in most other leptosporangiates, the two epibasal daughter cells (those nearest the apex of the gametophyte) give rise to the cotyledon and the stem; and the two hypobasal daughter cells to the foot and the primary root. Cotyledon, stem, and primary root each develop from an apical cell, and it is very probable that these apical initials are differentiated at the eight-celled stage of embryonal development (Fig. 181*E*).

FAMILY 4. MATONIACEAE

The Matoniaceae are the only Leptosporangiatae with a simultaneous development of sporangia that have the sori protected by an umbrella-shaped indusium. Aside from Dipteridaceae, it is the only family with simultaneously developing sporangia that dehisce transversely by means of an approximately vertical annulus.

The leaf architecture and certain sporangial features are similar to those in Gleicheniaceae. The Matoniaceae show considerable evolutionary progress over the Gleicheniaceae, in their more elaborate vascular organization, their indusial protection of sori, and their transverse dehiscence of sporangia by means of a vertical annulus.

Matonia is the only genus with living species, and its three species are found only in the Malayan region. Matoniaceae appeared late in the Triassic, apparently as an offshoot from the Gleicheniaceae. During the Jurassic and Lower Cretaceous the family became widespread with a distribution comparable to that of the cosmopolitan bracken fern of today.[2] The Matoniaceae, similar to the Gleicheniaceae, were driven toward the tropics by climatic changes toward the close of the Cretaceous. In contrast with the widespread tropical persistence that characterizes the present-day Gleicheniaceae, the Matoniaceae have disappeared from the tropical flora of today except in the Malayan region.

[1] Campbell, 1908.   [2] Seward, 1899.

Sporophytes of *M. pectinata* R. Br., the type species, have creeping dichotomously branched rhizomes with an average diameter of 7 mm. and an indefinite length. A rhizome bears leaves at intervals along the upper

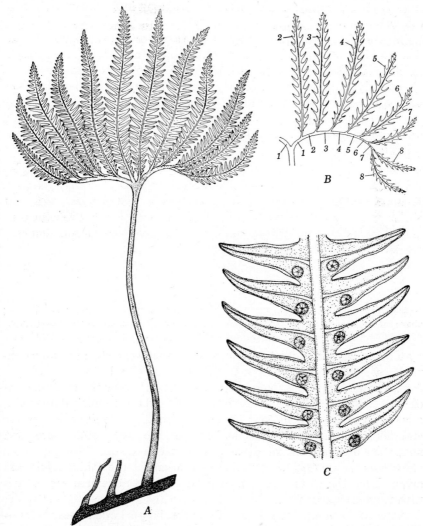

Fig. 182.—*Matonia pectinata* R. Br. *A*, sporophyte. *B*, diagram of a leaf blade showing relationship of successive dichotomies 1–1, 2–2, 3–3, etc. *C*, portion of a fertile pinna. (*A*, × ½; *C*, × 2.)

surface (Fig. 182*A*). One striking peculiarity of this species is the intermingling of young and old leaves along a rhizome. Leaves, which may attain a height of more than 2 meters, seem to have palmately divided blades. Actually, there is a repeated dichotomous branching (up to

20 or more times) of the blade and one in which successive forkings are always restricted to the dichotomy facing the leaf base (Fig. 182*B*). Lateral veins of the pinnules have one or more bifurcations. Anastomoses between branches of the lateral veins result in a more or less reticulate venation.

Stems of very young sporophytes have a protostelic vascular cylinder.[1] The protostele is replaced by an amphiphloic siphonstele after a stem has produced two to four leaves. With further development there is a change into a polycyclic condition. Early-formed polycyclic regions of a stem have a siphonostele surrounding a protostele; later-formed regions have the inner vascular cylinder siphonostelic. Steles at the apex of an old stem are tricyclic and with the innermost cycle protostelic or siphonostelic (Fig. 183).

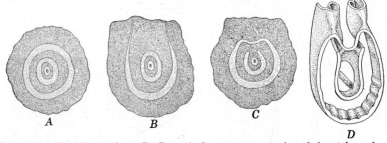

Fig. 183.—*Matonia pectinata* R. Br.   *A–C*, transverse sections below, through, and above the node of a rhizome.   *D*, stereodiagram of the vascular tissues of a node.   (*D, after Tansley and Lulham*, 1904.)   ($\times 3\frac{1}{3}$.)

The outer and middle siphonosteles of a tricyclic stele are only connected with each other at the nodes.[1] Connection is established by a downwardly projecting "compensating tongue" from the two edges of each leaf trace (Fig. 183*D*). Both the outer and the middle siphonosteles have a gap at each node, but that of the middle stele lies considerably anterior to that of the outer stele. Hence successive sections through a node show no gap in the middle stele until after a closure of the gap in the outer stele (Fig. 183*C*). Anterior to the gap of the middle stele and arising from the inner face is a simple vascular bridge that connects it with the innermost stele.

The xylem in all three siphonosteles consists of large tracheids intermingled with small, thin-walled, parenchymatous cells (Fig. 184). The outer siphonostele contains a variable number of small, mesarch, protoxylem masses that tend to lie toward the inner face of the xylem. There are also masses of protoxylem in the middle siphonostele. All three steles are amphiphloic, with the phloem on either side of the xylem but two or three cells in thickness. External to both the inner and outer phloem is a

[1] Tansley and Lulham, 1904.

narrow belt of pericyclic tissue. There is a typical endodermal layer immediately external to and immediately internal to both the outer and the middle steles. The innermost siphonostele generally has an endodermal layer only at its outer face. At each node there is a single leaf trace departing from the outer siphonostele. The trace is C-shaped, undivided, and similar in appearance to the single bundle running the length of the petiole.

The sori generally lie in two rows on a pinna, one on either side of, and a short distance from, the midrib (Fig. 182*C*). Large leaves with deeply

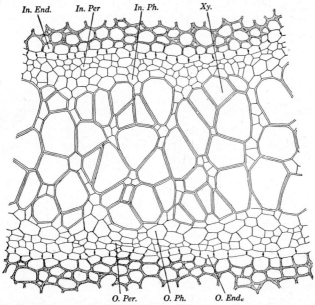

FIG. 184.—Transverse section through the middle siphonostele of a tricyclic rhizome of *Matonia pectinata* R. Br. (*In. End.*, inner endodermis; *In. Per.*, inner pericycle; *In. Ph.*, inner phloem; *O. End.*, outer endodermis; *O. Per.*, outer pericycle; *O. Ph.*, outer phloem; *Xy.*, xylem.) (× 160.)

incised pinnae may have more numerous and irregularly distributed sori. All sporangia on a leaf develop simultaneously. As in *Gleichenia*, sporangial development is preceded by an elevation of the receptacle above the surface of a pinna.[1] There is soon an overarching of the receptacular apex to form an umbrella-shaped indusium with a massive stalk (Fig. 185*A*). Differentiation of the six to nine sporangial initials does not take place until the indusium is well along in its development. The initials are differentiated from superficial cells of the indusial stalk, and their development into sporangia is in typical leptosporangiate sequence, with a potential formation of 64 spores.[1] Shortly after the sporangia

[1] Bower, 1899.

are ripe, there is a shedding of the indusium and a free exposure of the ring of sporangia surrounding the stump of the receptacle. Mature sporangia of *M. pectinata* R. Br. have a linear, obliquely vertical, annulus that causes a transverse dehiscence of the sporangial jacket (Fig. 185*B*).

Gametophytes of *Matonia* are unknown except for a few old ones found attached to young sporophytes.[1] These look like gametophytes of *Gleichenia* but nothing is known concerning their structure.

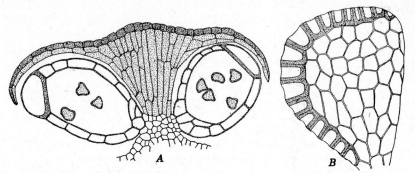

Fig. 185.—*Matonia pectinata* R. Br. *A*, vertical section through a receptacle and indusium. *B*, surface view of a mature sporangium. (*A*, × 80; *B*, × 120.)

FAMILY 5. DIPTERIDACEAE

The Dipteridaceae have sori in which sporangial development is essentially simultaneous. The sori are without indusia but have numerous capitate hairs. Dehiscence of sporangia is more or less transverse and by means of an obliquely vertical annulus.

The affinities of the family are with the Gleicheniaceae and Matoniaceae, but there is no close relationship to either. Living Dipteridaceae show a curious intermingling of primitive and advanced characters. On the primitive side there is the relatively simple vascular structure, the leaf architecture, the nearly simultaneous development of sporangia, and the primitive type of gametophyte. Advanced features include: the double leaf trace, the reticulate venation of the leaf blade, the small spore output per sporangium, and the nearly vertical annulus of a sporangium.

There is but one genus with living species. This genus (*Dipteris*) has six species, all of which are found only in the Malayan region. *Dipteris* was placed among the Polypodiaceae until it was shown[2] that there is a close relationship between it and certain fossil ferns that were conspicuous in the floras of the Triassic and Jurassic. Three of the fossil genera assigned to the Dipteridaceae had large lyre-shaped leaves; a fourth genus, of later origin, had leaves more like *Dipteris*. Except

---

[1] Bower, 1926.   [2] Seward and Dale, 1901.

that Dipteridaceae appeared somewhat earlier in the Triassic, the history of the family shows a remarkable parallelism to that of the Matoniaceae. Similar to the Matoniaceae they became widespread over Europe and North America during the Jurassic and disappeared from these areas toward the close of the Cretaceous. Similarly, also, the present-day representatives are found only in the Malayan region.

Sporophytes of *Dipteris* have creeping, dichotomously branched rhizomes that are covered with stiff brown scales. Leaves are borne in alternate succession on the upper side of a rhizome, and roots are irregularly distributed over its lower side. The rhizome shows the same inter-

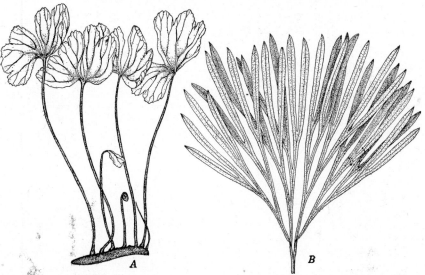

Fig. 186.—*A*, sporophyte of *Dipteris conjugata* (Kaulf.) Reinw. *B*, leaf of *D. Lobbiana* (Hook.) Moore. (*A*, × ½; *B*, × ⅜.)

mingling of old and young leaves as is found in *Matonia* (Fig. 186*A*). The lamina of a leaf may have a repeated dichotomous branching and an equal development of both dichotomies, *D. Lobbiana* (Hook.) Moore (Fig. 186*B*); or it may have but one dichotomy and a repeated dichotomous branching of the main vein, *D. conjugata* (Kaulf.) Reinw. Although both kinds of blades have a primitive type of primary venation, the veinlets are of an advanced type in that they form a reticulum in which many of the ultimate veinlets end blindly.

Young sporophytes have rhizomes with a protostelic vascular cylinder, but this soon gives way to a siphonostelic condition.[1] The siphonostele is amphiphloic and has an external and an internal endodermal layer. *D. conjugata* (Fig. 187) has a single trace departing to a leaf at

[1] De Bruyn, 1911.

each node.[1] The first-formed portion of the siphonostele of *D. Lobbiana* may also have one trace to a leaf, but later-formed portions always have two traces.[2]

The sori (Fig. 188*A*) may lie in two rows, one on either side of the midrib (*D. Lobbiana*), or they may be irregularly distributed over the

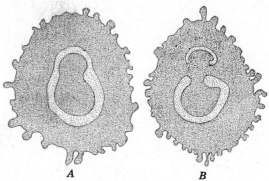

Fig. 187.—*Dipteris conjugata* (Kaulf.) Reinw. *A*, transverse section of a rhizome just below a node. *B*, through a node. (× 10.)

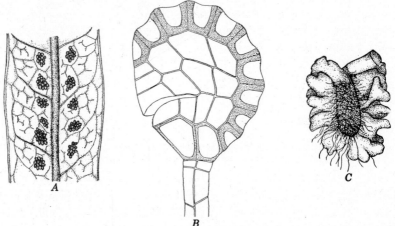

Fig. 188.—*A*, portion of a fertile pinna of *Dipteris Lobbiana* (Hook.) Moore. *B*, surface view of a mature sporangium of *D. conjugata* (Kaulf.) Reinw. *C*, gametophyte of *D. conjugata*. (*C, after Bower*, 1926.) (*A*, × 4; *B*, × 215; *C*, × 8.)

entire abaxial face of the blade (*D. conjugata*). Two species have been shown to have a simultaneous development of sporangia.[3] Young sori of *D. conjugata* produce sporangia in irregular sequence.[3] However, the sorus of this species is only an incipient mixed sorus, since older sori do not have the intermingling of mature and developing sporangia typical

---

[1] De Bruyn, 1911; Seward and Dale, 1901.   [2] De Bruyn, 1911; Bower, 1915.
[3] Armour, 1907.

of true mixed sori. Sporangial development is strictly leptosporangiate, and sporangia have a relatively small (64) potential output of spores. The stalk of a sporangium consists of four vertical rows of cells, two of which are visible when a stalk is seen from the side. In *D. conjugata* the length of a stalk is equal to the height of the spore case. Mature sporangia have an obliquely vertical annulus that almost completely encircles the sporangium (Fig. 188*B*). Dehiscence of a sporangium is approximately transverse, but there is no definite stomium.

Gametophytes of *Dipteris* (Fig. 188*C*) resemble the primitive gametophytes of *Osmunda* and *Gleichenia* in that they have an elongate midrib, flanked on either side by a thin much-convoluted wing.[1] The structure of the sex organs and the embryology of *Dipteris* are unknown.

FAMILY 6. HYMENOPHYLLACEAE

The Hymenophyllaceae differ from all other homosporous Leptosporangiatae but the Cyatheaceae in that the sporangia are formed in a basipetalous gradate succession on an elevated receptacle. The receptacle of Hymenophyllaceae is always surrounded by a cup-like or a two-lipped indusium. The chief difference between Hymenophyllaceae and Cyatheaceae is the structure of the sporophyte. Many Hymenophyllaceae are "filmy ferns" with semitransparent leaves one cell in thickness. This feature alone cannot be considered a distinctive character since certain species of *Todea* (one of the Osmundaceae) are also filmy ferns.

There are two genera in the family, *Hymenophyllum* and *Trichomanes*, each with about 230 species. The former has a two-lipped indusium, the latter a cup-like one. Both genera thrive best in tropical rain forests. Most of the species found in rain forests are epiphytes, but a few of them are terrestrial in habit.

In spite of their filmy structure many of the species are able to withstand desiccation and to recover after a considerable degree of drying and shriveling.[2] In this respect they resemble many liverworts and mosses, although their capacity to withstand desiccation is more limited.

Four or five species of *Trichomanes* have been found in the United States. A majority of these are known only from Florida, but one species (*T. Boschianum* Strum) is found on moist and dripping sandstone cliffs as far north as Kentucky. The geological record of the family is somewhat uncertain since most of the fossils that have been assigned to it are of questionable validity. However, one species (*Hymenophyllites quadridactylites* Gutbier), known from the Upper Carboniferous, seems to have much in common with the modern Hymenophyllaceae.[3]

---

[1] Bower, 1926. [2] Holloway, 1923; Shreve, 1911.
[3] Hirmer, 1927; Seward, 1910.

The sporophyte shows several primitive features. Among these are the protostelic vascular cylinder, the dichotomous venation of leaves, and the marginal receptacles. These features point to a relationship with the lower Leptosporangiatae and tend to show that the Hymeno-phyllaceae are a stock of relatively ancient origin. On the other hand, the gradate sorus and the nearly vertical annuli of sporangia show that

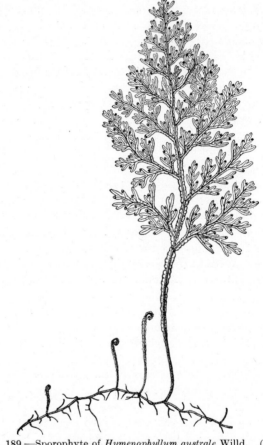

Fig. 189.—Sporophyte of *Hymenophyllum australe* Willd.   ($\times$ ½.)

there has been a considerable advance over primitive ferns as far as organization of the reproductive organs is concerned. Advance in struc-ture of the fructification does not appear to have lead to a higher type of fern because the plant body is ecologically restricted to a humid, feebly illuminated habitat. Thus, the Hymenophyllaceae may be looked upon as an evolutionary series ancient in origin and ending blindly because of ecological specialization.

Except for the indusia and receptacles there are no constant differences between *Hymenophyllum* and *Trichomanes*. With a very few exceptions, as *H. pulcherrimum* Col., the sporophyte of *Hymenophyllum* has a prostrate, creeping rhizome. This is sparingly branched because only occasionally is there a development of the axillary branch primordium formed at each node. Leaf primordia are formed in acropetalous succession and in a double row on the upper side of a rhizome. In many species, as in *H. australe* Willd., only one out of a half dozen successively formed primordia develops into a mature leaf. The others remain dormant, or they abort. Thus, there is a fairly long interval between successive mature leaves on a rhizome (Fig. 189). Since a dormant primordium may develop at any time into a leaf, it is not uncommon to find a spirally uncoiling young leaf between two fully mature ones. Irrespective of whether a leaf primordium continues development or not, a pair of adventitious roots is formed on the underside of a rhizome at each node. This accounts for the occurrence of several pairs of roots between two successive mature leaves. Intake of water through the roots is supplemented by absorption of water vapor condensing on the leaves. However, most species of *Hymenophyllum* seem to take in sufficient water through their roots to meet all needs of the plant.[1] A few species, as *H. cruentum* Cav., have an entire blade, but most of them have the blade divided into a succession of unequal dichotomies. Blades of the latter type always have a single vein in each shank of a dichotomy (Fig. 191*A*). Species with entire blades have a series of sori along the lateral margins, one at the terminus of each vein. Species with divided blades have a single sorus at the apex of each ultimate dichotomy. In both cases the receptacle is elevated but in neither does it project beyond the subtending indusium as in *Trichomanes*.

Stems of *Hymenophyllum*[2] have a relatively narrow cortex in comparison with those of most other ferns. All cells of the cortex may be thick-walled, or there may be thin-walled cells in the external portion and thick-walled ones in the internal portion. The vascular cylinder is protostelic. As is the case with most other ferns, the stele is externally delimited by an endodermal layer. The pericyclic layer internal to the endodermis may be one to several cells in thickness. It is always composed of thin-walled cells. Just within the pericycle is a layer of phloem, generally more than one cell in thickness. The phloem is separated from the xylem core by a band of conjunctive parenchyma one or more cells in thickness. There is considerable variation in structure of the xylem. Certain species with relatively large rhizomes, as *H. demissum* Swartz, have a continuous ring of metaxylem surrounding a central parenchymatous area in which the protoxylem is embedded.

[1] Shreve, 1911.   [2] Boodle, 1900.

Other species with large rhizomes, as *H. scabrum* A. Rich., have the metaxylem ring transversely interrupted on either flank. Metaxylem elements in the ventral arc of an interrupted ring are of smaller diameter than those in the dorsal arc (Fig. 190*A*). Some species with small rhizomes have an obliteration of the ventral arc of metaxylem. In such cases the protoxylem may be separated from the persistent dorsal arc by parenchyma (*H. cruentum* Cav.), or it may lie immediately next the lower face of the metaxylem (*H. fucoides* Swartz).

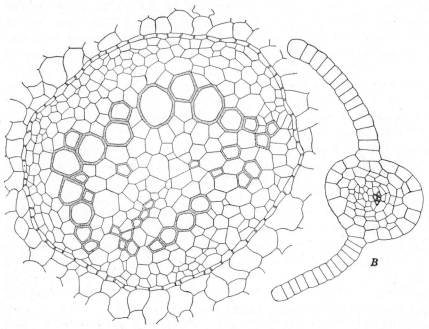

A

FIG. 190.—*Hymenophyllum australe* Willd. *A*, transverse section of a stele and inner portion or cortex of a rhizome. *B*, transverse section of a leaf. (*A*, × 325; *B*, × 140.)

Leaf traces are similar in structure to the steles from which they depart, and there is no interruption of the vascular cylinder when a trace is given off. As noted, above, there is a rudimentary or vestigial branch primordium in the axil of each leaf. The vascular supply within a primordium does not connect directly with the central cylinder. Instead, it is joined with, or departs from, the leaf trace some distance above the region where the latter is united with the stele.[1]

The most conspicuous difference between roots of *Hymenophyllum* and those of other ferns is the lack of a root cap.[2] The structure of a root proper resembles that of other Leptosporangiatae. In most species the stele is diarch, but it may be monarch if the root is of small diameter.[1]

[1] Boodle, 1900.   [2] Sadebeck, 1898.

A majority of the species are true filmy ferns and, except for the veins, have leaves one cell in thickness (Fig. 190*B*). Veins of leaves with a blade one cell in thickness may contain xylem and phloem, or they may be pseudo-veins in which there is no true vascular tissue. A few species, including *H. dilatatum* Schwartz, have leaf blades several cells in thickness in which the cells are organized into a solid tissue without intercellular spaces. The thin filmy leaf typical of most species is thought[1] to be a secondarily developed type resulting from adaptation to a hydrophytic environment. The thicker-leaved species, as *H. dilatatum*, have been regarded as being nearer the ancestral type than are those species with filmy leaves.[2] However, the fact that the first-formed leaves of thick-leaved species are one cell in thickness[3] indicates that species with the thick-leaved type are derived from, instead of more primitive than, those with a filmy type of leaf blade.

The sori are developed singly and at the distal end of a vein. They are terminal in position if the blade is divided, and lateral if it is undivided. Receptacular development is accompanied by the development of a subtending flap-like outgrowth, one cell in thickness, from both the adaxial and abaxial faces of the blade. The two-lipped indusium thus formed soon overarches the apex of a receptacle[4] and continues to ensheath the latter until the spores are shed (Fig. 191*A*–*B*). The first sporangial initials are differentiated at the apex of the receptacle and at a time when its basal portion is still meristematic. Succeeding sporangial initials appear in basipetalous succession, and sporangia at the receptacular apex may be at the spore-mother-cell stage before the lowermost initials are differentiated. Notwithstanding the gradate nature of the receptacle, the early stages in sporangial development resemble those of such primitive leptosporangiates as the Osmundaceae and the Gleicheniaceae. A sporangial initial is deeply embedded in the receptacle, and it produces only one or two stalk cells at each cutting face before dividing periclinally into jacket initial and primary archesporial cell (Fig. 191*B*). Succeeding stages of development are like those in typical leptosporangiates. The theoretical spore output[4] is generally 128 or 256, but it may be 512. A mature sporangium dehisces transversely by means of an obliquely vertical annulus (Fig. 191*C*).

The gametophyte of *Hymenophyllum* is an irregularly branched ribbon (Fig. 192*A*); that of *Trichomanes* is a profusely branched filament. Simplicity of the gametophyte among the Hymenophyllaceae is generally considered a derived condition, not a primitive one. Germination of spores takes place quite readily, but growth subsequent to the initial stages is at a very slow rate,[5] and gametophytes of *H. pulcherrimum* Col.

[1] Bower, 1908, 1923.   [2] Bower, 1908, 1926.   [3] Holloway, 1923.
[4] Bower, 1899.   [5] Goebel, 1888.

grown in culture[1] took more than three and a half years to reach maturity. While it is still within the sporangium,[2] a spore of *Hymenophyllum* develops into a three-celled germling, with three radiate internal walls. All three cells may divide transversely when a germling is shed from a sporangium, but only one of them continues development to form a filament five, six, or more cells in length. Following this the terminal cell of a filament becomes differentiated into an apical cell with two lateral

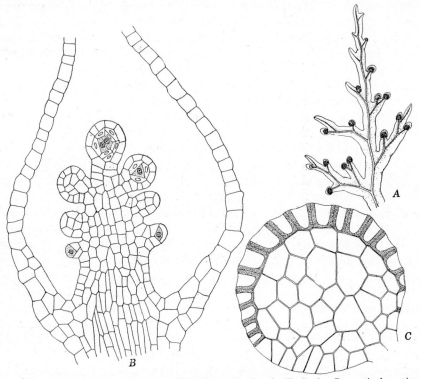

Fig. 191.—*Hymenophyllum australe* Willd.   *A*, tip of a fertile leaf.   *B*, vertical section through a receptacle.   *C*, surface view of a mature sporangium.   (*A*, × 2; *B*–*C*, × 140.)

cutting faces.[1]   The first-formed portion of a gametophyte produced by the apical cell is generally but two cells in breadth; later-formed portions are many cells broad and one cell in thickness.   Eventually the apical cell may be replaced by a group of apical initials.   The portion of the gametophyte lateral to the apical initial or initials never grows more rapidly than the growing point.   Thus, the gametophyte never assumes the heart-shaped outline typical of so many leptosporangiates.   *Hymeno-phyllum* differs from other ferns in that rhizoids are formed only at the margin of a gametophyte and generally in tufts.   Old gametophytes are

---

[1] Holloway, 1930.   [2] Goebel, 1888; Holloway, 1930.

irregularly branched. Branching may be due to a formation of two growing points at the thallus apex, but in most cases, it is due to a formation of lateral adventitious branches. Adventitious branches frequently develop from a single marginal cell of the prothallus. A young adventitious branch soon differentiates an apical cell that functions in the usual manner. Gametophytes of *Hymenophyllum* may multiply vegetatively either by progressive growth and death or by a formation of gemmae on the margins of prothallia.[1] A gemma is a three-rayed filament more or less like the three-rayed germling formed from a spore.

Sex organs of *Hymenophyllum* are generally borne on short adventitious branches that are more than one cell in thickness (Fig. 192*B*).

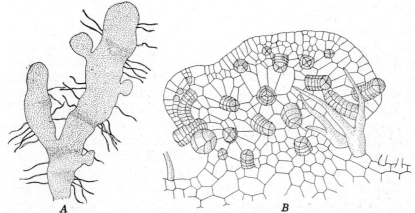

FIG. 192.—*A*, portion of a gametophyte of an undetermined species of *Hymenophyllum*. *B*, fertile lobe of gametophyte of *H. australe* Willd. (*B, after Goebel*, 1888.)

Such branches may bear only antheridia or may bear intermingled antheridia and archegonia. The antheridia are of an emergent type, have a jacket layer composed of several cells, and contain a larger number of antherozoids than antheridia of most Leptosporangiatae.[2] They are to be compared with antheridia of such primitive Leptosporangiatae as *Osmunda* and *Gleichenia* instead of with antheridia of advanced genera. An archegonium has a curved neck, several cells in height, that projects above the gametophyte. Although gametophytes bearing young sporophytes have been recorded, nothing is known concerning the embryology of *Hymenophyllum*. It is presumed that the young sporophytes resulted from a union of gametes, but there is a possibility that they may have been formed apogamously, as is known to be the case in certain species of *Trichomanes*.[3]

---

[1] Campbell, 1895.   [2] Campbell, 1895; Goebel, 1905.

[3] Bower, 1888; Georgevitch, 1910.

FAMILY 7.   CYATHEACEAE

The Cyatheaceae have a gradate sorus bearing sporangia that dehisce transversely by means of an obliquely vertical annulus.   The sori may be marginal or superficial in position and with or without an indusium.   Some members of the family are tree-like in habit; others are not.

Usually[1] the Cyatheaceae are held to include but six or seven genera that are grouped together chiefly because of their tree-like habit.   Even such a delimitation of the family is artificial since it has been shown[2] that there are differences in soral position and structure.   It has also been shown[3] that there are a number of other genera, ordinarily referred to the Polypodiaceae,[4] that have a gradate sorus more or less like that of the tree ferns.   A careful analysis of these ferns,[5] which include some 15 genera, shows that they fall into five families[6] when arranged according to a strictly natural system of classification.   Since the characters separating these one from another are not conspicuous, these gradate ferns are here grouped in one synthetic family, the Cyatheaceae.

The Cyatheaceae are tropical or subtropical in distribution.   The only representative of the family in this country is *Dennestaedtia adian-toides* (Humb. and Bonpl.) Moore, a rare fern in Florida[7] and one that is often placed in the Polypodiaceae.   Fossil remains of cyathaceous ferns are known from as far back as the Jurassic.[8]

The type genus, *Cyathea*, has about 180 species.   None of them are found in the United States, but 43 of them are listed[9] from Mexico, Central America, and the West Indies.   Some species of *Cyathea*, including the Central American *C. princeps* (Linden) E. Mayer, are tree-like in habit and attain a height of nearly 20 meters;[9] mature stems of certain other species are less than a meter in length.   Most species have an erect stem that may be unbranched and terminate in a crown of leaves, or branched and with a crown of leaves at the apex of each branch.   A majority of the species have large bi- to quadripinnate leaves.

C. medullaris Sw. (Fig. 193), native to Australia and several islands of the Pacific, is one of the hardier tree-like species.   It may be grown out of doors in this country in regions where the temperature does not fall more than 2 or 3° below the freezing point.   It is also one of the species frequently grown in greenhouses.   Mature plants growing under natural conditions in New Zealand attain a height of 6 to 15

[1] Christ, 1897; Diels, 1898; Maxon, 1909.   [2] Bower, 1899.
[3] Bower, 1899, 1910, 1912, 1913.   [4] Christ, 1897; Diels, 1898.   [5] Bower, 1926.
[6] Loxsomaceae, Dicksoniaceae, Plagiogyriaceae, Protocyatheaceae, Cyatheaceae.
[7] Small, 1931.   [8] Hirmer, 1927; Seward, 1910.   [9] Maxon, 1909.

Fig. 193.—Stand of *Cyathea medullaris* Sw. in Golden Gate Park, San Francisco, California. These plants are about 30 years old. (*Photograph by I. L. Wiggins.*)

meters.[1] In most cases the erect stem is unbranched; sometimes there is a single dichotomy. At the base of the stem, and extending upward for a meter or more, is a conical buttress of densely compacted adventitious roots. For a considerable distance above the buttress the surface of the stem is relatively smooth except for hexagonal scars of old leaves. Above this the stem surface is covered with a shaggy felt consisting of the half-decayed remains of old leaf bases and the adventitious roots borne below them. The stem terminates in a crown of 20 to 30 leaves.

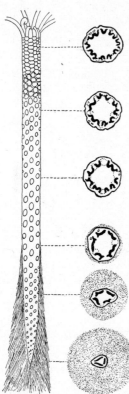

The blade of a leaf is 1.5 to 4 meters long and 0.9 to 1.5 meters broad; the length of a petiole is about equal to that of a blade. New leaves are developed throughout the growing season, and, although they are of immense size, they show the same spiral uncoiling as do most other Leptosporangiatae.

Basal support and anchorage of a stem is due in large part to the basal buttress-like mass of densely interwoven adventitious roots. The lowermost portion of a stem, exclusive of the root buttress, is an inverted cone that gradually broadens upward for a meter or more. Above this the stem is constant in diameter to the crown of leaves. There is no secondary thickening in stems of *Cyathea* or in those of any other Cyatheaceae.

A stem has a narrow cortex and a broad central cylinder. The central cylinder shows an ontogenetic recapitulation of the stelar theory in that it is protostelic for the first one or two nodes, siphonostelic for the next few nodes, and a poly-cyclic dictyostele above this.[2] The outer region of the polycyclic portion is a tubular dictyostele. Accordingly as it is cut at a low or a high level, there are,[3] respectively, two or three to many overlapping leaf gaps (Fig. 194). Meristeles of this dictyostele are convexly arched and have their poles turned outward next to the leaf gaps. Immediately internal to each meristele, and apparently a portion of it, is an arc of sclerenchymatous pith. There is a similar arc of sclerenchymatous cortical tissue immediately external to each meristele. A meristele is amphiphloic in organization and completely encircled

Fig. 194.—Diagram of a stem of *Cyathea* showing the vascular organization at successive levels. (*After Ogura, 1927.*)

[1] Cheeseman, 1925.   [2] Ogura, 1927; Stephenson, 1907.   [3] Ogura, 1927.

by an endodermal layer.[1] Between endodermis and phloem there is
a pericyclic layer a few cells in thickness. The xylem of a meristele
is composed of tracheids intermingled with parenchymatous cells.
Except for the sclerenchymatous arc internal to each meristele, the
interior of the central cylinder is a pith with numerous (50 to 150) small
vascular strands that are more or less concentrically arranged. The
rings and arcs of vascular strands represent much-dissected internal
steles,[2] more or less like those in polycyclic stems of *Matonia*. An arc
of strands is given off from the inner face of the outer vascular cylinder
below each leaf gap. Each arc runs diagonally inward and upward
past the gap toward the center of the pith. Here the strands branch
and anastomose. Half of this mass of strands departs at the next leaf,

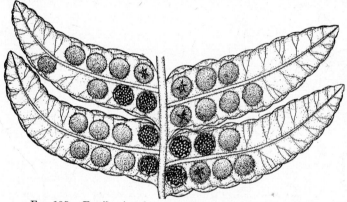

Fig. 195.—Fertile pinnules of *Cyathea medullaris* Sw.   ($\times$ 4.)

the remaining half departs at the second leaf above.[2] In addition to
receiving a portion of its trace supply from the internal vascular system,
the trace supply to a leaf also includes strands departing from the outer
dictyostele.

The relatively narrow cortex consists of three regions: the inner
sclerenchymatous region already mentioned, a median parenchymatous
region, and an outer sclerenchymatous one.[1] The parenchymatous
region contains numerous mucilage sacs.

There are several adventitious roots at the base of each petiole.
Some of the roots at a leaf base connect with the lower side of the gap
margins; others connect with the departing traces. Although roots are
produced below every leaf, those formed below leaves more than a meter
above the ground remain short and never penetrate the soil. There are
no unusual features in the structure of a root.[1]

[1] Ogura, 1927.   [2] Godwin, 1932.

Sori are developed as a leaf uncoils.　Each pinnule bears two rows of sori, one on either side of the midrib (Fig. 195).　Sori are first apparent as small swellings that soon become conical in shape.[1]　Sometimes, as in *C. dealbata* Sw.,[1] the indusium formed at the base of a sorus grows more rapidly than the receptacle and soon becomes a cup-like sheath overarching it.　In other cases, as in *C. medullaris* Sw., development of the indusium is relatively slow, and the only protection of young sporangia is that afforded by the precociously developing multicellular hairs from the receptacular surface (Fig. 196*A*).　Some species have a somewhat larger cell at the apex of a young receptacle, but there is no evidence indicating that it is an apical cell.[1]　Sporangial initials appear in basipetalous succession on a receptacle.　Development of an initial into

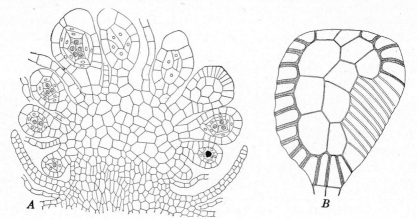

Fig. 196.—*Cyathea medullaris* Sw.　*A*, vertical section through a sorus.　*B*, surface view of a mature sporangium.　(× 145.)

a sporangium is in the usual leptosporangiate manner, with the formation of a tapetum two cells in thickness (Fig. 196*A*).　The archesporial cell of *C. dealbata* divides to form two or four spore mother cells.[1]　The resultant small number of spores (8 or 16) within the sporangium of this species is not characteristic of all species, since the theoretical number of spores in sporangia of *C. medullaris* is 64.　Mature sporangia are relatively small and are borne upon a stalk composed of four vertical rows of cells.　The annulus is an obliquely vertical row that incompletely encircles the sporangium (Fig. 196*B*).　One feature not found in previously described families is the belt of thin-walled cells, the stomium, that predetermines the precise spot at which transverse dehiscence will take place.

Germination of a spore begins with a rupture of the outer spore-wall layer, at the pyramidate pole, and a protrusion of the protoplast still

---

[1] Bower, 1899.

surrounded by the inner spore-wall layer. The first cell division is in a vertical plane. One daughter cell is the first prothallial cell; the other is the first rhizoid.[1] The first prothallial cell develops into a filament that rarely becomes more than five cells long. All cells of a filament but the lowermost (sometimes the lower two) then divide in a diagonal or a vertical plane. Young gametophytes of *Cyathea* and other Cyatheaceae are shorter and broader than those of the Polypodiaceae because of this early establishment of the plate stage. An apical cell is differentiated early in gametophytic development, sometimes as early as the four- or the five-celled stage; later on this cell is replaced by a group of apical initials. A mature gametophyte is heart-shaped and several cells in thickness in the region posterior to the apical notch. Sometimes, as in *C. dealbata* Sw.,[1] a gametophyte may be forked at the distal end and have two evident apical notches. Both the dorsal and the ventral surface of the cushion portion of a gametophyte may bear multicellular hairs 20 to 30 cells long and several cells broad at the base. The hairs originate from a single cell close to the growing point.

Antheridia are borne posterior and lateral to the apical cushion. They are generally formed on the ventral side but a few may be produced on the dorsal side. The initial of an antheridium is the outer daughter cell formed by diagonal division of a prothallial cell.[1] An initial divides transversely into a small wedge-shaped stalk cell that subtends half to three-quarters of its sister cell, the apical cell. The apical cell divides vertically by a peculiar ring-shaped wall similar to that in antheridia of Polypodiaceae (page 346). The outer cell, which more or less completely encircles its sister cells, is a jacket cell often called the "first ring cell."[2] It is very probable that, as in the Polypodiaceae, the inner cell divides into a primary androgonial cell and a dome cell by means of a periclinal curved wall. The dome cell divides anticlinally, by a vertical ring wall, into the second ring cell and the primary cover cell. In most cases the latter cell divides by means of a semicircular vertical wall. One of the daughter cells thus formed is the small opercular cell that is thrown off when an antheridium is mature.[1] Development of the jacket layer is accompanied by a division and redivision of the primary androgonial cell to form a number of androcytes. Antheridia of Cyatheaceae show a considerable advance over those of previously described Leptosporangiatae both in the reduction of the jacket layer to four cells and in the evolution of a special type of jacket cell, the ring cell.

Development of archegonia[1] takes place in an orthodox manner. The neck canal cell regularly has two nuclei, but sometimes it has four. The neck of an archegonium resembles that of Osmundaceae and Gleicheniaceae in that it is long and only slightly curved.

[1] Stokey, 1930.　　[2] Bauke, 1876; Schmelzeisen, 1933.

The demonstration[1] of antherozoids within the open neck of an archegonium containing a two-celled embryo indicates that embryonal development was initiated by gametic union. In other cases it is even more certain that the embryo developed apogamously.[2] Apogamous embryos of *Cyathea* are generally developed from a single cell in the axial row of a developing archegonium. Sometimes there is a parthenogenetic development of an egg.

The scanty observations on embryonal development[3] show that the first division of a zygote is vertical. It is very probable that the next division is also vertical and that the four organs of the embryo are established by the transverse divisions producing the octant stage. Somewhat older embryos show the typical leptosporangiate condition of a cotyledon and stem in the half embryo (epibasal half) facing the apex of the gametophyte and a root and foot in the hypobasal half.[4] During subsequent growth there is the usual more rapid development of cotyledon and primary root.

FAMILY 8. MARSILEACEAE

The Marsileaceae are distinguishable from all other Leptosporangiatae but the Salviniaceae by their heterospory. They differ from the latter family in that the structure containing the sporangia (the *sporocarp*) contains both microspores and macrospores.

As noted elsewhere (page 285) the two heterosporous families of ferns should be placed among the other Leptosporangiatae, instead of in a separate order or suborder. Many reasons have been brought forward[5] to show that the Marsileaceae are an offshoot from the Schizaeaceae. First of all, it is argued that the vegetative structure is that of primitive ferns no further advanced than the Schizaeaceae. Secondly, the sporocarp has been homologized with the enfolded fertile leaf or leaf segment of *Schizaea*. Lastly, the vestigial annulus in sporangia of Marsileaceae seems to be of the distinctive type found in Schizaeaceae. One major difficulty in relating the Marsileaceae to the Schizaeaceae is the structure of the sorus. In all Schizaeaceae the sporangia are borne singly and develop simultaneously; in the Marsileaceae the sporangia are borne in sori. Furthermore, the sorus in Marsileaceae is of a gradate type in which sporangia on the apex of the receptacle develop before those on the base of the receptacle. For these reasons the origin of the Marsileaceae should be sought among the families of Leptosporangiatae with gradate sori, namely, the Hymenophyllaceae and the Cyatheaceae. Sori of the first-named are always marginal; those of many Cyatheaceae

[1] Stokey, 1930.   [2] Stokey, 1918.   [3] Stokey, 1930; Stephenson, 1907.
[4] Stephenson, 1907.   [5] Bower, 1908, 1926.

lie some distance in from a leaf margin. Sori of Cyatheaceae are also generally protected by a cup-like or a flap-like indusium. Thus, as far as the sorus is concerned, there is a considerable basis for relating the Marsileaceae to the Cyatheaceae. The chief objection to this is the great difference in habit among the two families. Sporophytes of Cyatheaceae are generally large tree-like plants; those of Marsileaceae are small aquatic herbs. This is not as preposterous as it seems when one takes into consideration that such relationships between trees and small aquatic herbs occur among the angiosperms. An example of this is seen in the generally admitted close relationship between the Magnoliaceae and the Ranunculaceae; the latter including such aquatic herbs as *Ranunculus aquatilis* L. As is also well known, aquatic vascular

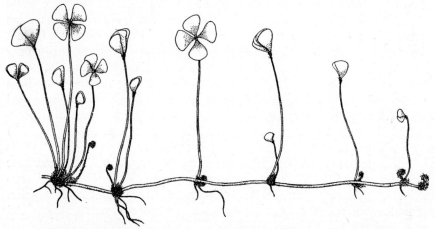

Fig. 197.—Sporophyte of *Marsilea vestita* Hook. and Grev. (Natural size.)

plants are generally simpler in structure than their terrestrial relatives. Thus, the simplicity of structure in sporophytes of Marsileaceae may be due to retrogression rather than to primitiveness.

The family includes three living genera: *Marsilea* with 56 species. *Pilularia* with 6 species, and the monotypic *Regnellidium*. All three genera are hydrophytes that grow rooted in the mud of marshes and shallow pools. The fossils that have been assigned to the Marsileaceae are so questionable in nature that the geological record of the family should be considered a blank.

At least six species of *Marsilea* are known to occur in the United States. Five of them are native to this country and found chiefly in the Gulf and Pacific Coast states. The sixth species (*M. quadrifolia* L.) is an introduced one that has become naturally established in certain ponds in New England. The sporophyte of *Marsilea* looks like an aquatic four-leaf clover (Fig. 197). It has a creeping, dichotomously branched rhizome capable of indefinite growth.   In *M. vestita* Hook. and Grev. a single plant may grow in all directions until it covers an area 25 meters or more in diameter.   The leaves are borne alternately along the upper side of a rhizome.   Internodes between successive leaves may be long or short.   There are one or more adventitious roots at each node and on the underside of the rhizome.   Elongating leaves posterior to a branch or stem apex have the circinate vernation typical of most Filicales.   Leaves of submerged individuals have long flexible petioles and leaf blades that float on the surface of the water.   When the same species grows on mud or damp soil, the leaves have short rigid petioles.   In either case, the blade is divided into four obovate to obcuneate pinnae.   Division of a blade into four pinnae results from two dichotomies arising in close succession to each other.   The veins of each pinna are dichotomously branched and have numerous cross connections that unite the vein system in a closed reticulum.   Most species resemble *M. vestita* in that sporocarps develop to maturity only on individuals that are not submerged.   The sporocarps are borne on short or long stalks (peduncles) inserted a short distance above the base of the petiole (Fig. 199*A*).   In most species the peduncle is unbranched and has a single sporocarp at its apex.   Some species have a dichotomously branched peduncle that bears 2 to 5 sporocarps (*M. quadrifolia*) or 6 to 26 of them (*M. polycarpa* Hook. and Grev.).

Rhizomes of *Marsilea* have an amphiphloic, solenostelic, vascular cylinder (Fig. 198).   Some species, including *M. vestita*, have conspicuous protoxylem masses that are exarch in position; other species, including *M. quadrifolia*, lack conspicuous protoxylem elements.   All species have the siphonostele externally and internally limited by an endodermal layer.   Just within the outer endodermis is a pericyclic layer one cell in thickness.   The structure of the pith depends upon environmental conditions.   Rhizomes of submerged plants generally have a parenchymatous pith; those of plants growing on mud have a more or less sclerotic pith.   The inner portion of the cortex is a solid tissue of thin-walled or sclerotic parenchyma.   External to this is an air-storage tissue (*aerenchyma*) with a single ring of air chambers.   The outermost portion of the cortex is a parenchymatous tissue, one to several cells in thickness.   An undivided leaf trace departs from the stele at each node.   It is similar in structure to the single vascular bundle in a petiole.   The latter has a V-shaped mass of xylem with the protoxylem exarch in position.   The xylem is successively surrounded by a band of phloem and an endodermal layer.   The portion of the petiole external to the endodermal layer is generally aerenchymatous.

The bean-shaped sporocarp of *Marsilea* (Fig. 199*A*) is generally interpreted as a modified fertile segment from the lower part of a leaf, but it has also been considered[1] homologous with the whole leaf. The chief argument for the latter interpretation is the resemblance of apical growth of a sporocarp to that of an entire leaf rather than to that of a pinna. However, both the nature of the vascular supply to the peduncle and the vascular system within the sporocarp seem to show that it is a leaf segment. Adherents of the leaf-segment theory variously interpret the sporocarp as resulting from an apposition of two pinnae[2] or from an enfolding of a single pinna. The single bundle in the peduncle and the single main vein in the sporocarp show that it is not a pair of pinnae.

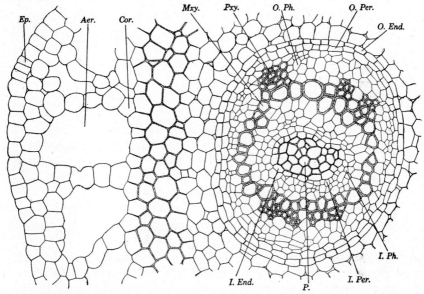

Fig. 198.—Transverse section through a rhizome of *Marsilea vestita* Hook. and Grev. (*Aer.*, aerenchyma; *Cor.*, cortex; *Ep.*, epidermis; *I. End.*, inner endodermis; *I. Per.* Inner pericycle; *I. Ph.*, inner phloem; *Mxy.*, metaxylem; *O. End.*, outer endodermis; *O. Per.*, outer pericycle; *O. Ph.*, outer phloem; *P.*, pith; *Pxy.*, protoxylem.) (× 215.)

Most of those who consider the sporocarp an enfolded pinna think that it is a pinnately divided one in which the pinnules have become fused with one another.[3] In the case of species with a single sporocarp at the base of a leaf, as *M. vestita* Hook. and Grev., it is very probable that there has been an enfolding of a single undivided pinna. The enfolding of a fertile pinna is similar to that found in *Schizaea*, that is, the sides of the under (abaxial) fertile face of a pinna are reflexed so that they oppose each other. The abaxial position of sporangia in *Schizaea* is clearly evident because they lie on the phloem side of the vascular bundle (see Fig. 175). This fact is more difficult of demonstration in *Marsilea* because the phloem in a vascular bundle completely encircles the xylem.

[1] Johnson, 1898, 1933.   [2] Busgen, 1890.   [3] Bower, 1926; Campbell, 1905.

However, the protoxylem in a leaf trace and a petiolar bundle is exarch in position, that is, on the abaxial side of a bundle. The protoxylem in the main bundle of a sporocarp lies at the inner face of the xylem. From this one may infer that there has been an enfolding of the abaxial face of the sporocarp. As already noted, the sporocarp of *Marsilea*

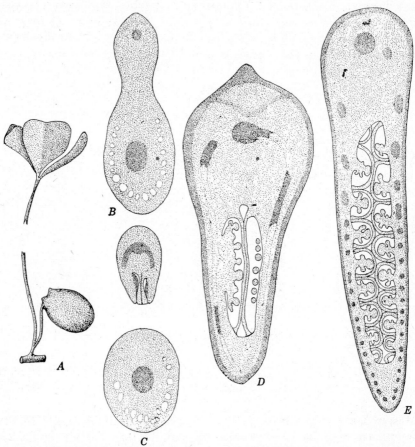

Fig. 199.—*Marsilea vestita* Hook. and Grev. *A*, leaf and sporocarp. *B–C*, two sections cut at different levels on a young sporocarp. The sections are cut in a transverse plane perpendicular to the flat surface. *D*, section of an older sporocarp cut in a transverse plane perpendicular to the flat surface. *E*, section of an older sporocarp cut in a longitudinal plane perpendicular to the flat surface. (*A*, × 3; *B–E*, × 45.)

is more like an enfolded pinna of the Cyatheaceae than an enfolded pinna of the Schizaeaceae. Its cyatheaceous nature is shown both by the gradate sorus and by the enclosure of the receptacle by an indusium (Fig. 200).

The vascular system is differentiated early in the ontogeny of a sporocarp. Interpreting a sporocarp in terms of a modified pinna, one may say that it has a midrib with 15 to 20 lateral veins on either side (Fig. 199*E*). The lateral veins on either side of a midrib alternate with one another, and each of them forks dichotomously midway between base and apex (Fig. 202*B*). Young sporocarps develop a linear receptacle at the point of forking of each lateral vein: hence, some distance in from the margin of the pinna. Similar to the lateral veins, the receptacles on opposite sides of a pinna alternate with one another. Axillary to each receptacle is a flap-like outgrowth, two cells in thickness, that projects forward to the pinna margin. These outgrowths are indusia. The two rows of indusia are so closely applied to each other that they

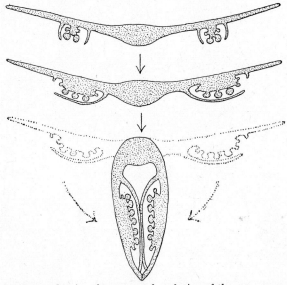

Fig. 200.—Diagrams showing the suggested evolution of the sporocarp of Maisiliaxeae by an enfolding of a pinnule of a cyatheaceous leaf. The sori are drawn as if opposite each other.

look like one solid tissue. For a time apical extension of the indusia keeps pace with that of the two pinna margins (Fig. 199*C*); later on, the leaf margins grow beyond the indusia and become so tightly applied to each other that the line of juncture is obliterated. Meanwhile each receptacle has become considerably elevated above the pinna surface, and each has differentiated a row of sporangial initials along its summit. Other sporangial initials are then differentiated in basipetalous succession along the flanks of a receptacle (Fig. 201*A*). The result is a typically gradate sorus in which sporangia at the summit are well along toward maturity before the lowermost ones begin to develop.

Sporangial initials at the apex of a receptacle develop into macrosporangia; those lower down develop into microsporangia. Both types of sporangia are strictly leptosporangiate in development.[1] Development in the two is alike up to the stage where each has a jacket one cell in thickness, a tapetal layer two cells in thickness, and 32 or 64 young spores (Fig. 201*B–E*). Only one of the spores in a macrosporangium matures. The others disintegrate and contribute to the multinu-

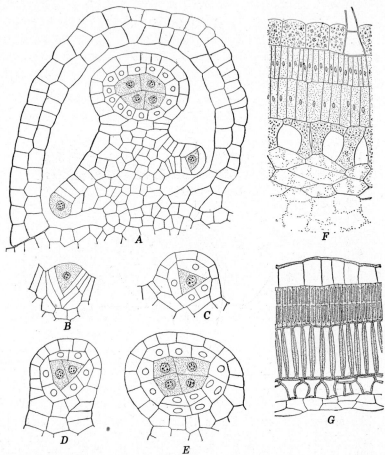

Fig. 201.—*Marsilea vestita* Hook. and Grev. *A*, vertical section of a receptacle and indusium. *B–E*, stages in the development of macrosporangia. *F–G*, transverse sections of young and old walls of sporocarps. (*A–E*, × 485; *F–G*, × 215.)

cleate plasmodium formed from the tapetum. All young spores in a microsporangium generally mature. The jacket layer of macrosporangia and microsporangia is homogeneous in structure and has no indication of an annulus. In another member of the family (*Pilularia*) the arrangement of thin-walled cells at the jacket apex is suggestive of the annulus of the Schizaeaceae.[2] As the sporangia are developing, there is a forma-

[1] Marschall, 1925.   [2] Campbell, 1904.

tion of a stony layer at the outer face of a sporocarp. In *M. vestita*, this begins with a periclinal division in the cell layer immediately beneath the epidermis (Fig. 201*F*). This is followed by an anticlinal division of each cell in the outer layer and a considerable elongation, in the anticlinal plane, of the cells in both layers. There is then a thickening of cell walls in both layers (Fig. 201*G*). Coincident with differentiation of the stony tissue, there is, except for sporangia and indusia, a gelatinization of all cells in the abaxial half of the sporocarp.

The sporocarp is now mature, and the spores capable of development into gametophytes, but it is very probable that under natural conditions sporocarps do not open until two or three years after they are mature. It is also very probable that opening is due to a partial decay of the

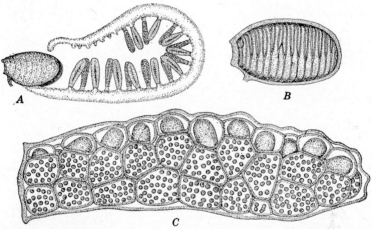

Fig. 202.—*Marsilea vestita* Hook. and Grev. *A*, extrusion of sorophore and receptacles from an opened sporocarp. *B*, empty half of a sporocarp wall, viewed from the concave side. *C*, a receptacle shortly after extrusion from a sporocarp. (*A*, × 2½; *B*, × 6; *C*, × 21.)

stony layer. A long delay in the opening of a sporocarp is immaterial because the spores within it remain viable for 20 to 30 years. The effective protection afforded by the stony layer and the long retention of viability by the spores is strikingly illustrated by the germination of spores from sporocarps that have been stored in 50 per cent alcohol for 20 years. At any time after it is mature, there is an immediate opening of a sporocarp if it is placed in water and a small piece of the stony layer is cut away. Within 15 to 20 minutes the gelatinous material within the sporocarp begins to imbibe water and to swell. This swelling splits the sporocarp wall into two valves. As more water is imbibed, the gelatinized abaxial half of the sporocarp (the *sorophore*) begins to project beyond the sporocarp wall. Since the sori are attached to the sorophore, they are gradually pulled from the sporocarp as the sorophore expands.

A fully expanded sorophore is a long gelatinous tube with a length 15 to 20 times that of the sporocarp (Fig. 202*A*). On either side of an expanded sorophore is a row of sori, alternate with one another. At the tip of a sorophore are a few small mammilate gelatinous projections, also alternate with one another. These are rudimentary sori that failed to develop. The indusia are intact, and the contained sporangia have an evident jacket when the sori are first freed from the sporocarp wall (Fig. 202*C*). There is, however, a gelatinization of the indusia and the

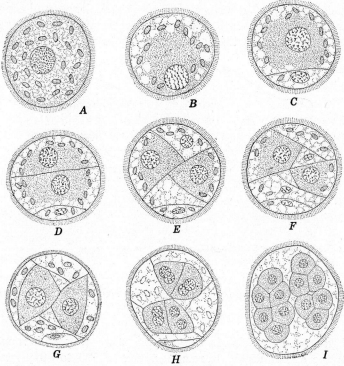

Fig. 203.—Stages in the development of microgametophytes of *Marsilea vestita* Hook. and Grev. (× 485.)

sporangial jackets five to six hours after extrusion. The developing gametophytes generally remain embedded in this watery gelatinous matrix until they are mature.

A microspore is globose in shape with a small pyramidate apex, the result of mutual pressure with sister spores in the tetrad. It has a relatively large, centrally located nucleus and numerous small starch grains scattered throughout the cytoplasm (Fig. 203*A*). Development of a microspore into a fully mature microgametophyte takes but 12 to 20 hours at ordinary room temperature. The first evident change in germination of a spore is a migration of the starch grains to the periphery of the cytoplasm. The nucleus then moves to one side of the spore, generally that opposite the pyramidate apex (Fig. 203*B*). Following a division of the nucleus, there is an asymmetrical division of the spore into a small lenticular cell (the prothallial cell) and a large apical cell (Fig. 203*C*). The apical cell has been described as next cutting off a basal cell,[1] but this is very doubtful, and all the evidence seems to show that it immediately divides into two antheridial initials in a plane diagonal to the prothallial cell (Fig. 203*D*). Both initials then cut off the first jacket cell by means of a curving wall diagonal to the previous plane of division.[2] The jacket cell in each antheridium does not divide again (Fig. 203*E*). The wedge-shaped sister cell divides periclinally into a small inner cell (the second jacket cell) and a large outer cell (Fig. 203*F*). Periclinal division of the outer cell forms the third jacket cell and the primary androgonial cell (Fig. 203*G*). The primary androgonial cell in each antheridium, by four series of simultaneous divisions, forms 16 androcytes (Fig. 203*H–J*). This is accompanied by a disintegration of the prothallial and a partial disintegration of the jacket cells. Metamorphosis of the androcytes into antherozoids is much the same as in other pteridophytes.[2] Up to this point the developing gametophyte is enclosed by the old spore wall. Shortly before the antherozoids are mature, there is a bursting of the spore wall and a protrusion of the antheridia beyond it. The antherozoids are liberated by a separation of the jacket cells from one another. Antherozoids of *Marsilea* differ from those of other ferns in that they have many more coils, sometimes a dozen or more. They are also unusual in that the flagella are only attached to the broad posterior coils.

Macrospores of *Marsilea* are ellipsoidal with a small hemispherical protruberance at the anterior pole (Fig. 204*A*). The spore wall about the protruberant portion is relatively thin and has three radiating ridges. Elsewhere the middle spore-wall layer is much thicker and radially fibrillar. The protruberant anterior portion of the protoplast consists of densely granular cytoplasm and a small lenticular nucleus; the remainder of the protoplast contains numerous large starch grains embedded in a watery cytoplasm. Development of a macrogametophyte to maturity is slightly slower than that of a microgametophyte and takes 14 to 22 hours. At the beginning of spore germination in *M. vestita* Hook. and Grev., there is some increase in the amount of granular cytoplasm at the anterior end, and the nucleus becomes spherical. Two or three hours after the inception of germination, there is a division of the nucleus,[3] and this is soon followed by a transverse cell division along the line of juncture between the densely granular and the watery portions

[1] Belajeff, 1898; Campbell, 1892.   [2] Sharp, 1914.   [3] Campbell, 1892.

of the cytoplasm (Fig. 204*B*). Although there is no further nuclear division in the large cell derived from the watery portion of the protoplast, there is a repeated division of the small cell formed from the papillate portion of the spore. The nature of this latter cell is somewhat doubtful. If it is interpreted as an archegonial initial, it is one unlike that of other pteridophytes since it gives rise to both neck and venter of the single archegonium. It is much more probable that it is an apical cell with

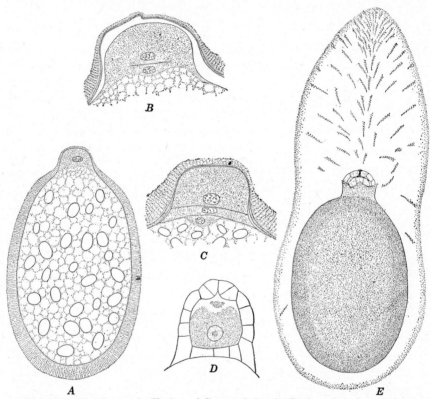

Fig. 204.—*Marsilea vestita* Hook. and Grev. *A*, longitudinal section of a macrospore. *B–D*, stages in the development of sterile tissue and archegonium of a macrogametophyte. *E*, surface view of a mature macrogametophyte with many antherozoids embedded in the surrounding gelatinous envelope. (*A*, × 120; *B–D*, × 215; *E*, × 80.)

four cutting faces, three lateral and one basal, which cuts off a single segment at each face before functioning as an archegonial initial. In *M. vestita* segments are not cut off in a regular sequence by the apical cell. Sometimes the first segment is cut off on the basal face (Fig. 204*C*). At other times, one, two, or three lateral segments are cut off before the basal one. Repeated anticlinal division in all four segments results in a vegetative tissue one cell in thickness. Development of an archegonial initial into an archegonium is the same as in other ferns.[1] It begins with a periclinal division of the initial into a primary cover cell and a central cell. Two successive anticlinal divisions of the primary cover cell form four quadrately arranged neck initials. An oblique division of each neck initial results in a short neck composed of two tiers of four cells each (Fig. 204D). Simultaneous with the development of the neck, there is a division of the central cell into a small lenticular primary canal cell and a large globose primary ventral cell. In some species, including *M. Drummondii* A. Br.,[2] the primary canal cell divides to form two small canal cells. In all species there is a division of the primary ventral cell into a small lenticular ventral canal cell and a large globose egg. The last step in archegonial development is a disintegration of the canal cell (or cells) and ventral canal cell and an opening of the archegonial neck.

A mature macrogametophyte is surrounded by a broad, ovoid, gelatinous envelope in which there is a more watery funnel-shaped portion radial to the archegonium. When gametophytes are grown in the laboratory, hundreds of antherozoids swarm about the archegonial end of the gelatinous envelope surrounding each macrogametophyte. Many of them enter the gelatinous envelope; some reaching the archegonium, others failing to do so. The body of an actively swarming antherozoid is coiled in a conical helix, but, as swarming continues, the spiral becomes laxer and laxer (Fig. 204E). The gelatinous envelope about a macrogametophyte contains many of these laxly coiled antherozoids after swarming ceases.

Embryonal development is generally due to a union of gametes, but it may also be due to parthenogenesis. The demonstration[2] of intact canal and ventral canal cells in archegonia with young embryos proves beyond all doubt that the latter were formed parthenogenetically (Fig. 76G). Because of abnormalities in the reduction divisions, macrospores of parthenogenetic individuals have a diploid number of chromosomes.[2]

Division of the zygote of *M. vestita* takes place two or three hours after fertilization and usually in a vertical plane. Vertical division of the zygote results from the fact that the macrogametophyte lies on its side. The plane of division is affected by gravity, and it has been shown[3] that a zygote may be made to divide transversely by orienting a macrogametophyte so that its long axis stands vertical to the force of gravity. The two daughter cells of a zygote also divide vertically,[4] but in a plane perpendicular to that of the first division. Two sister cells formed by this division develop, respectively, into cotyledon and stem

[1] Campbell, 1892; Strasburger, 1907. [2] Strasburger, 1907. [3] Leitgeb, 1878.
[4] Campbell, 1892.

of an embryo; the other two develop into its foot and root.   The embryo half developing into cotyledon and stem is generally called the anterior (epibasal) half, but there is no justification for this since the macrogametophyte is radially symmetrical and without anterior-posterior differentiation.   Embryonal development beyond the quadrant stage is in the manner typical of leptosporangiate ferns.   Development proceeds with great rapidity in *M. vestita* and embryos three days old consist of many cells (Fig. 205C).   Embryonal development is accompanied by a periclinal division of the adjoining gametophytic cells to form a calyptra two to three cells in thickness and one in which many of the super-

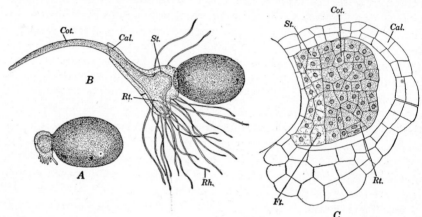

Fig. 205.—*Marsilea vestita* Hook. and Grev.   *A*, surface view of a macrogametophyte with a two-day old sporophyte.   *B*, surface view of a macrogametophyte with a six-day old sporophyte.   *C*, semidiagrammatic vertical section through a young sporophyte. (*Cal.*, calyptra; *Cot.*, cotyledon, *Ft.*, foot; *Rh.*, rhizoids; *Rt.* root; *St.*, stem.)   (*A–B*, × 30; *C*, × 325.)

ficial cells on the side of the calyptra facing the earth send out long rhizoidal projections (Fig. 205A).   All cells of the calyptra, including the rhizoids, contain numerous small chloroplasts.   Growth of the calyptra keeps pace with that of the embryo for the first four or five days; after this the cotyledon and primary root grow at a more rapid rate and burst through the calyptra (Fig. 205B).

FAMILY 9.   POLYPODIACEAE

The Polypodiaceae are the only family in which the sorus is of a mixed type.   The sporangium differs from that of most other ferns in its vertical annulus and its definite stomium in the region of transverse dehiscence.   Antheridia differ from those of most other ferns in that the jacket layer is composed of ring-shaped cells.

In some systems of classification[1] the Polypodiaceae include all genera in which the sporangium has a vertical annulus and a transverse dehiscence. A few genera with this type of sporangium have been shown[2] to have a gradate sorus or one that is not truly of a mixed type. Even when these are removed from the family, there remain some 85 genera (with approximately 2,600 species) in which there is a mixed sorus. Because of the great variation in soral position, soral protection, and vegetative structure, this great assemblage has been held[3] to be one of polyphyletic origin rather than a natural group. If this be true, evolution of a mixed sorus in different phyletic lines has always been accompanied by a shift of the annulus to a vertical position and an evolution of a definite stomium in the sporangium. Such a parallel evolution has also involved the production of a distinctive type of antheridium in the gametophyte generation. Evolution of the same type of sorus, the same type of sporangium, and the same type of antheridium in several different phyletic lines seems to be too remarkable a coincidence. It is much more probable that the Polypodiaceae are monophyletic in origin but subject to considerable variation in many features. The derivation of the family seems to be from the cyatheaceaus group.

The family is a relatively recent one, and there is no satisfactory evidence showing that it existed during the Paleozoic.[4] Most of the fossils referred to the family are known from the Coenozoic. However, there are two or three Jurassic ferns that have a good claim to be included in the Polypodiaceae.[5]

About 36 genera and 209 species of Polypodiaceae are native to the United States.[6] These represent 80 to 90 per cent of all ferns native to this country. Even in Florida, which has a subtropical climate favorable for development of a wide variety of ferns, the polypods outnumber the others three to one.[7]

The bracken fern (*Pteridium*) is widely distributed in the United States. The bracken of the eastern part of this country is *P. latiusculum* (Desv.) Hieron.; that of the region west of the Great Plains is a variety (*pubescens* Underw.) of the European *P. aquilinum* (L.) Kuhn. The brackens are frequently placed in the genus *Pteris* and generally as a single species (*Pteris aquilinum* L.). *Pteridium* differs from *Pteris* in that it has an inconspicuous indusium at the inner face of a sorus. A more conspicuous diagnostic character is the presence of several bundles in a petiole, instead of a single one as in *Pteris*.[8]

Brackens grow in woods, in thickets, and on dry open slopes. The stem grows horizontally and a few centimeters beneath the surface of the

---

[1] Christ, 1897; Diels, 1898.   [2] Bower, 1899, 1910, 1912, 1913.   [3] Bower, 1928.
[4] Seward, 1910.   [5] Hirmer, 1927; Seward, 1910.   [6] Maxon *in litt.*
[7] Small, 1931.   [8] Diels, 1898.

ground (Fig. 206).   It is long and slender, has numerous dichotomous forkings, and is capable of indefinite growth.   When progressive death and decay of older parts of a rhizome extends to a point at which branch-

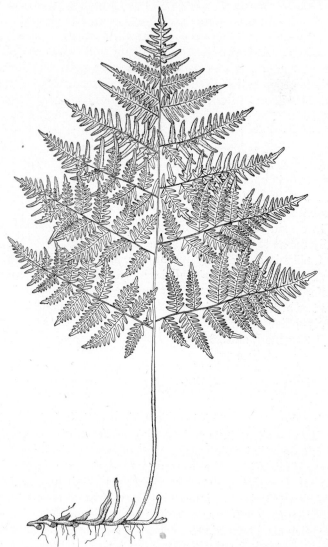

Fig. 206.—Sporophyte of *Pteridium aquilinum* var. *pubescens* Underw.   ($\times \frac{1}{3}$.)

ing has occurred, the two branches continue development as separate plants.   Increase in the number of individuals is generally due to this vegetative multiplication instead of to a formation of new plants by gametic union.   Small, slender, sparingly branched adventitious roots are borne singly at irregular intervals along a rhizome. Leaves are borne alternately on the upper side of a rhizome and separated from one another by long internodes. Leaves of the eastern bracken may attain a height of 2 meters; those of the western bracken may grow to twice this height. The blade and petiole of a leaf are about equal in length. A blade is triangular in outline and generally tripinnately divided in the lower portion. Sporangia are borne in linear sori, abaxial to a transverse vein-like receptacle connecting the ends of the forked veins in a pinnule. The sorus is surrounded by a two-lipped indusium. The conspicuous outer lip is reflexed and overlaps the sorus and its sporangia. The inconspicuous inner lip is a sheet one cell in thickness and lies axillary to the receptacle (Fig. 208*B*).

Unlike most other ferns, the apical cell of a stem (at least in *P. latiusculum*) has two cutting faces that alternately cut off ventral and

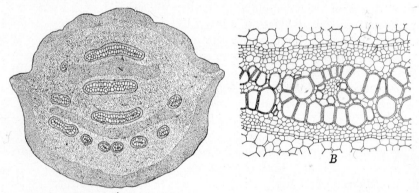

A

Fig. 207.—*Pteridium latiusculum* (Desv.) Hieron. *A*, transverse section of a rhizome. *B*, transverse section of a meristele. (*A*, × 9; *B*, × 65.)

dorsal segments.[1] The first portion of a stem matured from derivatives of an apical cell has a siphonostelic central cylinder.[2] Later-matured portions are polycyclic and have two concentric cylinders of vascular tissue.[3] Different from the polycyclic stele of *Matonia*, the outer cylinder in *Pteridium* is a much-dissected dictyostele (Fig. 207*A*). The inner cylinder is dissected into two more or less arcuate strips. As in most other polycyclic stems, both cylinders contribute to the trace supply departing to a leaf.[3] Meristeles in both the inner and outer cylinders are completely encircled by an endodermal layer (Fig. 207*B*). Internal to the endodermis is a pericyclic layer one to two cells in thickness. Abutting on the inner face of the pericycle is a layer of protophloem, one cell in thickness. It is composed of small sieve tubes and somewhat larger phloem parenchyma cells.[1] The endodermis, pericycle, and proto-

[1] Chang, 1927.   [2] Jeffrey, 1917.   [3] Tansley and Lulham, 1904.

phloem arise from a common mother-cell layer.[1] The innermost portion of the phloem contains large sieve tubes. At the center of the xylem mass are one or two small strands of protoxylem. External to the protoxylem and more or less completely separated from it by small parenchymatous cells are large scalariform elements, the metaxylem. These are generally called tracheids, but they are comparable to vessels since there are no closing membranes in pits on the end walls. The outermost portion of the xylem consists of small parenchymatous cells. The portion of the pith internal to the inner cylinder is wholly parenchymatous; that between outer and inner cylinders is partly parenchymatous and partly sclerenchymatous. The sclerenchymatous portion may more or less completely encircle the inner cylinder (*P. aquilinum*), or it may lie in two strips, one flattened, the other arcuate (*P. latiusculum*). The cortex consists of an inner parenchymatous region encircled by a broad band of sclerenchymatous tissue. The band of sclerenchyma is not continuous. Instead, it is interrupted on either flank by a tongue of parenchyma, continuous with that of the inner cortical region. The parenchymatous portion of the sclerotic band is generally interpreted as an aerating region (pneumatophore).

Adventitious roots are developed from an apical cell differentiated in the mother-cell layer giving rise to endodermis and pericycle.[1] This cell is of the usual pyramidal type found in roots. The stele in mature portions of a root is generally diarch.

Primordia of leaves are formed close to the growing point of a rhizome. Growth of embryonic leaves is at a slow rate, and in most cases they do not unfold until two years after their inception. During the first year there is the formation of an embryonic petiole, that becomes 2 to 4 cm. long. During the second year there is the formation of an embryonic, spirally coiled blade at the apex of the petiole. At the beginning of the third year, elongation of the petiole pushes the coiled upper portion through the soil, and the rapidly elongating above-ground portion then uncoils from base to apex.

Petioles of mature leaves have several vascular bundles. Pinnules of the blade (Fig. 208*B*) have a structure resembling that of a dicotyledonous leaf blade. Just beneath the upper epidermis is a palisade layer, one to three cells in thickness. Below this is a spongy parenchyma with conspicuous intercellular spaces. Stomata are present in the lower epidermis only.

The position and general appearance of a sorus have been described above. Sori are strictly marginal in origin (Fig. 208*A*), and the outer and inner indusial flaps arise lateral to a very young receptacle.[2] Most sori (Fig. 208*B*) are of the mixed type, but those on certain pinnules may

---

[1] Chang, 1927.   [2] Bower, 1918.

show a tendency toward a basipetalous gradate organization. Stalk and capsule of a sporangium are derived from a single initial, a superficial cell of the receptacle. Development of a sporangium is strictly leptosporangiate. After elongating somewhat above the surface of the receptacle, the sporangial initial divides transversely into an inner and an outer cell. The inner cell may or may not divide. In either case, it or its daughter cells eventually become indistinguishable from other cells of the receptacle. The outer cell, by three successive diagonal divisions, gives rise to a pyramidal apical cell that cuts off four to five segments from each of its three lateral cutting faces (Fig. 209*A–B*).

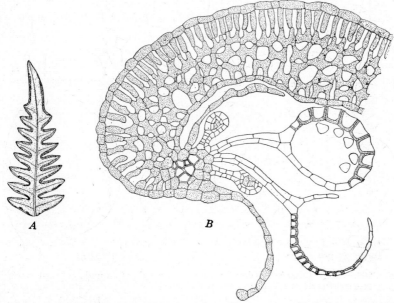

Fig. 208.—*Pteridium aquilinum* var. *pubescens* Underw. *A*, a fertile pinna. *B*, semi-diagrammatic transverse section of a pinnule and sorus. (*A*, × 1½; *B*, × 160.)

The last three segments cut off contribute to the sporangial jacket; those cut off previously go to form the stalk. After this the apical cell divides periclinally into a flat outer cell (a jacket initial) and an inner pyramidal cell, the archesporial cell (Fig. 209*C*). This latter cell functions as an internal apical cell that successively cuts off a tabular tapetal initial from each of its four cutting faces (Fig. 209*D*). By anticlinal and periclinal division the tapetal initials develop into a tapetal layer two cells in thickness (Fig. 209*F–G*). The cell remaining after cutting off of the tapetal initials is the primary sporogenous cell. Theoretically, this undergoes four successive divisions to form 16 spore mother cells. Sometimes, either because of an abortion of certain spore mother cells or a failure to form a full complement of them, there is not the expected output of 64 spores.[1] Meanwhile there has been an anticlinal division and redivision of the four jacket initials. In the case of certain other Polypodiaceae[2] it has been shown that the last-formed initial develops into the upper half of the sporangial jacket and the other three initials into the lower half (Fig. 209*H–I*). Development of each initial into a portion of the jacket is according to a regular, although complicated, succession. The sequence of division is such that

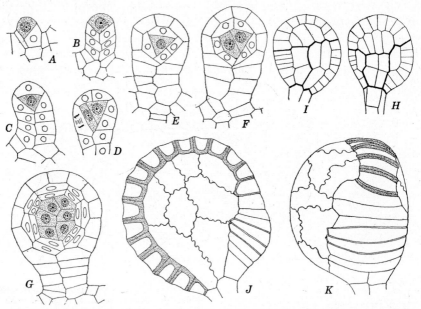

Fig. 209.—*A–G*, stages in the development of sporangia of an undetermined species of *Pteris*. *H–I*, diagrams of a jacket of a young sporangium of *Aspidium filix-mas* in which the portion derived from each of the four jacket initials is outlined with a heavy line. *J–K*, side and front surface views of mature sporangia of *Pteridium aquilinum* var. *pubescens* Underw. (*H–I*, based on *Müller*, 1893.) (*A–G*, × 325; *J–K*, × 215.)

the two flattened faces of the jacket layer have a different cellular arrangement. The annulus is a vertical row of cells that starts at the sporangial base and encircles about three-fourths of the sporangium. It is derived in part from the first initial and in part from the fourth. Immediately below the free end of the annulus and derived from the third initial is a vertical strip of four cells that develops into the stomium. Mature stomial cells are thin-walled; mature cells of the annulus have a thickening of their radial and inner tangential walls (Fig. 209*J–K*).

Similar to other Polypodiaceae, the spores of *Pteridium* remain viable for some time after they are shed. Spores of many Polypodiaceae

[1] Bower, 1899.   [2] Müller, 1893.

may remain viable for more than a year. The longest well-authenticated record for the retention of viability is the germination of spores of *Asplenium Serra* Langsd.-Fisch. from herbarium material 48 years old.[1] It is very probable that under natural conditions the spores of *Pteridium aquilinum* L. do not germinate until the spring after they are shed,[2] but spores of other Polypodiaceae may develop into gametophytes in the same year they are shed   Such gametophytes may produce embryos in the fall or in the following spring.

Germination of a *Pteridium* spore begins with a rupture of the two outer spore-wall layers, at the pyramidate pole, and a protrusion of the protoplast, still surrounded by the innermost wall layer.   The protruding portion cuts off a small colorless cell that elongates to form the first rhizoid.   The large green sister cell develops into a filament three to

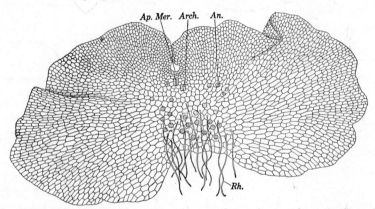

Fig. 210.—Ventral view of a mature gametophyte of an undetermined species of *Nephrolepis*.   (*An.*, antheridium; *Ap. Mer.*, apical meristem; *Arch.*, archegonium; *Rh.* rhizoid.)   (× 17.)

six cells in length. The terminal cell of a filament, by two obliquely vertical divisions, gives rise to an apical cell that alternately cuts off segments right and left.[2]   The other cells of a filament usually do not divide again.   Division and redivision of segments cut off from the apical cell result in a plate-like sheet, one cell in thickness.   If conditions for growth are favorable and it is not crowded by neighboring ones, a young gametophyte gradually becomes heart-shaped because of a more rapid growth of portions lateral to the growing apex.   Sooner or later the apical cell is replaced by a group of apical initials.   Eventually the gametophyte becomes like that of other Polypodiaceae and more than one cell in thickness in the region posterior to the apical notch (Fig. 210).   Gametophytes growing under unfavorable conditions may develop into branched filaments or into irregularly branched straps.

[1] Fischer, 1911.   [2] Lagerberg, 1906.

Such gametophytes produce antheridia only. However, if they are transferred to a favorable environment, the subsequently developed portion is cordate and bears both archegonia and antheridia.

Antheridial development in *Pteridium*[1] is the same as in other Polypodiaceae.[2] An antheridial initial originates as a papillate protrusion from a vegetative cell. The protruding portion soon becomes cut off by a transverse wall. The antheridial initial thus formed looks like a very young rhizoid, but may be distinguished from it on account of its greater breadth. The first division of an initial is by means of a funnel-shaped, diagonally vertical, wall. The lower margin of a

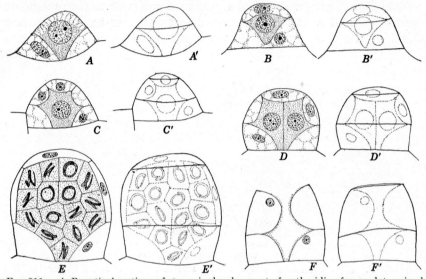

Fig. 211.—*A–F*, optical sections of stages in development of antheridia of an undetermined species of *Nephrolepis*. *A'–F'*, surface views of the same antheridia. (× 650.)

"funnel wall" generally intersects the transverse wall at the base of an initial, but sometimes it does not do so. The peripheral cell, which completely encircles its sister cell, is a jacket cell known as the "first ring cell" (Fig. 211*A–A'*). This cell does not divide again. Its sister cell divides, by means of a periclinal curved wall, into the dome cell and the primary androgonial cell (Fig. 211*B–B'*). The dome cell elongates somewhat and then divides anticlinally by means of a funnel wall. One daughter cell is the "second ring cell" of the antheridial jacket, the other is the cap cell (Fig. 211*C–C'*). In most Polypodiaceae there is no division of the cap cell. In a few cases[3] it divides into two daughter cells. Meanwhile the primary androgonial cell has divided and redivided to form 30 to 50 androcytes. An antheridium is fully mature after

[1] Lagerberg, 1906.   [2] Atkinson, 1894; Campbell, 1905; Strasburger, 1869.
[3] Hartmann, 1931.

metamorphosis of the androcytes into antherozoids has been completed (Fig. 211*D–E*, *D'–É'*). A mature antheridium has a jacket layer composed of two ring cells and either one or two cap cells. It contains 30 to 50 spirally coiled antherozoids, each with 20 to 30 flagella in the anterior portion.

An abundant supply of moisture is an essential condition for the opening of ripe antheridia. Intake of water results in a considerable swelling of the jacket cells, and the resultant pressure causes a lid-like tilting or a shedding of the cap cell (Fig. 211*F–F'*). If an antheridium has two cap cells, there is a tilting or shedding of only one of them.[1]

The formation of archegonia is restricted to the portion of a gametophyte immediately posterior to the apical notch. Archegonial develop-

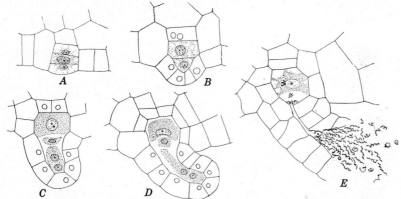

FIG. 212.—Stages in the development of archegonia of *Onoclea sensibilis* L. The thallus apex is towards the left. (× 325.)

ment in *Pteridium*[2] and other Polypodiaceae[3] is not markedly different from that in other Filicales. An initial cell gives rise to a basal cell, a central cell, and a primary cover cell (Fig. 212*A*). The primary cover cell divides to form four neck initials, and from these is developed a neck five to seven cells in height (Fig. 212*B–D*). The neck of an archegonium, unlike that in most other ferns, is strongly curved toward the posterior end of the gametophyte. The central cell gives rise to a binucleate primary canal cell, a ventral canal cell, and an egg (Fig. 212*C–D*). The canal and ventral canal cells disintegrate into a gelatinous mass that is partially extruded when the neck opens by a spreading apart and dissociation of its uppermost cells.

Free-swimming antherozoids respond positively to certain chemotactic stimuli,[4] and entrance of antherozoids into an archegonium is undoubtedly

[1] Hartmann, 1931.   [2] Lagerberg, 1906.
[3] Atkinson, 1894; Campbell, 1905; Yamanouchi, 1908.
[4] Pfeffer, 1884; Shibata, 1911.

due to a chemotactic response. Many antherozoids frequently enter the gelatinous mass protruding from the archegonial neck (Fig. 212*E*). Several antherozoids may reach the base of a neck, but usually only one of them enters the egg.[1]

The development of the embryo (Fig. 213) is much the same from genus to genus among the Polypodiaceae. In *Gymnogramme sulphurea* Desv.[2] the young zygote enlarges somewhat and secretes a cell wall. Following this it divides vertically and in a plane perpendicular to the long axis of the gametophyte. The daughter cell toward the apex of the

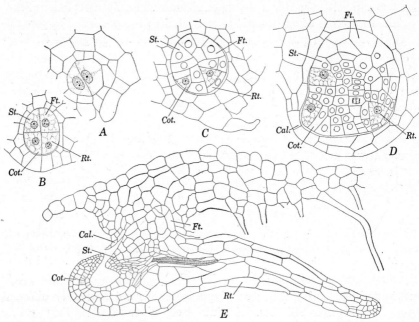

Fig. 213.—*Onoclea sensibilis* L.   *A–D*, stages in the development of embryos.   *E*, a young sporophyte after bursting through the calyptra.   (*Cal.*, calyptra; *Cot.*, cotyledon; *Ft.*, foot; *Rt.*, root; *St.*, stem.)   (*A–D*, × 215; *E*, × 80.)

gametophyte is the anterior or epibasal cell, its sister is the posterior or hypobasal cell, and the wall separating them is often called the basal wall. These two cells divide vertically in a plane perpendicular to the basal wall. The two new walls thus formed constitute the median wall of an embryo. Each of the four cells next divides transversely. The four organs of a young sporophyte (cotyledon, primary root, stem, and foot) may each be referred to a definite portion of the eight-celled embryo. The two epibasal cells nearest the archegonial neck produce the cotyledon, and the two other epibasal cells produce the stem. The two hypobasal cells nearest the archegonial neck produce the primary root, and the two

[1] Shaw, 1898; Yamanouchi, 1908.   [2] Vladesco, 1935.

remaining hypobasal cells give rise to the foot. There is an approximately simultaneous division of each cell of the octant stage and a similar division in the 16-celled stage. The apical cells of cotyledon and primary root are first definitely recognizable at the 32-celled stage. After the 32-celled stage there is not a simultaneous division of cells in each quadrant, and those of the cotyledonary and root quadrants divide more rapidly than those of other quadrants. For a while enlargement of an embryo is accompanied by a compensatory enlargement of the surrounding archegonium. Eventually, however, enlargement of cotyledon and primary root ruptures the ensheathing archegonial tissue. After this the cotyledon grows outward and forward beneath the gametophyte and then grows upward through the apical notch. The primary root also grows transversely for a time, but it soon bends downward and grows into the soil. The stem portion of a young sporophyte begins the formation of leaves soon after the cotyledon is fully unfolded. Young sporophytes of *Pteridium* may develop six or more leaves during the first year.[1] These are simpler in structure than are leaves produced during the second and succeeding years. A gametophyte persists until a young sporophyte has two or more leaves, but the gametophyte does not appear to contribute much to the nutrition of a sporophyte after the cotyledon is fully expanded.

FAMILY 10. PARKERIACEAE

The Parkeriaceae are the only aquatic, homosporous, leptosporangiate ferns. The sporangia are borne singly on the abaxial face of the leaf blade.

There is but one genus, *Ceratopteris*. There are those[2] who argue that there is no justification for a separation of it from the polypodiaceous series. *Ceratopteris* is undoubtedly related to the polypodiaceous ferns. However, the sporangial characters and the antheridial structure are so distinctive that there is ample warranty for following those[3] who separate it from the Polypodiaceae.

Ceratopteris is hydrophytic in habit and of world-wide distribution throughout tropical and subtropical regions. Sometimes it grows on damp soil, but generally it is a true aquatic, either free-floating or rooted in the mud. It grows in running or quiet, fresh or brackish water and from sea level to an altitude of 600 meters. There are four species.[4] Two of these, *C. pteridioides* (Hook.) Hieron. and *C. deltoidea* Benedict are found in Florida and along the Gulf Coast.[5]

The sporophyte is an annual. New sporophytes may develop as a result of gametic union or may develop from adventitious buds persisting

---

[1] Lagerberg, 1906.   [2] Bower, 1928.   [3] Christ, 1897; Diels, 1898.
[4] Benedict, 1909.   [5] Small, 1931.

from leaves of plants of the previous year.   A sporophyte has a short prostrate or erect stem (Fig. 214).   The leaves, which are of two kinds, are borne alternately on a stem.   The sterile leaves are erect or spreading and have a broad, two- to four-times divided, pinnate or trifoliate blade. Petioles of plants rooted in mud run horizontally for a short distance and then bend abruptly upward; those of free-floating plants do not have this elbow-like bending in the lower portion.   At the base of the petiole of each sterile leaf is a complete or incomplete whorl of adventitious roots.   Fertile leaves are always taller than sterile ones and two

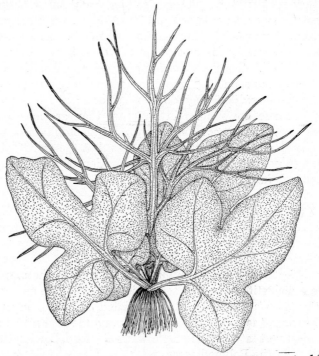

FIG. 214.—Sporophyte of *Ceratopteris pterioides* (Hook.) Hieron.   (× ⅓.)

to five times divided into narrow strap-like segments.   The sporangia are subsessile and lie in one or two rows parallel to, and some distance inward from, the margin of a segment.   According to the species,[1] a sporangium has a vertical annulus of 4 to 10 cells that causes an irregular dehiscence or a vertical annulus of 20 to 70 cells that causes a transverse dehiscence (Fig. 215C).   Sporangia of one species contain 16 spores, those of other species contain 32.

The small stem of *Ceratopteris* is fleshy in texture.   The first-formed portion of it has a protostelic central cylinder.[2]   Above this there is a

[1] Benedict, 1909.   [2] Ford, 1902.

dictyostelic siphonostele. Later-formed portions of a stem may have medullary vascular strands that are connected with the trace supply of leaves.[1] It is very probable that such portions of a stem have a polycyclic organization more or less like that in *Cyathea* (page 322). Meristeles in stem of *Ceratopteris* are each surrounded by an endodermal layer[2] that appears to have originated from the same mother-cell layer as the pericycle internal to it.

Adventitious roots arise endogenously from the endodermal layer of a leaf bundle.[2] Roots of *Ceratopteris* are similar in structure to those of *Schizaea* (page 297) and *Azolla* (page 355). The pericycle, endodermis, and innermost cortical layer are each six cells in perimeter, and the three arise from a common mother-cell layer. The cortex also resembles that of *Azolla* in its six intercellular spaces.

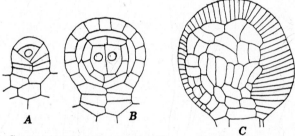

Fig. 215.—*Ceratopteris pterioides* (Hook.) Hieron. *A–B*, vertical sections of young sporangia. *C*, surface view of an older sporangium. (*After Kny*, 1875.) (*A–B*, × 200; *C*, × 100.)

Sporangial initials are differentiated some distance inward from a leaf margin.[1] Sporangial development is strictly leptosporangiate.[3] An initial first cuts off three to four stalk cells from each of its three cutting faces.[4] Unlike most other ferns there is no subsequent elongation of these stalk cells. Development of a capsule[5] takes place in the usual manner and has a formation of a tapetum two cells in thickness (Fig. 215*A*–*B*). The archesporial cell may give rise to four or eight spore mother cells.

Spore germination begins with a rupture of the outer spore-wall layer and a protrusion of the protoplast, still surrounded by the inner spore-wall layer. There is next a formation of one or two rhizoids.[3] Following this there may or may not be an immediate differentiation of an apical cell (Fig. 216*A*). In the latter case a gametophyte may even develop to a stage where it bears antheridia without establishing an apical cell. There is a strong dimorphic tendency among gametophytes of *Ceratopteris*. Certain of them tend to remain small and produce numerous antheridia

[1] Bower, 1928.   [2] Ford, 1902.   [3] Kny, 1875.   [4] Bower, 1928; Kny, 1875.
[5] Ford, 1902; Kny, 1875.

along their margins (Fig. 216*B*).   Others tend to be relatively large and produce both kinds of sex organs (Fig. 216*C*).   Gametophytes of the first type are spatulate in outline, those of the second are more or less cordate.   In some cases the cordate outline results from a more rapid growth of wings lateral to the apical region, in other cases it results from a production of one or two lateral adventitious outgrowths.[1]

Usually antheridia are formed only from marginal cells of a gametophyte.[1]   Antheridia of *Ceratopteris* (Fig. 216*D–E*) differ from those of

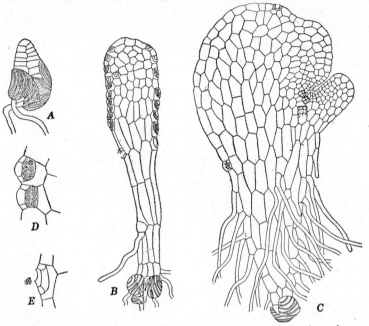

Fig. 216.—*Ceratopteris pterioides* (Hook.) Hieron.   *A*, germination of spore.   *B*, gametophyte with antheridia.   *C*, gametophyte with antheridia and archegonia.   *D–E*, antheridia.   (*After Kny*, 1875.)   (*A*, × 75; *B*, × 40; *C*, × 50; *D–E*, × 160.)

other Leptosporangiatae in that they are embedded.[2]   These antheridia are not of the embedded type found in the Eusporangiatae.   Instead, they appear to be a modification of the polypodiaceous type and one in which the initial cell divides transversely in a plane below the surface of the gametophyte, not flush with it.

The meager observations on embryonal development[1] seem to show that it is of the usual leptosporangiate type.

[1] Kny, 1875.

[2] The embedded antheridia found in gametophytes of certain Leptosporangiatae (Black, 1909; Pfeiffer, Norma E., 1912; Ferguson, 1911) are really combined antheridia and archegonia.   There is a strong presumption that gametophytes with these abnormal sex organs only produce sporophytes apogamously.

FAMILY 11. SALVINIACEAE

The Salviniaceae are to be distinguished from all other Leptosporangiatae but the Marsiliaceae by their heterospory. They differ from the Marsiliaceae in the indusial nature of the sporocarp wall and in the fact that a sporocarp contains only microsporangia or only macrosporangia.

The mode of sporangial development shows that the family is to be referred to the Leptosporangiatae. Adaptation of the plant body to a free-floating habit has resulted in such specialization that structural relationships with other ferns have been obscured, and enclosure of the sporangia within a sporocarp has obliterated one of the most distinctive phylogenetic indices, the annulus. The indusial nature of the sporocarp wall and the elevated receptacle on which the sporangia are borne have

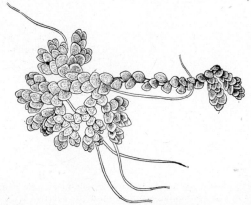

Fig. 217.—Sporophyte of *Azolla filiculoides* Lam. (× 4.)

been cited to show a relationship to the Hymenophyllaceae.[1] The gradate basipetalous receptacle of a microsporocarp also seems to be like the receptacle of Hymenophyllaceae, but the history of its development shows that it is dissimilar since the whole receptacle in the Salviniaceae is derived from a single sporangial initial. Because of this, it is better to consider the Salviniaceae a family of uncertain position among the Leptosporangiatae.

The family includes two living genera: *Salvinia*, with 13 species, and *Azolla*, with five species. *Salvinia* has at least one species native to the United States. *Azolla*, which occurs westward and southward of Lake Ontario, has two species native to this country; *A. caroliniana* Willd. in the East and *A. filiculoides* Lam. in the West. Several fossil species of *Salvinia* have been found in horizons from the middle of the Early Coenozoic (Miocene) onward.[2]

[1] Bower, 1928; Campbell, 1918.   [2] Hirmer, 1927; Seward, 1910.

Sporophytes of *Azolla* (Fig. 217) resemble gametophytes of leafy Jungermanniales. They grow free-floating on the surface of permanent pools and backwaters of sluggish streams. Repeated vegetative multiplication by progressive growth and death and by abscission of lateral branches often results in a carpet of plantlets dense enough to conceal the water. Such free-floating masses of *Azolla* can frequently be recognized from a considerable distance because of their distinctive reddish color.

The pinnately branched, horizontally floating stem bears a long adventitious root here and there along the under side. A stem and its branches are densely clothed with small, alternately arranged, overlapping leaves. Each leaf is divided into two lobes of approximately equal size. The thick upper (dorsal) lobe is aerial and green; the thin lower (ventral) lobe is submerged and nearly colorless. It is thought that intake of water is through the ventral leaf lobes rather than through the roots. The

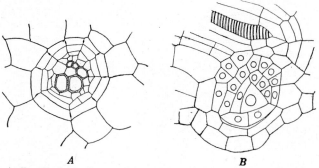

A   B

Fig. 218.—*Azolla filiculoides* Lam. *A*, transverse section of stele of a stem. *B*, longitudinal section of a stem containing a primordium of a root. (*A*, × 325; *B*, × 650.)

space enclosed by an overarching of juvenile leaves at each branch apex always contains a blue-green alga, *Anabaena Azollae* Strasb. One or more hormogones of the imprisoned *Anabaena* always move into a special chamber formed within the dorsal lobe of a young leaf. The alga multiplies within the chamber and persists within it as long as a leaf remains alive. The relationship between alga and host is not merely that of a space parasitism. Experiments[1] seem to show that there is a true symbiosis in which the *Anabaena* fixes free nitrogen for the host. The universal occurrence of the same species of *Anabaena* within *Azolla* indicates that dispersal of the latter is effected by a transportation of vegetative portions rather than by a dissemination of spores. It is very probable that aquatic birds are the chief agency in dispersing the *Azolla*.

Growth of a stem is by means of a three-sided apical cell that successively cuts off a segment from each cutting face. The embryonic region of a stem is upwardly recurved. The mature region, which is close

[1] Oes, 1913.

to the growing point, has a small central cylinder. In *A. filiculoides* Lam. it is impossible to draw a sharp distinction between central cylinder and cortex because the pericycle, endodermis, and innermost cortical layer are derived from a common mother-cell layer. The endodermal and pericyclic layers are each one cell in thickness and nine cells in perimeter (Fig. 218*A*). When seen in transverse section, the region internal to the pericycle contains about six xylem elements and about twice as many phloem elements. The central cylinder seems to be protostelic in organization, but adaptation to an aquatic life has been accompanied by so great a reduction of the vascular tissues that it is impossible to determine this with certainty. The cortical region is five to eight cells in thickness and composed of thin-walled parenchymatous cells without intercellular spaces.

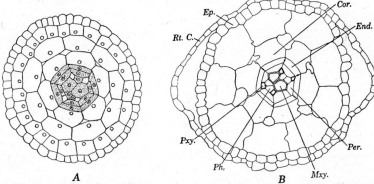

A   *B*

Fig. 219.—*Azolla filiculoides* Lam. Transverse sections through immature and mature portions of a root. (*Cor.*, cortex; *End.*, endodermis; *Ep.*, epidermis; *Mxy.*, metaxylem; *Per.*, pericycle; *Ph.*, phloem; *Pxy.*, protoxylem; *Rt. C.*, root cap.) (× 325.)

Each adventitious root is formed from a single cell of the mother layer giving rise to pericycle, endodermis, and innermost cortical layer. This cell soon gives rise to a pyramidal apical cell with four cutting faces, one toward the outer side and three lateral (Fig. 218*B*). Segments from the external face contribute to a root cap that ensheaths tissues of the root proper long after they are mature. Eventually, however, older tannin-filled portions of the cap are sloughed off. Segments cut off from the three lateral faces of an apical cell contribute to the remainder of the root. As seen in transverse section, tissues of maturing (Fig. 219*A*) and mature regions (Fig. 219*B*) in roots of *A. filiculoides* Lam. are diagrammatically arranged. At the outside is an epidermal layer of many cells. Internal to this are two layers of cortical cells; the outer with nine cells, the inner with six. Successively within the inner cortical layer and derived from the same mother-cell layer are a six-celled endodermal layer and a six-celled pericyclic layer. Two pericyclic cells opposite each other divide anticlinally, and one daughter cell in each pair matures into a protoxylem element. Two other protoxylem elements are also matured from cells internal to the pericycle. In addition to these four protoxylem elements a mature central cylinder has two large metaxylem elements and four phloem ones. Root hairs are not formed until a root has attained about half its ultimate length. They are formed in transverse belts and from embryonic epidermal cells near the growing point that are still ensheathed by the root cap. The embryonic epidermal cell divides diagonally into two daughter cells, one of which matures into a root hair, the other into an ordinary epidermal cell. As long as growth continues there is a formation of root hairs just back of the growing point. After the apical cell

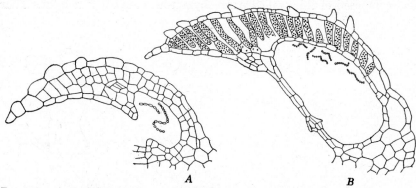

A   *B*

Fig. 220.—*Azolla filiculoides* Lam. Longitudinal sections through the dorsal lobe of an immature and a mature leaf. (*A*, × 215; *B*, × 80.)

ceases to function, it may divide into a number of cells each of which elongates into a root hair.[1]

A young leaf soon becomes differentiated into a dorsal and a ventral lobe. The distal half of a mature ventral lobe is one cell in thickness; the proximal half is more than one cell in thickness and has a single layer of large chambers. This portion of the ventral lobe may contain a few chloroplasts. Early in development of the dorsal lobe, there is the formation of a cavity on the adaxial face and near the leaf base (Fig. 220*A*). The cavity opens externally by a large circular pore. One or more hormogones of *Anabaena* migrate into this cavity and eventually become permanently imprisoned within it by a development of proliferous outgrowths from the margin of the pore. A mature dorsal lobe (Fig. 220*B*) has an upper and a lower epidermis, the former with numerous one- or two-celled hairs. Except for a small vein, the remaining tissue is a palisade parenchyma with large intercellular spaces.

Only the lowermost leaf of a branch is fertile. According to the species this forms two or four sporocarps in the axil of the dorsal lobe.[2]

[1] Leavitt, 1902.   [2] Strasburger, 1873.

In the youngest stage at which a sporocarp can be recognized, there is a macrosporangial initial that has cut off one or two stalk segments at its inner face.[1] At the same time a ring of cells, the beginning of the indusium, is recognizable at the base of the young stalk (Fig. 221*A*). Development of an indusium is more rapid than that of a sporangium, and it soon becomes a cup-like sheath, two cells in thickness, that projects beyond the developing sporangium. Indusia overarching sporangia

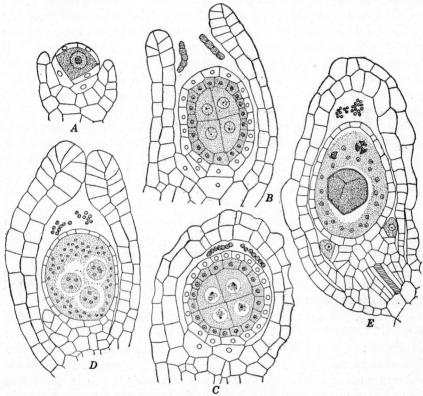

Fig. 221.—*Azolla filiculoides* Lam. Stages in the development of macrosporangia and the surrounding sporocarp wall (indusium). (*A–C*, × 650; *D–E*, × 325.)

always contain one or more hormogones of *Anabaena*. Eventually the opening at the distal end of an indusial cup becomes closed by an approximation of the free margins (Fig. 221*B*, *D*). Development of the macrosporangial initial into a macrosporangium (Fig. 221*B–E*) takes place in a typically leptosporangiate manner.[2] A macrosporangium has a tapetal layer one cell in thickness and eight macrospore mother cells. During meiosis the tapetum breaks down into a multinucleate plasmodium in

[1] Pfeiffer, Wanda M., 1907.   [2] Campbell, 1893; Pfeiffer, Wanda M., 1907.

which the number of nuclei may continue to increase. Each of the 32 young macrospores forms a thin spore wall.

One conspicuous difference between development of this macrosporangium and sporangia of other Leptosporangiatae is the repeated division of the stalk cells to form a massive columnar stalk. An even more striking difference is the functioning of certain superficial stalk cells as initials of additional sporangia (Fig. 221*E*). Sporangial initials differentiated in stalks of macrosporangia are always microsporangial.

Irrespective of their nature, all sporocarps have a similar ontogeny up to this stage of development. Their subsequent history depends upon the behavior of the macrosporangium. One young macrospore in a macrosporangium may begin enlargement to form a functional macrospore (Fig. 221*E*). In such a case there is no further development of the juvenile microsporangia below the macrosporangium. Enlargement of the functional macrospore is accompanied by a formation of four quadrately arranged alveolar bodies (*massulae*) by the plasmodial tapetum. The functional macrospore lies in the large massula at the base of a sporangium. The three massulae in the upper portion may contain one or more small nonfunctional macrospores. When the macrospore is mature, there is a transverse rupture of the surrounding macrosporangium and indusium. The distal portion of indusium and macrosporangium, as well as the three massulae with nonfunctional spores, remain attached to the massula containing the macrospore (Fig. 223*A*). The portions attached to the macrospore and its massula have been called the "swimming apparatus"[1] because they were thought to be filled with air and thus to give buoyancy. Repeated observations on ripe spores after indusial rupture shows that they never float but always sink.[2]

A macrosporangium may have a disintegration of all spores within it instead of a development of one of them into a functional macrospore.[3] When this takes place, the microsporangial initials on its stalk develop into mature microsporangia and additional microsporangial initials are differentiated in basipetalous succession (Fig. 222*A*). Thus, depending on the fate of the macrosporangium, all sporocarps on a leaf may be macrosporocarps, all may be microsporocarps, or there may be both kinds. Development of microsporangia is leptosporangiate and has the formation of a long narrow stalk (Fig. 222*B–D*, *G*). Similar to a macrosporangium there are eight spore mother cells and a tapetal layer one cell in thickness. There is also a breaking down of the tapetum into a multinucleate plasmodium during meiosis (Fig. 222*C*). All 32 microspores are functional. When first formed, they are evenly distributed throughout the plasmodium; later on they move to the periphery of the plasmodium (Fig.

---

[1] Strasburger, 1873. [2] Campbell, 1893.
[3] Goebel, 1905; Pfeiffer, Wanda M., 1907; Strasburger, 1889.

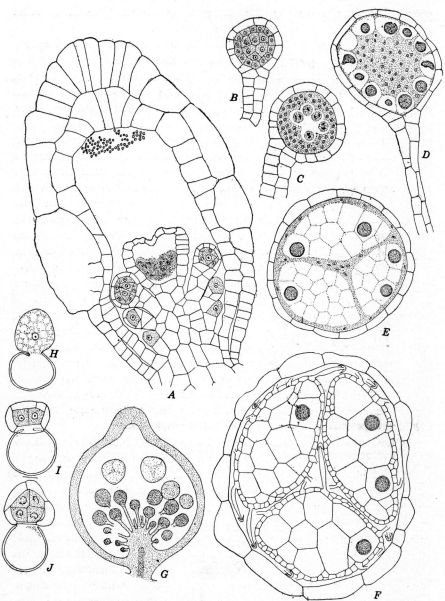

FIG. 222.—*Azolla filiculoides* Lam. *A*, longitudinal section of a young microsporangial sporocarp. *B*, microsporangium at a late stage in development of sporogenous tissue. *C–F*, stages in the development of massulae within microsporangia. *G*, longitudinal section of a nearly mature sporocarp. *H–J*, stages in development of microgametophytes. (*A–F*, × 325; *G*, × 60; *H–J*, × 650.)

222*D*). Following this, the plasmodium gives rise to four or more quadrately arranged alveolar massulae, each of which contains several microspores embedded in the peripheral portion (Fig. 222*E*). Massulae of species belonging to the section *Euazolla*, which includes *A. filiculoides* Lam., develop numerous elongate hooked processes (*glochidia*) on their surfaces (Fig. 222*F*). Massulae of species belonging to the section *Rhizosperma* lack glochidia. When a microsporocarp is ripe, there is a breaking of the indusium and a rupture of each sporangial jacket. The liberated massulae float away. In the case of *A. filiculoides* several microsporic massulae may become attached to a macrosporic massula by means of their glochidia (Fig. 223*B*). Neither macrospore nor microspore has begun development into a gametophyte at the time this attachment takes place.

A microspore remains embedded within a massula during the entire course of its development into a gametophyte. The time interval between spore germination and full development of a microgametophyte is much the same as with a macrogametophyte, that is, a week or so. Germination begins with a bursting of the outer spore-wall layer and a protrusion of the cytoplasm and nucleus, still surrounded by the inner wall layer (Fig. 222*H*). The protruberant portion becomes the single antheridial initial by formation of a cross wall near the apex of the spore cavity.[1] The large vegetative cell within the spore cavity cuts off a small lenticular cell and then divides no further.[2] The antheridial initial develops into an antheridium with eight androcytes and a jacket layer of a few cells (Fig. 222*I–J*). It is very probable that the mature antherozoids escape from the surrounding massula by a gelatinization of the latter.

Development of a macrospore into a mature gametophyte takes about a week.[1] The first indication of germination is an increase in size of the macrospore nucleus. Following a division of the nucleus there is a cutting off of a small lenticular cell at the upper end of the macrospore. The large sister cell, which contains numerous starch grains, does not divide again, but it does become multinucleate. The lenticular cell divides vertically into two daughter cells of unequal size.[1] The larger of these may divide either vertically or horizontally. In either case the young macrogametophyte soon becomes a lenticular disk two cells in thickness (Fig. 223*B*). It is at this stage that one of the median cells in the upper layer functions as the first archegonial initial. Up to this time the macrospore wall has remained intact. Shortly after this, it ruptures, and the developing gametophyte protrudes through the opening. The macrogametophyte eventually becomes a protruberant hemispherical mass five to eight cells in thickness. At first it has but one archegonium,

[1] Campbell, 1893.   [2] Belajeff, 1898; Campbell, 1893.

that formed from the first initial. If there is no fertilization of the egg in this archegonium, additional archegonial initials are differentiated lateral to it. If these fail to function, further archegonia are produced until a dozen or more have been formed (Fig. 223C). Archegonial development is much the same as in other ferns. An initial divides periclinally into a central cell and a primary cover cell (Fig. 224A). Two successive anti-clinal divisions of the cover cell produce four quadrately arranged neck initials (Fig. 224B). The neck initials, by oblique and transverse division,

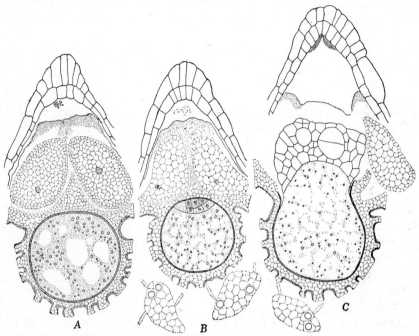

Fig. 223.—*Azolla filiculoides* Lam. *A*, macrospore within a massula and adjoined by other macrosporangial massulae and the apical portion of the indusium. *B*, an early stage in the development of a macrogametophyte. *C*, a mature macrogametophyte within a two-celled embryo. In *B* and *C* microsporic massulae are attached to a macrosporic massula by their glochidia. (× 160.)

give rise to a short neck three to four cells in height. Meanwhile, there has been a division of the central cell into a small lenticular primary canal cell and a large primary ventral cell (Fig. 224D). The primary canal cell pushes up into the developing neck. It may remain undivided or may divide to form two neck cells (Fig. 224E). Sometimes the primary ventral cell divides into a small lenticular ventral canal cell and a large egg.[1] In other cases it appears to function directly as the egg. Opening of the archegonium probably takes place in the usual manner.

[1] Campbell, 1893.

A zygote of *Azolla* elongates vertically and then divides transversely (Fig. 224*F*).   Each daughter cell then divides in a plane perpendicular to that of the preceding division.[1]   As in most other Leptosporangiatae, each of the four parts of an embryo can be traced back to a cell of the quadrant stage.   The two cells nearest the neck give rise to the cotyledon and stem; the two inner ones produce the foot and primary root (Fig. 224*G*).   Cotyledon, stem, and primary root each grow by means of an apical cell.   The chief difference between embryonal development in *Azolla* and that in other leptosporangiates is the relative rate at which the various organs develop.   In *Azolla*, development of the stem is almost as

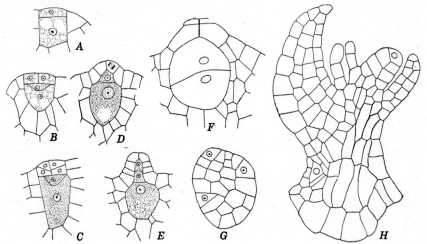

Fig. 224.—*Azolla filiculoides* Lam.   *A–E*, stages in the development of archegonia. *F*, two-celled embryo.   *G*, young embryo.   *H*, embryo at an advanced stage of development.   (× 325.)

rapid as that of the cotyledon (Fig. 224*H*).   On the other hand the primary root develops at a very slow rate.   The slow development of the root, as compared with that in other leptosporangiates, cannot be ascribed to the hydrophytic habit of the plant because other hydrophytic ferns, as *Marsilia*, have a rapid development of the primary root.   It is very probable that retardation of root development is due to the fact that the cotyledon and first-formed leaves function as water-absorbing organs.

Bibliography

Arber, E. A. Newell.   **1906.**   *Ann. Bot.* **20**: 215–232.   [Primofilices.]

Armour, Helen M.   **1907.**   *New Phytol.* **6**: 238–244. 4 figs.   [Sporangia, *Dipteris.*]

Atkinson, G. F.   **1894.**   The study of the biology of ferns by the collodion method. New York. 134 pp. 163 figs.

Baas-Becking, L. G. M.   **1921.**   *Recueil Trav. Bot. Néerland.* **18**: 333–372. 2 pl. 48 figs.   [Stele of Eusporangiatae.]

[1] Campbell, 1893.

BARTOO, D. R. **1929.** *Bot. Gaz.* **87**: 642–652. 12 figs. [Root, *Schizaea.*]

    1929A. *Ibid.* **88**: 322–331. 20 figs. [Sporangia, *Schizaea.*]

    1930. *Ibid.* **89**: 137–153. 27 figs. [Anatomy, *Schizaea.*]

BAUKE, H. **1876.** *Jahrb. Wiss. Bot.* **10**: 49–116. 5 pl. [Gametophyte, *Cyathea.*]

BELAJEFF, W. **1898.** *Bot. Zeitg.* **56**: 141–194. 2 pl. [Microgametophyte, *Azolla, Marsilea.*]

BENEDICT, R. C. **1909.** *Bull. Torrey Bot. Club* **36**: 463–476. 3 figs. [*Ceratopteris.*]

BENSON, MARGARET. **1911.** *Ann. Bot.* **25**: 1045–1057. 3 pl. 3 figs. [*Botryopteris.*]

BERTRAND, C. E., and F. CORNAILLE. **1904.** *Compt. Rend. Acad. Sci. Paris* **139**: 346–348. [Primofilices.]

BERTRAND, P. **1909.** Études sur la fronde des Zygoptéridées. Lille. 286 pp. 16 pl. 37 figs.

    1911. Nouvelles remarques sur la fronde des Zygoptéridées. Autun. 38 pp. 4 pl. 5 figs.

    1913. *Progr. Rei Bot.* **4**: 182–302. 59 figs. [Primofilices.]

    1933. *Bull. Soc. Bot. France* **80**: 527–537. 12 figs. [Primofilices.]

BLACK, CAROLINE A. **1909.** *Bull. Torrey Bot. Club.* **36**: 557–571. 3 pl. [Embedded sex organs, Polypodiaceae.]

BOODLE, L. A. **1899.** *Ann. Bot.* **13**: 377–394. 1 pl. [Anatomy, *Ophioglossum.*]

    1900. *Ibid.* **14**: 455–496. 3 pl. [Anatomy, Hymenophyllaceae.]

    1901. *Ibid.* **15**: 359–421. 3 pl. [Anatomy Schizaeaceae.]

    1901A. *Ibid.* **15**: 703–747. 2 pl. [Anatomy, *Gleichenia.*]

    1903. *Ibid.* **17**: 511–537. 3 figs. [Anatomy, *Schizaea.*]

BOODLE, L. A., and W. E. HILEY. **1909.** *Ibid.* **23**: 419–432. 1 pl. 3 figs. [Anatomy, *Gleichenia.*]

BOWER, F. O. **1888.** *Ibid.* **1**: 269–305. 3 pl. [Apogamy, *Trichomanes.*]

BOWER, F. O. **1889.** *Ibid.* **3**: 305–392. 5 pl. [Sporangia, *Osmunda.*]

    1896. Studies in the morphology of spore-producing members. II. Ophioglossaceae. London. 86 pp. 9 pl. 3 figs.

    1897. *Phil. Trans. Roy. Soc. London*, Ser. B, **189**: 35–81. 5 pl. [Sporangia, Marattiales.]

    1899. *Ibid.* **192**: 29–138. 6 pl. [Sporangia, Leptosporangiatae.]

    1908. The origin of a land flora. London. 727 pp. 361 figs.

    1910. *Ann. Bot.* **24**: 423–450. 2 pl. 5 figs. [Polypodiaceae, cyatheaceous ferns.]

    1911. *Ibid.* **25**: 537–553. 2 pl. [Anatomy, *Ophioglossum.*]

    1911A. *Ibid.* **25**: 277–298. 3 pl. [Anatomy, *Ophioglossum.*]

    1912. *Ibid.* **26**: 269–323. 7 pl. [Polypodiaceae, cyatheaceous ferns.]

    1913. *Ibid.* **27**: 443–477. 3 pl. 2 figs. [Cyatheaceous and polypodiaceous ferns.]

    1915. *Ibid.* **29**: 495–529. 2 pl. 19 figs. [Anatomy, *Dipteris.*]

    1918. *Ibid.* **32**: 1–68. 43 figs. [Sporangia, *Schizaea.*]

    1923. The ferns. Vol. 1. Cambridge. 359 pp. 309 figs.

    1926. *Ibid.* Vol. 2. Cambridge. 344 pp. 271 figs.

    1928. *Ibid.* Vol. 3. Cambridge. 306 pp. 175 figs.

    1935. Primitive land plants. London. 658 pp. 449 figs.

BREBNER, G. **1902.** *Ann. Bot.* **16**: 517–552. 2 pl. 2 figs. [Anatomy, Marattiales.]

BRITTON, ELIZABETH G., and ALEXANDRIA TAYLOR. **1901.** *Bull. Torrey Bot. Club* **28**: 1–19. 6 pl. [Gametophyte, *Schizaea.*]

BROWN, DOROTHY W. **1920.** *Ibid.* **47**: 339–345. 10 figs. [Apogamy, *Osmunda.*]

BRUCHMANN, H. **1904.** *Bot. Zeitg.* **62**: 227–247. 2 pl. [Gametophyte, *Ophioglossum.*]

BRUYN, HELENA DE. **1911.** *Ann. Bot.* **25**: 761–772. 2 pl. [Anatomy, *Dipteris.*]

BURLINGAME, L. L. **1907.** *Bot. Gaz.* **44**: 34–56. 2 pl. [Sporangium, Ophioglossales.]

BUSGEN, M. **1890.** *Flora* **73**: 169–182. 1 pl. [Sporocarp, *Marsilea*.]

CAMPBELL, D. H. **1892.** *Proc. California Acad. Sci.* 2 ser. **3**: 183–205. 2 pl. [Gametophytes and embryo, *Marsilea*.]

1892. *Ann. Bot.* **6**: 49–94. 4 pl. [Gametophyte and embryo, *Osmunda*.]

1893. *Ibid.* **7**: 155–187. 3 pl. [Gametophyte and embryo, *Azolla*.]

1894. *Ibid.* **8**: 1–20. 2 pl. [Gametophyte, *Marattia*.]

1895. The structure and development of mosses and ferns. 1st ed. New York. 544 pp. 266 figs.

1904. *Amer. Nat.* **38**: 761–775. 9 figs. [Relationships, Marsileaceae.]

1905. The structure and development of mosses and ferns. 2d. ed. New York. 657 pp. 322 figs.

1907. *Ann. Jard. Bot. Buitenzorg* 2 ser. **6**: 138–194. 11 pl. [Gametophyte, *Ophioglossum*.]

1908. *Ibid.* **8**: 69–102. 8 pl. [Gametophytes, Marattiales, *Gleichenia*.]

1911. The Eusporangiatae. *Carnegie Inst. Washington Publ.* **140**: 1–229. 13 pl. 192 figs.

1918. The structure and development of mosses and ferns. 3d. ed. New York. 708 pp. 322 figs.

1921. *Amer. Jour. Bot.* **8**: 303–314. 7 figs. [Stele of Eusporangiatae.]

CHANG, C. Y. **1927.** *Bot. Gaz.* **83**: 288–306. 18 figs. [Anatomy, *Pteridium*.]

CHARLES, GRACE M. **1911.** *Ibid.* **51**: 81–101. 4 pl. 3 figs. [Anatomy of young sporophyte, *Marattia*.]

CHEESEMAN, T. F. **1925.** Manual of the New Zealand flora. Wellington. 1163 pp.

CHRIST, H. **1897.** Die Farnkräuter der Erde. Jena. 388 pp. 293 figs.

CHRYSLER, M. A. **1910.** *Ann. Bot.* **24**: 1–18. 2 pl. 16 figs. [Fertile spike, Ophioglossales.]

1925. *Bull. Torrey Bot. Club* **52**: 126–132. 1 pl. [Fertile spike, Ophioglossales.]

CROSS, G. L. **1931.** *Bot. Gaz.* **92**: 210–217. 8 figs. [Embryo, *Osmunda*.]

DIELS, L. **1898.** Cyatheaceae. Polypodiaceae, Parkeriaceae, and Schizaeaceae. In A. Engler and K. Prantl, Die natürlichen Pflanzenfamilien. Teil. 1. Abt. 4. Pp. 113–371. 121 figs.

FAULL, J. H. **1901.** *Bot. Gaz.* **32**: 381–420. 4 pl. [Anatomy, *Osmunda*.]

FERGUSON, MARGARET C. **1911.** *Ibid.* **51**: 443–448. 2 pl. [Embedded sex organs, Polypodiaceae.]

FISCHER, H. **1911.** *Beih. Bot. Centralbl.* **27**, Abt. 1: 54–59. [Gametophytes, Polypodiaceae.]

FORD, SIBILLE, O. **1902.** *Ann. Bot.* **16**: 95–121. 1 pl. 8 figs. [Anatomy, *Ceratopteris*.]

GEORGEVITCH, P. **1910.** *Jahrb. Wiss. Bot.* **48**: 155–170. 30 figs. [Apogamy and apospory, *Trichomanes*.]

GODWIN, H. **1932.** *New Phytol.* **31**: 254–264. 7 figs. [Anatomy, *Cyathea*.]

GOEBEL, K. **1880–1881.** *Bot. Zeitg.* **38**: 545–552, 561–571. 1 pl. **39**: 697–706, 713–720. 1 pl. [Development of sporangia.]

1888. *Ann. Jard. Bot. Buitenzorg.* **7**: 74–119. 4 pl. [Gametophyte, *Hymenophyllum*.]

1905. Organography of plants. English ed. Translated by I. B. Balfour. Part 2. Oxford. 707 pp. 417 figs.

1915. Organographie der Pflanzen. 2 Auf. 2d Teil. Jena. 694 pp. 730 figs.

1930. *Ibid.* 3 Auf. 2d. Teil. Jena. 736 pp. 850 figs.

GRAHAM, R. **1935.** *Bot. Gaz.* **97**: 156–168. 24 figs. [Primofilices from Illinois.]

GWYNNE-VAUGHAN, D. T. **1911.** *Ann. Bot.* **25**: 525–536. 1 pl. 5 figs. [Anatomy, *Osmunda*.]

HARTMAN, M. ELIZABETH. **1931.** *Bot. Gaz.* **91**: 252–276. 27 figs. [Antheridia, Polypodiaceae.]

HIRMER, M. **1927.** Handbuch der Paläobotanik. Bd. 1. Munchen. 708 pp. 817 figs.

HOLLOWAY, J. E. **1923.** *Trans. New Zealand Inst.* **54**: 577–618. 21 pl. [Ecology, Hymenophyllaceae.]

1930. *Ann. Bot.* **44**: 269–284. 32 figs. [Gametophyte, Hymenophyllaceae.]

JEFFREY, E. C. **1917.** The anatomy of woody plants. Chicago. 478 pp. 306 figs.

JOHNSON, D. S. **1898.** *Ann. Bot.* **12**: 119–145. 3 pl. [Sporocarp, *Marsilea*.]

1933. *Bull. Torrey Bot. Club* **60**: 555–564. 1 pl. [Sporocarps, Marsileaceae.]

JONKMAN, H. F. **1880.** *Arch. Néerland. Sci. Exactes et Nat.* **15**: 199–224. 3 pl. [Gametophyte, Marattiales.]

KIDSTON, R., and D. T. GWYNNE-VAUGHAN. **1907.** *Trans. Roy. Soc. Edinburgh* **45**: 759–780. 6 pl. [Fossil Osmundaceae.]

1908. *Ibid.* **46**: 213–232. 4 pl. [Fossil Osmundaceae.]

1909. *Ibid.* **46**: 651–667. 8 pl. [Fossil Osmundaceae.]

1910. *Ibid.* **47**: 455–477. 4 pl. [Fossil Osmundaceae.]

KNY, L. **1875.** *Nova Acta K. Leop.-Carol. Deutsch. Ak. d. Naturf.* **37**, No. 4: 1–66. 8 pl. [*Certaopteris*.]

KRÄUSEL, R., and H. WEYLAND. **1926.** *Abhandl. Senckenbergischen Naturf. Ges. Frankfurt a/M.* **40**: 115–155. 15 pl. 46 figs. [*Cladoxylon*.]

KUBÄRT, B. **1917.** *Denkschr. Akad. Wiss. Wien* (Math.-Nat. Kl.) **93**: 551–584. 7 pl. 26 figs. [*Anachoropteris*.]

LAGERBERG, T. **1906.** *Ark. Bot.* **6**, No. 5: 1–28. 5 pl. [Gametophyte, *Pteridium*.]

LANG, W. H. **1902.** *Ann. Bot.* **16**: 23–56. 3 pl. [Gametophyte, *Ophioglossum*.]

LEAVITT, R. G. **1902.** *Bot. Gaz.* **34**: 414–419. 1 pl. [Root hairs, *Azolla*.]

LEITGEB, H. **1878.** *Sitzungsber. Akad. Wiss. Wien* (Math.-Nat. Kl.) **77**[1]: 222–242. 1 pl. [Embryology, *Marsilea*.]

MAHESHWARI, P., and B. SINGH. **1934.** *Jour. Indian Bot. Soc.* **13**: 103–123. 3 pl. 44 figs. [Anatomy, *Ophioglossum*.]

MANTON, IRENE. **1932.** *Jour. Genetics.* **25**: 423–430. 4 figs. [Apospory, *Osmunda*.]

MARSCHALL, CORNELIA C. **1925.** *Bot. Gaz.* **79**: 85–94. 9 figs. [Sporangia, *Marsilea*.]

MAXON, W. R. **1909.** Cyatheaceae. In North American flora. Vol. 16. Part 1. New York. pp. 65–88.

1925. *Nation. Geogr. Mag.* **47**: 541–586. 45 figs. [Ferns.]

MÜLLER, C. **1893.** *Ber. Deutsch. Bot. Ges.* **11**: 54–72. 1 pl. 2 figs. [Sporangia, Polypodiaceae.]

OES, A. **1913.** *Zeitschr. Bot.* **5**: 145–163. 1 fig. [*Anabaena* in leaves of *Azolla*.]

OGURA, Y. **1927.** *Jour. Faculty Sci. Imp. Univ. Tokyo. Sect. 3 Botany* **1**: 141–350. 74 figs. [Anatomy, *Cyathea*.]

PETRY, L. C. **1914.** *Bot. Gaz.* **57**: 169–192. 16 figs. [Anatomy, *Ophioglossum*.]

1915. *Ibid.* **59**: 345–365. 2 pl. 6 figs. [Apical cell, *Ophioglossum*.]

PFEFFER, W. **1884.** *Unters. Bot. Inst. Tübingen.* **1**: 363–482. [Chemotaxis, antherozoids.]

PFEIFFER, NORMA E. **1912.** *Ibid.* **53**: 436–438. 4 figs. [Embedded sex organs, Polypodiaceae.]

PFEIFFER, WANDA M. **1907.** *Ibid.* **44**: 445–454. 2 pl. [Sporocarps, *Azolla*.]

POTONIÉ, H. **1921.** Lehrbuch der Paläobotanik. 2d ed. Berlin. 537 pp. 326 figs.

RAUWENHOFF, N. W. P. **1891.** *Arch. Néerland. Sci. Exactes et Nat.* **24**: 157–231. 7 pl. [Gametophyte, *Gleichenia*.]

RENAULT, B. **1875.** *Ann. Sci. Nat. Bot.* 6 ser. **1**: 220–240. 6 pl. [*Botryopteris*.]

1876. *Ibid.* **3**: 1–29. 4 pl. [Sporangia, *Botryopteris*, *Etapteris*.]

Rogers, Lenette M. **1923.** *Bot. Gaz.* **75**: 75–85. 3 pl. [Gametophyte, *Lygodium*.]
1927. *Cellule* **37**: 327–352. 3 pl. [Gametophyte, *Lygodium*.]
Sadebeck, R. **1898.** Hymenophyllaceae. In A. Engler and K. Prantl, Die natürlichen Pflanzenfamilien. Teil 1, Abt. 4. Pp. 91–112. 11 figs.
Schmelzeisen, W. **1933.** *Flora* **127**: 46–80. 5 pl. 5 figs. [Gametophyte, *Cyathea*.]
Scott, D. H. **1910.** *Ann. Bot.* **24**: 819–820. 1 fig. [*Botryopteris*.]
1920. Studies in fossil botany. 3d ed. Vol. 1. London. 434 pp. 190 figs.
Seward, A. C. **1899.** *Phil. Trans. Roy. Soc. London* Ser. B. **191**: 171–209. 4 pl. [*Matonia*.]
1910. Fossil plants. Vol. 2. Cambridge. 624 pp. 265 figs.
Seward, A. C., and Elizabeth Dale. **1901.** *Phil. Trans. Roy. Soc. London* Ser. B. **194**: 487–513. 3 pl. [Anatomy, *Dipteris*.]
Sharp, L. W. **1914.** *Bot. Gaz.* **58**: 419–431. 2 pl. [Microgametophyte, *Marsilea*.]
Shaw, W. R. **1898.** *Ann. Bot.* **12**: 261–285. 1 pl. [Fertilization, Polypodiaceae.]
Shibata, K. **1911.** *Jahrb. Wiss. Bot.* **49**: 1–60. 3 figs. [Chemotaxis, antherozoids.]
Shreve, F. **1911.** *Bot. Gaz.* **51**: 184–209. 8 figs. [Ecology, Hymenophyllaceae.]
Small, J. K. **1931.** Ferns of Florida. New York. 237 pp. 107 figs.
Steil, W. N. **1919.** *Trans. Amer. Microsc. Soc.* **38**: 271–273. 2 figs. [Gametophytes, Polypodiaceae.]
Stephenson, G. B. **1907.** *Trans. and Proc. New Zealand Inst.* **40**: 1–16. 5 pl. [Embryo, *Cyathea*.]
Stokey, Alma G. **1918.** *Bot. Gaz.* **65**: 97–102. 10 figs. [Apogamy, Cyatheaceae.]
1930. *Ibid.* **90**: 1–45. 186 figs. [Gametophyte, *Cyathea*.]
Strasburger, E. **1869.** *Jahrb. Wiss. Bot.* **7**: 390–422. 2 pl. [Fertilization, Polypodiaceae.]
1873. Ueber Azolla. Leipzig. 86 pp. 7 pl.
1889. Histologische Beiträge. Heft 2. Jena. 186 pp. 4 pl.
1907. *Flora* **97**: 123–191. 6 pl. [Apogamy, *Marsilea*.]
Tansley, A. G., and Edith Chick. **1903.** *Ann. Bot.* **17**: 493–510. 2 pl. 1 fig. [Anatomy, *Schizaea*.]
Tansley, A. G., and R. B. Lulham. **1904.** *New Phytol.* **3**: 1–17. 59 figs. [Anatomy, *Pteridium*.]
1905. *Ann. Bot.* **19**: 475–519. 3 pl. 5 figs. [Anatomy, *Matonia*.]
Thomas, A. P. W. **1902.** *Ibid.* **16**: 165–170. [Gametophyte, *Schizaea*.]
Thompson, J. M. **1920.** *Trans. Roy. Soc. Edinburgh* **52**: 715–735. 4 pl. 9 figs. [Anatomy, *Schizaea*.]
Twiss, Edith M. **1910.** *Bot. Gaz.* **49**: 168–181. 2 pl. [Gametophytes, Schizaeaceae.]
Underwood, L. M., and R. C. Benedict. **1909.** Marattiales. In North American flora. Vol. 16. Part 1. New York, pp. 15–23.
Vladesco, A. **1935.** *Rev. Gén. Bot.* **47**: 422–434, 513–528, 564–592, 644–656, 684–720, 741–771. 107 figs. [Embryology, Polypodiaceae.]
West, C. **1915.** *Ann. Bot.* **29**: 409–422. 1 pl. 14 figs. [Anatomy, Marattiales.]
1917. *Ibid.* **31**: 77–99. 1 pl. 9 figs. [Mycorrhiza, Marattiales.]
1917A. *Ibid.* **31**: 361–414. 2 pl. 33 figs. [Anatomy, Marattiales.]
Wettstein, R. von. **1933–1935.** Handbuch der systematischen Botanik. 4th ed. Leipzig. 1149 pp. 709 figs.
Williams, S. **1928.** *Trans. Roy. Soc. Edinburgh* **55**: 795–805. 7 figs. [Sporangia, *Osmunda*.]
Yamanouchi, S. **1908.** *Bot. Gaz.* **45**: 145–175. 3 pl. [Gametophytes, Polypodiaceae.]
Zimmermann, W. **1930.** Die Phylogenie der Pflanzen. Jena. 452 pp. 250 figs.

INDEX

Page references in **bold face** refer to pages on which the subject is illustrated or is especially described.

A

Abscission, 211

Acrogynae, 45, **61–68**
    classification of, 67
    relationships of, 62

Acrogyny, 57, 64
    nature of, 24

Actinostele, **125, 130, 149, 152, 172,** 256, 260, 262
    exarch, **170,** 207, 226, 227, **228,** 233
    nature of, 125
    polyarch, 278, **279**
    tetrarch, **241**
    triarch, **229**

Aerenchyma, 328, **329**

Air chamber, **11,** 12, **22,** 23, **25, 30, 213**
    development of, 13

Air pore, 23, **25, 30,** 43

Algae, relationship, to Bryophyta, 2
    to Pteridophyta, 115

Alternation of generations, 1
    antithetic, 5
    in Bryophyta, 1, 4
    homologous, 4
    origin of, 4–6
    in Pteridophyta, 1, 132–135

Amblystegium riparium, **99**

Amphigastria, **63,** 68

Amphithecium, 19, 26, 36, 40, **79,** 80, 82, 90, 94
    formation of, 105

Anabaena Azollae, 354, **356, 357**

Anachoropteridaceae, **259–260**

Anachoropteridales, **259–260**
    relationships of, **249**

Anachoropteris, 254, **259–260**

Anacrogynae, **48–61,** 68
    classification of, 49
    relationships of, 49

Anacrogyny, 48, 70
    nature of, 28

Andreaea, **92–95**
    petrophila, **93, 94**

Andreaeaceae, **92–95**

Andreaeales, **92–95**

Andreaeobrya, **92–95**
    characteristics of, 84, 92
    relationships of, **6**

Androcyte, **15,** 39, 45, 102, 157, 178, 190, **214,** 215, 244, **272, 292, 305,** 325, 335, **346, 359,** 360

Androcyte mother cell, 15, 45, 244, 272

Androgonial cell, 15, **44,** 69, **70, 78,** 79, **89, 101,** 102, **157, 177,** 178, **189,** 190, **346**
    primary, 15, **44,** 69, **70,** 79, 88, **89, 101,** 102, **157, 177,** 178, **189, 214,** 215, 244, 272, **292,** 325, **334,** 335, **346**

Androgonial tissue, **272, 292, 305, 334,** 335

Anemia, 294, 299

Aneura, 50

Aneuraceae, 50

Annularia radiata, 231

Annulus, **106,** 256, **258,** 259, **290,** 291, **298,** 299, **304, 310, 312, 318, 324, 344, 351**
    of strobilus, 240

Antheridial cell, **189**
    primary, 14, **44,** 79

Antheridial chamber, **14, 51,** 57, 78

Antheridiophore, **34**
    development of, 33

Antheridium, **25,** 27, **28, 34, 51, 58, 93, 281, 319, 345, 352**
    development of, **14, 15,** 24, **38, 44,** 54, **70, 78,** 88, **89, 101, 157, 177,** 178, **243, 272,** 291, **292, 305,** 325, **346, 359,** 360
    embedded, 352*n.*
    initial of, 14, 43, 69, 78, 244, **292, 305,** 325, **334,** 335
    of Jungermanniales, 42

R